PROGRESS IN CLINICAL AND BIOLOGICAL RESEARCH

1983 TITLES

Please see pages following the index for previous titles in this series

13th International Cancer Congress, Part B

BIOLOGY OF CANCER (1)

13th International Cancer Congress, Part B

BIOLOGY OF CANCER (1)

Proceedings of the 13th International Cancer Congress
September 8–15, 1982
Seattle, Washington

Editors

Edwin A. Mirand
Roswell Park Memorial Institute
Buffalo, New York

William B. Hutchinson
Fred Hutchinson Cancer Research Center
Seattle, Washington

Enrico Mihich
Roswell Park Memorial Institute
Buffalo, New York

ALAN R. LISS, INC. • NEW YORK

Address all Inquiries to the Publisher
Alan R. Liss, Inc., 150 Fifth Avenue, New York, NY 10011

Copyright © 1983 Alan R. Liss, Inc.

Printed in the United States of America.

Library of Congress Cataloging in Publication Data

International Cancer Congress (13th : 1982 : Seattle,
    Wash.)
    13th International Cancer Congress.

    (Progress in clinical and biological research ; 132)
    Includes bibliographies and indexes.
    Contents: pt. A. Current perspectives in cancer --
pt. B. Biology of cancer (1) -- pt. C. Biology of
cancer (2) -- pt. D. Research and treatment -- pt. E.
Cancer management.
    1. Cancer--Congresses. I. Mirand, Edwin A.,
1926–   . II. Hutchinson, William B. III. Mihich,
Enrico. IV. Title. V. Title: Thirteenth International
Cancer Congress. VI. Series. [DNLM: 1. Medical
oncology--Congresses. W1 PR668E v.132 / QZ 200 I604
1982z]
RC261.A2I56 1982a   616.99′4   83-48399
ISBN 0-8451-0132-3 (set)
ISBN 0-8451-0175-7 (pt. B)

Contents

XI. FUNCTIONAL ASPECTS OF CELL MEMBRANES

Contributors

S. Ackerman, The Wistar Institute of Anatomy and Biology, Philadelphia, PA **[9]**

R. Andreesen, Department of Tumorbiology, Max Planck Institut für Immunbiologie, Freiburg, Federal Republic of Germany **[393]**

Thomas M. Aune, Department of Pathology and Laboratory Medicine, The Jewish Hospital of St. Louis, St. Louis, MO **[335]**

K. Ayres, Department of Microbiology, The University of Chicago, Chicago, IL **[251]**

Heinz Bauer, Institut für Virologie, Justus-Leibig-Universität Giessen, Giessen, West Germany **[19]**

W. Berdel, Department of Oncology and Hematology, Technical University, Medical Faculty, München, Federal Republic of Germany **[393]**

E. Bonmassar, Department of Experimental Medicine, Second University of Rome, Rome, Italy **[435]**

Gerhard Bonse, Abt. Pflanzenschutz, Bayer AG, Wuppertal, West Germany **[175]**

Carmia Borek, Department of Radiology and Pathology, Columbia University College of Physicians and Surgeons, New York, NY **[105]**

C. Bruce Boschek, Institut für Virologie, Justus-Liebig-Universität Giessen, Giessen, West Germany **[19]**

D. Bunick, The Wistar Institute of Anatomy and Biology, Philadelphia, PA **[9]**

Y.C. Cheng, Department of Pharmacology, University of North Carolina, Chapel Hill, NC **[49]**

Judith D. Cohn, Dulbecco Laboratory, Salk Institute, San Diego, CA **[355]**

E. Copelan, Department of Medicine, Division of Hematology and Oncology, Ohio State University, College of Medicine, Columbus, OH **[3]**

Janet D. Crow, Cell Genetics Section, National Cancer Institute, Bethesda, MD **[127]**

Guy de-Thé, Laboratory of Epidemiology and Immunovirology of Tumors, Faculty of Medicine Alexis Carrel, Lyon, France **[37]**

Wolfgang Dekant, Institute of Toxicology, University of Würzburg, Würzburg, West Germany **[175]**

Joseph A. DiPaolo, Laboratory of Biology, National Cancer Institute, Bethesda, MD **[141]**

M.A. Epstein, Department of Pathology, University of Bristol Medical School, Bristol, United Kingdom **[61]**

The number in brackets is the opening page number of the contributor's article.

Gerard I. Evan, Department of Microbiology, University of California at San Francisco, San Francisco, CA [355]

M.C. Fioretti, Institute of Pharmacology, University of Perugia, Perugia, Italy [435]

Norbert E. Fusenig, Institute for Biochemistry, German Cancer Research Center, Heidelberg, Federal Republic of Germany [91]

Ronald Glaser, Department of Medical Microbiology and Immunology, College of Medicine and Comprehensive Cancer Center, The Ohio State University, Columbus, OH [49]

K. Goerttler, Department of Experimental Pathology, German Cancer Research Center, Heidelberg, Federal Republic of Germany [219]

E. Gorelik, Surgery Branch, The National Cancer Institute, Bethesda, MD [425]

Hiroshi Hamada, Cell Genetics Section, National Cancer Institute, Bethesda, MD [127]

G.J. Hämmerling, Institute für Immunologie und Genetik, Deutsches Krebsforschungszentrum, Heidelberg Im Neuenheimer Feld, Heidelberg, Federal Republic of Germany [375]

E. Hecker, Department of Biochemistry, German Cancer Research Center, Heidelberg, Federal Republic of Germany [219]

Charles Heidelberger, University of Southern California Comprehensive Cancer Center, Los Angeles, CA [83]

Gary B. Henderson, Division of Biochemistry, Department of Basic and Clinical Research, Scripps Clinic and Research Foundation, La Jolla, CA [415]

Dietrich Henschler, Institute of Toxicology, University of Würzburg, Würzburg, West Germany [175]

R. Marian Hicks, Department of Cell Pathology, School of Pathology, Middlesex Hospital Medical School, London, United Kingdom [205]

Kanji Hirai, Department of Molecular Biology, Tokai University School of Medicine, Bohseidai, Isehara, Japan [71]

Kazuyoshi Ikuta, Department of Pathology, Research Institute for Microbial Diseases, Osaka University, Suita, Osaka, Japan [71]

Casper Jersild, Regional Bloodtransfusion Center, Aalborg Hospital, Aalborg, Denmark [299]

Takeo Kakunaga, Cell Genetics Section, National Cancer Institute, Bethesda, MD [127]

Hajime Karasuyama, Department of Immunology, Faculty of Medicine, University of Tokyo, Tokyo, Japan [345]

Peter Karran, Imperial Cancer Research Fund, Mill Hill Laboratories, London, United Kingdom [241]

Shiro Kato, Department of Pathology, Research Institute for Microbial Diseases, Osaka University, Suita, Osaka, Japan [71]

Toshiki Kitahara, Department of Immunology, Faculty of Medicine, University of Tokyo, Tokyo, Japan [345]

Eva Klein, Department of Tumor Biology, Karolinska Institutet, Stockholm, Sweden [325]

Erik Kriek, Chemical Carcinogenesis Division, Netherlands Cancer Institute, Amsterdam, The Netherlands [161]

Margaret L. Kripke, Cancer Biology Program, NCI-Frederick Cancer Research Facility, Frederick, MD [279]

W. Kuon, Institute für Immunologie und Genetik, Deutsches Krebsforschungszentrum, Heidelberg Im Neuenheimer Feld, Heidelberg, Federal Republic of Germany [375]

K. Larson, Department of Microbiology, The University of Chicago, Chicago, IL [251]

John Leavitt, Linus Pauling Institute, Palo Alto, CA [127]

Edwin S. Lennox, Department of Tumor Biology, MRC Laboratory of Molecular Biology, Cambridge, United Kingdom [355]

M.G. Lewis, Department of Veterinary Pathobiology, Ohio State University, College of Veterinary Medicine, Columbus, OH [3]

Tomas Lindahl, Imperial Cancer Research Fund, Mill Hill Laboratories, London, United Kingdom [241]

V. Lindgren, Department of Microbiology, The University of Chicago, Chicago, IL [251]

Anthony D. Lowe, Department of Tumor Biology, MRC Laboratory of Molecular Biology, Cambridge, United Kingdom [355]

D. Lutz, Department of Biochemistry, German Cancer Research Center, Heidelberg, Federal Republic of Germany [219]

L.E. Mathes, Department of Veterinary Pathobiology, Ohio State University, College of Veterinary Medicine, Columbus, OH [3]

Daniel Medina, Department of Cell Biology, Baylor College of Medicine, Houston, TX [187]

M. Modolell, Department of Tumorbiology, Max Planck Institut für Immunobiologie, Freiburg, Federal Republic of Germany [393]

A.J. Morgan, Department of Pathology, University of Bristol Medical School, Bristol, United Kingdom [61]

J.F. Morton, Morton Collectanea, University of Miami, Coral Gables, FL [219]

Paul G. Munder, Department of Tumor Biology, Max Planck Institut für Immunbiologie, Freiburg, Federal Republic of Germany [393]

Larry Nathanson, Nassau Hospital, Mineola NY; and School of Medicine, SUNY at Stony Brook, NY [387]

J.R. North, Department of Pathology, University of Bristol Medical School, Bristol, United Kingdom [61]

Atsuo Ochi, Department of Immunology, Faculty of Medicine, University of Tokyo, Tokyo, Japan [345]

R. Oepke, Department of Tumorbiology, Max Planck Institute für Immunbiologie, Freiburg, Federal Republic of Germany [393]

Ko Okumura, Department of Immunology, Faculty of Medicine, University of Tokyo, Tokyo, Japan [345]

R.G. Olsen, Department of Veterinary Pathobiology, Ohio State University, College of Veterinary Medicine, Columbus, OH **[3]**

W. Pahlke, Department of Tumorbiology, Max Planck Institute für Immunbiologie, Freiburg, Federal Republic of Germany **[393]**

Giorgio Parmiani, Division of Experimental Oncology B, Istituto Nazionale Studio e Cura dei Tumori, Milano, Italy **[363]**

James F. Perdue, Lady Davis Institute for Medical Research, Sir Mortimer B. Davis Jewish General Hospital, Montreal, Quebec, Canada **[405]**

Carl W. Pierce, Department of Pathology and Laboratory Medicine, The Jewish Hospital of St. Louis, St. Louis, MO **[335]**

Miriam C. Poirier, Laboratory of Cellular Carcinogenesis and Tumor Promotion, National Cancer Institute, Bethesda, MD **[289]**

L. Romani, Institute of Pharmacology, University of Perugia, Perugia, Italy **[435]**

Evi Rüsch, Institut für Immunologie und Genetik, Deutsches Krebsforschungszentrum, Heidelberg Im Neuenheimer Feld, Heidelberg, Federal Republic of Germany **[375]**

D. Sagher, Department of Microbiology, The University of Chicago, Chicago, IL **[251]**

Yoshiaki Satoh, Department of Dermatology, Tokyo Medical and Dental University, Tokyo, Japan **[267]**

M. Shinitzky, Department of Membrane Research, The Weizmann Institute of Science, Rehovot, Israel **[425]**

W. Sindelar, Surgery Branch, The National Cancer Institute, Bethesda, MD **[425]**

R. Sklar, Department of Microbiology, The University of Chicago, Chicago, IL **[251]**

Y. Skornick, Department of Surgery, Rokach Hospital, Tel-Aviv, Israel **[425]**

M.I. Stiff, Department of Veterinary Pathobiology, Ohio State University, College of Veterinary Medicine, Columbus, OH **[3]**

Jay Stoerker, Department of Medical Microbiology and Immunology, College of Medicine and Comprehensive Cancer Center, The Ohio State University, Columbus, OH **[49]**

B. Strauss, Department of Microbiology, The University of Chicago, Chicago, IL **[251]**

Osias Stutman, Department of Cellular Immunology, Memorial Sloan-Kettering Cancer Center, New York, NY **[311]**

Tomio Tada, Department of Immunology, Faculty of Medicine, University of Tokyo, Tokyo, Japan **[345]**

Hiraku Takebe, Radiation Biology Center, Kyoto University, Kyoto, Japan **[267]**

Teruko Tamura, Institut für Virologie, Justus-Liebig-Universität Giessen, Giessen, West Germany **[19]**

Walter G. Verly, Department of Biochemistry, Faculté des Sciences, Université de Liège, Liège I, Belgium **[261]**

J. Weber, Department of Biochemistry, German Cancer Research Center, Heidelberg, Federal Republic of Germany **[219]**

R. Weinmann, The Wistar Institute of Anatomy and Biology, Philadelphia, PA **[9]**

O. Westphal, German Cancer Center, Heidelberg, Federal Republic of Germany **[393]**

Takashi Yagi, Radiation Biology Center, Kyoto University, Kyoto, Japan **[267]**

Seiichi Yamada, Department of Immunology, Faculty of Medicine, University of Tokyo, Tokyo, Japan **[345]**

Katsumi Yamauchi, Department of Immunology, Faculty of Medicine, University of Tokyo, Tokyo, Japan **[345]**

Shen K. Yang, Department of Pharmacology, School of Medicine, Uniformed Services University of the Health Sciences, Bethesda, MD **[151]**

R. Zandomeni, The Wistar Institute of Anatomy and Biology, Philadelphia, PA **[9]**

Yi Zeng, Institute of Virology, Chinese Academy of Medical Sciences, Beijing, People's Republic of China **[37]**

Foreword

The papers presented in the Plenary Lectures and the Congress Symposia at the 13th International Cancer Congress, September 8–15, 1982, Seattle, Washington, are included in these volumes. The United States was the official host of the Congress, which was held under the auspices of the International Union Against Cancer (UICC), and the Fred Hutchinson Cancer Research Center, Seattle, Washington was the host institution.

Dr. William B. Hutchinson of the Fred Hutchinson Cancer Research Center was the Congress President and Dr. Edwin A. Mirand of Roswell Park Memorial Institute, Buffalo, New York, was the Secretary-General.

The scientific program of the Congress contained over 4,000 presentations. The National Program Committee, chaired by Dr. Enrico Mihich of Roswell Park Memorial Institute, felt that it would be appropriate to include only the papers from the Plenary Lectures and the Congress Symposia to keep the number of volumes at a reasonable level. These papers are presented in five volumes.

Volume A — Final Report of the Secretary-General that includes the organizational details of the scientific program
        — Plenary Lectures
Volumes B & C — Basic science topics in oncology
Volumes D & E — Clinical oncology topics

Since it would be impossible to cover all the areas of oncology presented at the Congress, by presenting the plenary and symposia sessions, we attempted to select the most rapidly advancing and promising areas of clinical and basic research. A good index of the growth in the field of oncology can be obtained by comparing the publications of this meeting with the last cancer congress publications (12th International Cancer Congress) held in Buenos Aires from October 5–10, 1978.

Looking over the topics covered herein, one can only marvel at the tremendous rate of progress and the increase in interest in oncology in the past four years. This reflects the developments in molecular biology as it relates to cancer viral and chemical carcinogenesis, in the design and evaluation of clinical trials, biological response modifiers, cancer nursing, psychosocial aspects of cancer, etc.

On behalf of the Congress officers, we wish to express our gratitude to the National Program Committee and to all the scientists, physicians, dentists, nurses, and other participants engaged in oncology who attended this Congress and who made it a success. I am sure that both the scientific and social interchange which was experienced at the Seattle meeting will have a positive, lasting effect on our lives. We hope to see you at the 14th International Cancer Congress to be held in Budapest, Hungary in 1986 to further the scientific and social interaction.

The editors are deeply indebted to all the authors for their outstanding contributions to these volumes.

We wish to express thanks and appreciation to Catherine O'Leary, Lisa Barone, Linda Beverage, Kevin Craig, Ann M. Gannon, Ramon Melendez, Amy Mirand and Lucy Mirand, all of whom aided in various ways in the preparation of these volumes.

Finally, we wish to acknowledge the support of the National Cancer Institute, American Cancer Society, Pacific Northwest Regional Commission for their generous support of the 13th International Cancer Congress.

Edwin A. Mirand

Preface to Part B

What causes a seemingly normal cell to become cancerous? Is the answer to be found in immunology, genetics, biology, the environment? Or is the answer to be found in a combination of these elements or some others?

Answers to these questions have been the focus of cancer research in laboratories, worldwide, for many years.

Results of recent laboratory studies have provided immunologic, genetic, biological and molecular "events" that have helped to identify the specific agents, properties, and conditions that are critical to understanding cancer etiology.

In this volume, prominent investigators examine and explore these major scientific advances, and bring the subject of cancer etiology into perspective. Primary emphasis is on the mechanisms and dynamics involved in cell proliferation, transformation, and regulation; chemical carcinogenesis and its formation; and tumor antigenic and antitumor antibodies. The projected potential of the diagnostic and prognostic value of this research is also delineated by the authors.

Edwin A. Mirand

CONGRESS SYMPOSIA

VIRAL ANTIGENS AS REGULATORS OF CELL PROLIFERATION
Weil, R., Switzerland, Chairman; Friend, C., USA,
Co-Chairman; Arena

Mechanism of SV40- and Polyoma-Induced Phenotypic
Reprogramming of the Host Cells. *Weil, R.,
Khandjian, E. W. and Matter, J-M., Geneva
Switzerland. (By Title Only)

Herpes Virus Antigens in Transformation and
Tumorigenesis. *McDougall, J., USA. (By Title Only)

Immunosuppressive Properties of a Feline Retrovirus
15,000 Dalton Protein. *Olsen, R. G., Mathes, L. E.,
Lewis, M. G., Stiff, M. I., and Copelan, E.,
Columbus, OH USA.

Mechanism of Initiation of RNA Polymerase II.
*Bunick, D., Zandomeni, R., Ackerman, S. and
Weinmann, R., Philadelphia, PA USA.

The Study of Molecular Functions of the Transforming
Protein PP60^{SRC} of Rous Sarcoma Virus by the Use of
Monospecific Antibodies. *Bauer, H., Tamura, T.
and Boschek, B. C., Giessen, W. Germany.

Please note: Papers that are listed as "By Title
Only" were presented at the 13th International
Cancer Congress, but are not included in these
volumes.

1

13th International Cancer Congress, Part B
Biology of Cancer (1), pages 3–7
© 1983 Alan R. Liss, Inc., 150 Fifth Avenue, New York, NY 10011

IMMUNOSUPPRESSIVE PROPERTIES OF A FELINE RETROVIRUS 15,000 DALTON PROTEIN

R.G. Olsen, Ph.D.,[a,b] L.E. Mathes, Ph.D.,[a] M.G. Lewis, M.S.,[a] M.I. Stiff, Ph.D.,[a] E. Copelan, M.D.[c] The Ohio State Univ., [a]Dept. of Vet. Pathobiology, 1925 Coffey Rd., [b]Cancer Center, [c]The College of Medicine, 410 W. 10th Ave., Columbus, Ohio 43210

The generalized immune dysfunctions associated with feline leukemia virus disease is often times manifested weeks after feline retrovirus infection but months before appearance of frank neoplasia. Immune dysfunctions associated with this disease are multiple, of which the most apparent is a generalized immunosuppression that is manifested by increased mortality and morbidity of viral and bacterial diseases. It has been reported that greater than 50% of feline leukemia infections in cats are diagnosed as having generalized viral and bacterial diseases, abortion, fetal absorption and glomerular nephritis (Essex et al., 1975).

Other defects in the immune system associated with feline leukemia include atrophy of the thymus, and pericortical lymphoid depletion (Hoover et al., 1973). This often precedes the onset of lymphosarcoma by several months. During the preneoplastic state, animals exhibit frank dysfunctions of cellular immunity as shown by the failure to reject skin grafts and by depression of the cats peripheral blood lymphocyte blastogenic response to phytomitogens. Lymphocyte functions associated with feline leukemia virus disease also include reduction in lymphocyte membrane conA receptor mobility (capping) as well as a decrease in the lymphocyte blast transformation (Olsen et al., 1980).

Recently, we demonstrated that feline leukemia is also associated with disorder of the suppressor cell function (Stiff and Olsen, 1982). It was demonstrated that suppressor cell function decreased during the early stages of feline retrovirus disease.

ASSOCIATION OF IMMUNOSUPPRESSION WITH FELINE RETROVIRUS PROTEIN

The mechanism by which FeLV infection induces suppression in the preneoplastic stage is unknown. It is tempting to speculate that FeLV infection and subsequent transformation of T-cells is responsible for the T-cell dysfunctions. However, much evidence has accumulated that suggests that FeLV transformation is independent of FeLV-associated immunosuppression.

The first evidence that abrogation of immune functions may be the property of feline retroviral products or viral structural components (virion) was a result of administering inactivated FeLV in young kittens. Kittens that received killed FeLV and then were challenged with oncogenic FeLV/FeSV exhibited larger tumor growth and a higher percentage of progressive malignancies than the control kittens (kittens that did not receive killed FeLV) (Olsen et al., 1977).

The putative role of FeLV structural components in the FeLV-associated immunosuppression is consistent with the clinical findings that immunosuppression precedes transformation, often by months. In addition, this concept is compatible with the findings that FeLV induces diseases other than neoplastic diseases.

ASSOCIATION OF FeLV-STRUCTURAL COMPONENT WITH INTERFERENCE OF FELINE LYMPHOCYTE FUNCTIONS

Inactivated FeLV, in addition to causing tumor enhancement and abrogating tumor immunity, was shown to interfere with three different lymphocyte functions: lymphocyte blastogenesis, lymphocyte membrane lectin receptor mobility, and mixed lymphocyte reaction (Olsen et al., 1980). It was reported that micrograms of inactivated FeLV were suppressive to feline lymphocyte blastogenesis (Hebebrand et al., 1977). As an extension of these studies, it was shown that conA-induced lymphocyte capping was likewise reduced when lymphocytes were incubated with killed FeLV (Nichols et al., 1979).

In an attempt to delineate which feline virion moeities were responsible for the suppressive properties on lymphocyte functions, Mathes et al developed a scheme to fractionate and recover FeLV components and test each component for suppression of mitogen-induced LBT. These workers identified a fraction of FeLV that was isolated by its insolubility in aqueous buffers that possessed suppressive properties equal to inactivated FeLV. Other FeLV proteins (i.e., gp70, p27) did not possess this biological property. Further purification of the FeLV suppressive fraction revealed a 15,000 (FeLV p15E) dalton protein on polyacrylamide gel electrophoresis (Mathes et al., 1979).

Purified FeLV p15E was shown to be suppressive to the mitogen-induced LBT at a concentration of 0.2 ug/well.

In vivo administration of FeLV p15E reduced the cats' response to FOCMA and increased the cats' susceptibility to FeLV disease (Mathes et al., 1979). The in vivo biologic effects of FeLV p15E was very similar to the effects of inactivated FeLV. In addition to tumor enhancement and decreased FOCMA antibody response, it was shown that administration of FeLV p15E interferes with the apparent helper effect of T-lymphocytes. Studies showed that FeLV p15E interferes with the apparent conversion of IgM to IgG FOCMA antibody. Cats given FeLV p15E develop persistent IgM FOCMA antibody with only low levels of IgG. This profile (i.e., persistent IgM antibody to FOCMA) is similar to the antibody profiles produced by cats that possess progressor FeLV/FeSV tumors or persistent viremic cats (Olsen et al., 1981).

MECHANISM OF FeLV p15E SUPPRESSION

The site of cellular impairment that culminates in feline retrovirus-associated immunosuppression is unknown. Evidence to date indicates that the T-lymphocyte and not the immune accessory cells are adversely effected by FeLV p15E exposure.

Recent studies by Copelan et al. (unpublished data) have shown that FeLV proteins do not impair monocyte function as assessed by Interleukin I production. However, Interleukin II production by activated T-lymphocytes was decreased by more than 90% and T-cell proliferation to Interleukin II was decreased by more than 50% by exposure to FeLV p15E.

In an attempt to delineate the effects of FeLV p15E on prostaglandin-mediated functions, Lewis et al. (unpublished)

observed that the suppressive effect of FeLV on the normal
mitogenesis of feline peripheral blood lymphocytes was partially reversed by the addition of a prostaglandin inhibitor.
Incubation of the lymphocytes with a concentration of 10^{-7}
M indomethacin or aspirin (prostaglandin inhibitors) caused
the FeLV suppressive effect to be reduced by up to 80%. The
addition of the inhibitor to an LBT without FeLV added
caused little or no effect upon the lymphocyte stimulation.

Current research in immune modulation has shown a link
between the prostaglandin system, interleukin production and
cell function. With further study of the interaction of
FeLV with these immune parameters, we hope to determine the
site of FeLV-induced immune dysfunction.

Essex M, Hardy WD Jr, Cotter SM, Jakowski RM, Sliski A (1975). Naturally occurring persistent feline oncornavirus infections in the absence of disease. Infect. Immun. 11: 470.

Hebebrand LC, Mathes LE, Olsen RG (1977). Inhibition of Concanavalin A stimulation of feline lymphocytes by inactivated feline leukemia viruses. Cancer Res 37:4532.

Hoover EA, Perryman LE, Kociba GJ (1973). Early lesions in cats inoculated with feline leukemia virus. Cancer Res 33:145.

Mathes LE, Olsen RG, Hebebrand LC, Hoover EA, Schaller JP, Adams PW, Nichols WS (1979). Immunosuppressive properties of virion polypeptide, a 15,000 dalton protein, from feline leukemia virus. Cancer Res 39:950.

Olsen RG, Hoover EA, Schaller JP, Mathes LE, Wolff LH (1977). Abrogation of resistance to feline oncornavirus disease by immunization with killed feline leukemia virus. Cancer Res 37:2082.

Olsen RG, Mathes LE, Hebebrand LC, Hoover EA, Nichols WS (1980). Animal model of human disease. 98:857.

Olsen RG, Mathes LE, Nichols SW (1981). FeLV-related immunosuppresion. In Olsen RG (ed): "Feline Leukemia," Boca Raton, Florida: CRC Press, p. 149.

Stiff MI, Olsen RG (1982). Loss of the short-lived suppressive function of peripheral leukocytes in feline retrovirus-infected cats. J Clin Lab Immunol 7:133.

13th International Cancer Congress, Part B
Biology of Cancer (1), pages 9–18
© 1983 Alan R. Liss, Inc., 150 Fifth Avenue, New York, NY 10011

MECHANISM OF INITIATION OF RNA POLYMERASE II

D. Bunick, R. Zandomeni, S. Ackerman and
R. Weinmann

The Wistar Institute of Anatomy and Biology
36th Street at Spruce
Philadelphia, PA 19104

Recent developments in recombinant DNA technology
have allowed the introduction of small restriction enzyme
fragments into prokaryotic vectors and the amplification
of these DNA fragments in large amounts. Thus high concentrations of highly purified viral and cellular eukaryotic
promoters can be attained in vitro. A parallel development
of in vitro RNA polymerase II transcriptional systems
which retain the in vivo fidelity of initiation has greatly
aided in our understanding of transcriptional phenomena
(Weil et al. 1979, Manley et al. 1980). The assays
currently in use measure specific size RNAs generated by
initiation at a specific site on the DNA template and
elongation up to the cutting site of a restriction enzyme.
Termination occurs at that site because the DNA-dependent
RNA polymerase II runs off the template. This assay depends on a successful initiation of the RNA polymerase II
at the correct promoter site followed by elongation and
runoff to produce an RNA of a defined size. The steps involved in the initiation process have not been analyzed
in detail in eukaryotic systems. Fractionation of the extracts that are used in in vitro transcriptional systems
reveals that, in addition to the RNA polymerase II, at
least four distinct chromatographic fractions are required
for obtaining runoff RNAs (Matsui et al. 1981). It is
unclear which of these factors are required for the actual
initiation. It is also unclear whether the low efficiency
of transcription of these in vitro systems (1% of the templates give just one transcript/hour) reflects the efficiency of initiation, or the efficiency of the transition

to elongation and successful completion of runoff RNA products. To analyze the molecular events surrounding the initiation of transcription, we have used nucleotide analogs,
which act as "mutant" substrates and interact abnormally
with the transcriptional machinery. The combined use of
template mutants in the promoter DNA sequence and mutant
enzymes or factors in the transcriptional machinery can be
used to complement this analysis. To separate the events
of transcriptional initiation and capping, we used
nucleotide analogs with β-γ-imido substitutions, which are
highly resistant to hydrolysis of the γ-triphosphates
(Yount et al. 1971). We demonstrate here that uncapped
imidotriphosphate containing 5' ends can be obtained in
this system. In addition, we found an unexpected requirement for hydrolysis of the β-γ bond of ATP for successful initiation of transcription by eukaryotic RNA
polymerase II.

RESULTS

     In vitro transcriptional extracts (prepared as des-
cribed by Manley et al. 1980) were incubated with DNA
template containing the murine leukemia virus long terminal repeat (MuLV LTR). This DNA template contains the
MuLV LTR promoter, which initiates a transcript with the
sequence m^7GpppGmpCp... (van Beveren et al. 1980). The
correctly initiated RNA has a length of 540 nucleotides,
when analyzed in urea-polyacrylamide gels (Fig. 1 and
Fuhrman et al. 1981). The nucleotide analog β-γ-imido-
GTP (GMP-PNP) has a phosphohydrolase-resistant γ-phosphate.
It can be used for RNA transcription, instead of GTP, as
cleavage of the α-β bond results in efficient incorporation
(Bunick et al. 1982). However the β-γ-imido substitution
does not allow capping if GMP-PNP is located at the 5' end
of a transcript, because the cleavage of this bond is a
requirement for capping (Venkatesan et al. 1980). Incubation of in vitro reactions in the presence of GMP-PNP with
the MuLV LTR template indicates that transcription can
occur in the presence of the imido analog (Fig. 1, lane 2).
Presumably, the transcript is initiated with a 5' G, and
the imido-substituted triphosphate resists hydrolysis.
Thus, we assume that the 5' ends of the MuLV LTR
transcripts are uncapped.

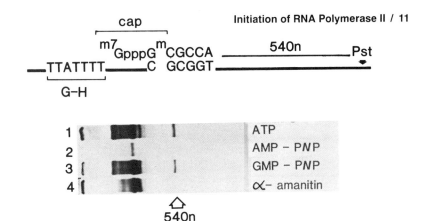

Fig. 1. The DNA template coding strand of the MuLV LTR is
shown schematically in the upper panel. The sequences
corresponding to the Goldberg-Hogness or TATA box (G-H) as
well as the sequences around the site of transcription initiation are indicated. The RNA runoff product (already
capped) with the 5' end sequences and extending 540 n up to
the Pst site is also shown. All sequence data are from
Fuhrman et al. (1981). The template, a Pst fragment inserted into pBR322, was a generous gift of Dr. S. Fuhrman. The
lower panel shows an autoradiogram of a 5% polyacrylamide
urea gel containing the transcripts obtained after electrophoresis of RNA made in vitro in the presence of the MuLV-
LTR template digested with Pst 1. The 540 n runoff RNA is
indicated by the arrow, as determined from the mobility of
ϕX174 Hae III-digested end-labeled DNA fragments. The in
vitro reactions contained 10 μl of HeLa whole cell extract
prepared as described (Manley et al. 1980), 25 μg/ml of
Pst-digested [α-^{32}P]DNA, 100 μM each of ATP, UTP and GTP
and 10 μM of [α-^{32}P]CTP 40 Ci/mM, 5 μCi, 10 μM creatine
phosphate, 65 mM KCl and 7 mM MgCl$_2$. After 60 min at 30°C
the RNA was phenol-chloroform-extracted, ethanol-
precipitated and dissolved in 90% deionized formamide.
Electrophoresis was at 1000 Volts for 3 hr, as described by
Sanger and Coulson (1978) in a 5% acrylamide-8 M urea
0.4-mm gel run from left to right. Autoradiography was
overnight at -70°C using Lightning Plus (DuPont) inten-
sifying screens and Kodak XRP-1 film. Lane 1 corresponds
to a complete reaction, in lane 2 the ATP was substituted
by AMP-PNP (100 μM), and in lane 3 the GTP was substituted
by GMP-PNP. In lane 4 the incubation was performed in the
presence of 1 μg/ml of α-amanitin, enough to inhibit
completely RNA polymerase II (Lindell et al. 1970).

To demonstrate that the transcripts do indeed contain uncapped 5' ends, we labeled the ends by the nearest neighbor technique. Briefly, RNA was synthesized in vitro on the MuLV LTR template in the presence of GMP-PNP and labeled with $[\alpha\text{-}^{32}P]$CTP. At the 5' ends of the transcripts, T2 ribonuclease digestion should release a tetraphosphate with 3'-labeled phosphate indicated in Fig. 2. RNA labeled in vitro in the presence of $[\alpha\text{-}^{32}P]$CTP and GMP-PNP was eluted from a gel like the one in Fig. 1, digested with T2 ribonuclease, and analyzed by thin-layer chromatography on polyethylene-imino cellulose (PEI) plates as described by Celma et al. (1977) (Fig. 2). We detected a spot (lane a) that comigrates with a tetraphosphate marker generated by in vitro transcription of poly-dGdC with E. coli RNA polymerase and T2 ribonuclease digestion (Fig. 2, lane d). As expected for a 3'-labeled tetraphosphate, the radioactive phosphate is removed by P1 digestion both in the MuLV transcript and in the case of the marker, as shown in lanes b and c, Fig. 2. Thus we show that normal sized runoff transcripts can be generated containing a free 5'-triphosphate end. Similar results were reported for the adenovirus early region IV promoter (Bunick et al. 1982). For this latter case, the T1 ribonuclease oligonucleotide analysis revealed that the only distinct 5' oligonucleotide results when UMP-PNP is used as a substrate. In this case transcripts could be initiated with either A or U (Fire et al. 1981), and no preference for either type was found when UMP-PNP was used. In addition, the release of the tetraphosphate demonstrates that this bond is not methylated at the 2'-O-ribose position. Thus capping is required for methylation to occur, as in the case of the EIV transcription unit (Bunick et al. 1982).

With promoters that start their transcripts at an A, such as the case of the ε-globin (Baralle et al. 1980), no uncapped transcripts were obtained. The normal 460 n runoff RNA of the BamHl-digested ε-globin template could be easily detected (Fig. 3). However, when ATP was substituted for AMP-PNP, the corresponding transcripts were not detected (Fig. 3, lane 2). The imidonucleotide AMP-PNP acts as a competitive inhibitor of specific RNA polymerase II transcription, as shown in mixing experiments where AMP-PNP acts in the presence of low amounts of ATP (Fig. 3, lane 3). Similar results were obtained previously for the adenovirus major late promoter (Bunick et al. 1982). We

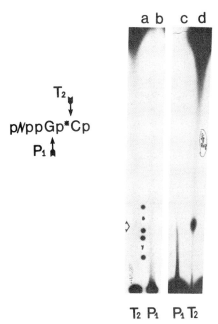

T₂ P₁   P₁ T₂

Fig. 2. Analysis of 5' ends of RNA polymerase II products. Specific MuLV-LTR 540 n runoff RNA from a reaction like the one in Fig. 1 containing 300 μCi of [α-^{32}P]CTP and 100 μM GMP-PNP was eluted and subjected to ribonuclease T2 or P1 complete digestion (lanes a and b). The samples were then spotted on a polyethylene imino-cellulose plate (Brinkman) and developed with 0.6 M phosphate, pH 3.5 (Celma et al. 1977). A marker made from in vitro transcription of poly-dGdC with E. coli RNA polymerase and GMP-PNP and [α-^{32}P]CTP was run in lanes c and d. Exposure was for 2 weeks for lanes a and b and for 4 hr for the insert in lanes c and d. The position of the dye markers (β-xylenecyanol blue, Y; orange, G and GMP-PNP) are indicated.

have shown that this absence of transcription is not due to the lack of capping of A-initiated transcripts because the transcripts initiated with G, like MuLV LTR, are also inhibited by AMP-PNP (Fig. 1, lane 3). Thus, this ATP requirement is a transcriptional requirement for cleavage of the β-γ bond in faithful transcription systems. This requirement is at the level of initiation of transcription, as preinitiated transcription complexes are able to elongate their RNA in the presence of AMP-PNP (Bunick et al. 1982).

DISCUSSION

Capping (Shatkin 1976) and transcription of eukaryotic mRNAs are closely linked (Babich et al. 1980, Salditt-Georgieff et al. 1981). Initiation of transcription must occur very close to (Ziff, Evans 1978, Evans et al. 1977) or at the site of (Contreras et al. 1981, Hagenbüchle, Schibler 1981) the capped mRNA precursor.

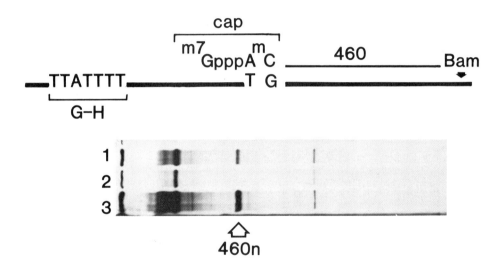

Fig. 3. Analysis of transcription of the human ε-globin gene. A segment of DNA containing the human ε-globin promoter sequences is shown schematically in the upper panel (Baralle et al. 1980). The sequences on the coding strand for both the G-H box and the initiation site are indicated, as well as the first nucleotides of the capped transcript. When the DNA template is cut with the restriction enzyme Bam H1, a 460 n RNA runoff product is expected (Proudfoot et al. 1980). The lower panel shows the results of analyzing the RNAs resulting from incubations with ATP (lane 3) or AMP-PNP (lane 2) or a mixture of both (50 μM ATP; 150 μM AMP-PNP) (lane 1). The arrow indicates the migration position of the 460 n RNA runoff product. Electrophoresis, from left to right, was as described in Fig. 1.

The inability by several groups (Vennstrom et al. 1978, Bunick, Weinmann 1980) to isolate uncapped RNA polymerase II transcripts suggested that the two reactions were coupled (Gidoni et al. 1981). The data presented here indicate that in the in vitro transcriptional system, capping is not required to obtain full-length runoff RNA transcripts. This is in agreement with the findings in the reovirus system (Banerjee 1980) where capping is also not required. We conclude from these results that the initiation site of transcription of the mRNA precursor coincides with the cap site in the mature mRNA. Thus, at least for these transcripts, no secondary modifications of the length of the RNA seem to occur at the initiation site, unlike U1 RNA which reportedly undergoes secondary modifications (Murphy et al. 1982). Whether capping is important for polyadenylation, splicing or nucleocytoplasmic transport of mRNAs remains to be determined. The T2 sensitivity of the bond between the 5'-end GMP-PNP and the following $[\alpha-^{32}P]CMP$ suggests that the 2'-O-ribose of the latter is not methylated, and capping is required for this methylation to occur.

The requirement for cleavage of the $\beta-\gamma$ bond of ATP for specific initiation is unique to the RNA polymerase II of eukaryotes. Additional evidence for this requirement at the level of initiation comes from the internal incorporation of $[\alpha-^{32}P]AMP$-PNP into viral RNA in nuclei isolated from adenovirus-infected cells, and the absolute failure to incorporate into the 5' ends of the adenovirus major late promoter transcript (Bunick et al. 1982). Furthermore labeled AMP-PNP can also be incorporated into RNA in the regular runoff assay, if added to preinitiated RNA in the reaction, i.e., elongation of preinitiated RNA molecules can occur in the presence of AMP-PNP (Bunick et al. 1982) but new initiations cannot occur when the analog is present. This requirement is a distinguishing feature between the specific initiation in the whole cell extract and the nonspecific initiation of purified (Schwartz, Roeder 1975) RNA polymerase II on naked DNA templates (Bunick et al. 1982).

The requirement of hydrolysis of the $\beta-\gamma$ bond could be functionally significant. For example, ATP requiring topoisomerases (Cozzarelli 1980) could be used for the unwinding of the DNA double helix, a necessary step for transcription initiation (Wang et al. 1977). The recognition process of the promoter itself, or phosphorylation or modification of a protein in the initiation complex could be additional steps where this requirement may exist.

ACKNOWLEDGMENTS

We thank Drs. M. Shander and S. Fuhrman for providing us with plasmids containing ε-globin and MuLV LTR, respectively. D. Bunick was supported with funds from 5T32-07922 and S. Ackerman with funds from 2T32 CA-09717. This work was supported with grants CA-10815, CA-21124 and AI-13231 from the National Institutes of Health.

REFERENCES

Babich A, Nevins JR, Darnell JE (1980). Early capping of transcripts from the adenovirus major late transcription unit. Nature 287:246.

Banerjee AK (1980). 5'-Terminal cap structure in eukaryotic messenger ribonucleic acids. Microbiol Rev 44:175.

Baralle FE, Shoulders CC, Proudfoot NJ (1980). The primary structure of the human ε-globin gene. Cell 21:621.

Bunick D, Weinmann R (1980). Use of thiotriphosphates for the study of in vitro initiation in adenovirus-infected cell nuclei. Biochim Biophys Acta 610:331.

Bunick D, Zandomeni R, Ackerman S, Weinmann R (1982). Mechanism of RNA polymerase II-specific initiation of transcription in vitro: ATP requirement and uncapped runoff transcripts. Cell 29:877.

Celma ML, Pan J, Weissman SM (1977). Studies of low molecular weight RNA from cells infected with adenovirus 2. II. Heterogeneity at the 5'-end of VA-RNA 1. J Biol Chem 252:9043.

Contreras R, Fiers W (1981). Initiation of transcription by RNA polymerase II in permeable, SV40-infected or non-infected CV1 cells: evidence for multiple promoters of SV40 late transcription. Nucl Acids Res 9:215.

Cozzarelli NR (1980). DNA topoisomerases. Cell 22:327.

Evans RM, Fraser N, Ziff E, Weber J, Wilson M, Darnell JE (1977). The initiation sites for RNA transcription in Ad2 DNA. Cell 12:733.

Fire A, Baker CC, Manley JL, Ziff EB, Sharp PA (1981). In vitro transcription of adenovirus. J Virol 40:703.

Fuhrman SA, van Beveren C, Verma I (1981). Identification of a RNA polymerase II initiation site in the long terminal repeat of murine leukemia viral DNA. Proc Natl Acad Sci USA 78:5411.

Gidoni D, Kahana C, Canaani D, Groner Y (1981). Specific initiation of transcription of SV40 early and late genes occurs at the various cap nucleotides including cytidine. Proc Natl Acad Sci USA 78:2174.

Hagenbuchler O, Schibler U (1981). Mouse β-globin and adenovirus 2 major late transcripts are initiated at the cap sites in vitro. Proc Natl Acad Sci USA 78:2283.

Lindell TJ, Weinberg F, Morris PW, Roeder RG, Rutter WJ (1970). Specific inhibition of nuclear RNA polymerase II by α-amanitin. Science 170:447.

Manley JL, Fire A, Cano A, Sharp PA, Gefter ML (1980). DNA-dependent transcription of adenovirus genes in a soluble whole cell extract. Proc Natl Acad Sci USA 77:3855.

Matsui T, Segall J, Weil PA, Roeder RG (1981). Multiple factors required for accurate initiation of transcription by RNA polymerase II. J Biol Chem 255:11992.

Murphy JT, Burgess RR, Dahlberg JE, Lund E (1982). Transcription of a gene for human U1 small nuclear RNA. Cell 29:265.

Proudfoot NJ, Shander MHM, Manley JL, Gefter ML, Maniatis T (1980). Structure and in vitro transcription of human globin genes. Science 209:1329.

Salditt-Georgieff M, Harpold M, Chen-Kiang S, Darnell JE (1980). The addition of 5' cap structures occurs early in hnRNA synthesis and prematurely terminated molecules are capped. Cell 19:69.

Sanger F, Coulson A (1978). The use of thin acrylamide gels for DNA sequencing. FEBS Lett 87:107.

Schwartz LB, Roeder RG (1975). Purification and subunit structure of DNA-dependent RNA polymerase II from the mouse plasmacytoma MOPC 315. J Biol Chem 250:3221.

Shatkin AJ (1976). Capping of eukaryotic mRNAs. Cell 9:645.

van Beveren C, Goddard JG, Beans A, Verma IM (1980). Structure of Moloney murine leukemia viral DNA: Nucleotide sequence of the 5' long terminal repeat and adjacent cellular sequences. Proc Natl Acad Sci USA 77:3307.

Venkatesan S, Gershowitz A, Moss B (1980). Purification and characterization of mRNA guanylyltransferase from HeLa cell nuclei. J Biol Chem 255:2829.

Vennstrom B, Pettersson U, Philipson L (1978). Initiation of transcription in nuclei isolated from adenovirus-infected cells. Nucl Acids Res 5:205.

Wang JC, Jacobsen JH, Saucier JM (1977). Physico-chemical studies on the interaction between DNA and RNA-polymerase. Unwinding of the DNA helix by Escherichia coli RNA polymerase. Nucl Acids Res 4:1225.

Weil PA, Luse DS, Segall J, Roeder RG (1979). Selective and accurate initiation of transcription at the Ad2 major late promoter in a soluble system dependent on purified RNA polymerase II and DNA. Cell 18:469.

Yount RG, Babcock D, Ballantyne W, Ojala D (1971). Adenylyl-imidodiphosphate, an adenosine triphosphate analog containing a P-N-P linkage. Biochemistry 10:2484.

Ziff EB, Evans RM (1978). Coincidence of the promoter and capped 5' terminus of RNA from the adenovirus 2 major late transcription unit. Cell 15:1463.

13th International Cancer Congress, Part B
Biology of Cancer (1), pages 19–33
© **1983 Alan R. Liss, Inc., 150 Fifth Avenue, New York, NY 10011**

THE STUDY OF MOLECULAR FUNCTIONS OF THE TRANSFORMING PROTEIN PP60^{SRC} OF ROUS SARCOMA VIRUS BY THE USE OF MONOSPECIFIC ANTIBODIES

Heinz Bauer, Teruko Tamura and C. Bruce Boschek

Institut für Virologie, Fachbereich Humanmedizin der Justus-Liebig-Universität Giessen D-6300 Giessen, West Germany

INTRODUCTION

Cellular transformation by Rous sarcoma virus (RSV) is caused by a single viral gene, src, which encodes a phosphoprotein of 60,000 d molecular weight (pp60^{src}) that has the function of a tyrosine-specific phosphotransferase (reviewed in Erikson, 1981). Evidence has been accumulating which indicates that phosphorylation of cellular proteins by this protein kinase plays an important role in the transformation mechanism (Sefton et al., 1980). In fact, a variety of proteins have been shown to be phosphorylated in tyrosine residues upon RSV-transformation. Most of these proteins have been defined mainly by molecular weight, and only few of them have been correlated with proteins of known functions, for instance a 130K protein which appears to be vinculin (Sefton et al., 1981), and a 38K phosphoprotein (Radke et al., 1980), which has been found associated with malic dehydrogenase activity (Rübsamen et al., 1982).

On the other hand, a variety of structural and metabolic alterations have been described to occur upon RSV-transformation, but their relationship with the function of pp60^{src} is not precisely known. They concern, for instance, elements of the cytoskeleton (Boschek et al., 1981) and such fundamental pathways such as glycolysis and metabolism of cyclic nucleotides and divalent cations (reviewed in Bauer et al., 1982). Interestingly, about 5 % of pp60^{src} molecules have been found to be complexed with two phosphoproteins in which form it appears to have reduced kinase activity (Hunter and Sefton, 1980; Brugge et al., 1981; Oppermann et al., 1981).

It appears that $pp60^{src}$ functions in a pleiotropic manner by interacting with different cellular target molecules either by its protein kinase activity or by other thus far unknown functions. Studies with transformation-defective, temperature-sensitive RSV mutants have in fact suggested a pleiotropic or multifunctional effect of $pp60^{src}$ (Calothy and Pessac, 1976; Becker et al., 1977; Friis et al., 1977; Weber and Friis, 1979). However, the extent of pleiotropism and the structural and metabolic consequences of the primary effects of $pp60^{src}$ are by no means clear.

One attempt to study the function of $pp60^{src}$ in more detail is to determine its intracellular localization. Such studies have been performed in several laboratories by immunocytochemical or cell fractionation methods using immune sera from RSV tumor-bearing animals (TBR serum), and $pp60^{src}$ has been found in different cellular compartments. The bulk of $pp60^{src}$ has been described to be associated with or located very near the inner face of the cytoplasma membrane (Willingham and Pastan, 1979), particularly at cell-cell contact sites and in focal adhesion plaques (Rohrschneider, 1979; 1980). $pp60^{src}$ has also been observed in the cytoplasm (Brugge et al., 1978; Rohrschneider, 1979; Willingham and Pastan, 1979), at the periphery of the nucleus (Rohrschneider, 1979), and in lower amounts at the outer cell surface (Barnekow et al., 1980). Whether these results reflect functions of $pp60^{src}$ at different cellular sites is not yet known, since immune sera from tumor-bearing animals have been used in those studies. These sera are not monospecific for $pp60^{src}$ and may possibly have reacted with molecules other than $pp60^{src}$.

The question of antibody specificity may be circumvented by using monospecific antibodies prepared against individual epitopes of $pp60^{src}$ and thus may be highly specific for that protein. Such antibodies may also allow the detection of specific configurations of $pp60^{src}$ possibly paralleling one or the other of its functional stages. A given configuration may be characterized by the exposure of specific epitopes. The fact that $pp60^{src}$ has more than one antigenic site is evident from the various degrees of cross-reactivity by individual TBR-sera when tested against $pp60^{src}$ of different origins (Rübsamen et al., 1979). Therefore, monospecific antisera to $pp60^{src}$ epitopes may allow the study of structural and functional relationships of this protein. One approach in this direction would be the preparation of monoclonal antibodies according to the method of Köhler and Milstein (1975). To our knowledge, no pp60^{src}-specific monoclonal antibodies have been described, and our own attempts to prepare such antibodies have failed, when pp60^{src} was used as immunogen.

An alternative approach for obtaining monospecific antibody is the immunization against synthetic peptides which correspond to certain regions of the protein. This method has been successfully used in several cases, when peptide sequences were predicted from the nucleotide sequence of the respective gene (Sutcliffe et al., 1980; Walter et al., 1980, 1981; Wang and Goldberg, 1981).

In this report, preliminary results will be presented on the production of monospecific antibodies prepared against 6 oligopeptides identical to amino acid sequences of pp60^{src}. The main subject will be concerned with the preparation of monoclonal antibodies in the mouse, and the isolation of specific antibodies from TBR-serum against a synthetic peptide containing the 6 amino acid residues at the carboxy terminus of pp60^{src}, and finally the use of such antibodies for the localization of pp60^{src}.

RESULTS

Antibodies prepared against 6 oligopeptides from the right half of pp60^{src}.

According to an "antigenicity plot" by Hopp and Woods (1981) which essentially searches for regions with a high hydrophilicity, we have chosen several peptide sequences from pp60^{src} as predicted from the nucleotide sequence of the src-gene of the Prague strain of RSV (D. Schwartz, R. Tizard, and W. Gilbert, personal communication). Thus far, six peptides synthesized by Drs. R. Birr and R. Pipkorn at the Max-Planck-Institut für Medizinische Forschung in Heidelberg, coupled with key lympet hemocyanin (KLH) have been used for immunization of each one rabbit. Peptide number I (in the order from the C' to the N'terminus) (409 Arg-Leu-Ile-Glu-Asp-Asn-Glu 415) yielded antibodies which precipitated a distinct amount of pp60^{src}, and peptide IV (457 Lys-Gly-Arg-Val-Pro-Tyr 463) and peptide V (500 Arg-Lys-Asp-Pro-Gly-Gly-Arg 506) induced antibodies with weak pp60^{src} reactivity. No pp60^{src} was detected with antibodies against the other three peptides.

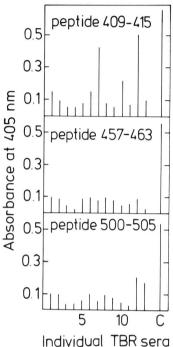

Figure 1. Screening of 13 different TBR-sera by ELISA for antibodies reactive with either of three synthetic peptides.
C represents, as a positive control, or rabbit antiserum prepared against the respective peptide.

To test whether antisera against native pp60^{src} contain antibodies against peptides I, IV and V, 13 different TBR-sera were tested in an ELISA for reaction with these peptides. Peptide monospecific antibodies were used as positive controls. As shown in Fig. 1, two of the TBR-sera have a rather strong, and 2 to 3 a weak reaction against peptide I, but none of the sera contains significant amounts of antibodies against peptide IV and only 2 sera reacted weakly with peptide V. These preliminary results suggest that peptide I represents an antigenic site of native pp60^{src} fairly well, and peptide IV and V may be similar to or part of other antigenic sites.

While these peptide-specific antibodies have not yet been further analyzed, we have studied antibodies prepared against a carboxy terminal peptide (C'peptide) in more detail as will be described in the following.

Antigenicity of native pp60^{src} in the carboxy terminal region.
The C'peptide (NH2 Tyr-Val-Leu-Glu-Val-Ala-Glu COOH) prepared by Bachem, Bubendorf/Switzerland, contains the 6

carboxy terminal amino acids of pp60^{src} as predicted from
the nucleotide sequence of the src-gene of the Schmidt-
Ruppin strain of RSV (Czernilofsky et al., 1980), and an
additional N-terminal tyrosine for purpose of linkage to a
carrier protein. G. Walter and coworkers have found that
this peptide induced pp60^{src} reactive antibodies in rabbits
(pers. communications). We were interested first in examining
whether this peptide region is immunogenic in native pp60^{src}.
To test this, a total of 28 different TBR-sera, all reactive
with pp60^{src}, were examined for specific binding with the
C'peptide; ten sera were tested by immunoprecipitation of
^{125}I-labelled C'peptide which was conjugated to ovalbumine
(OA-C'peptide), and 18 were tested by the ELISA. Three out
of these 28 sera were found to contain significant amounts
of C'peptide reactive antibodies. The specificity of the
reaction was demonstrated in a competition experiment in
which the precipitition of radiolabeled C'peptide could be
inhibited to 80 - 100 % by preincubation of sera with
either C'peptide alone or C'peptide coupled to carrier
proteins, but not by preincubation with carrier alone (data
not shown).

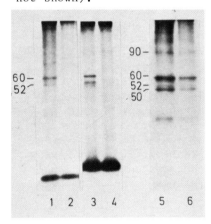

Figure 2. Immunoprecipitation
with extracts from ^{32}P-ortho-
phosphate-labelled SR-RSV-A
transformed CEC.
1) R-C'IgG (10 μg); 2) R-C'IgG
after pretreatment with C'peptide; 3) TBR-C'IgG (3 μg);
4) TBR-C'IgG after pretreatment
with C'peptide; 5) total TBR-
IgG (10 μg); 6) Total TBR-IgG
after treatment with C'peptide

   C'peptide-specific IgG isolated from TBR-serum (TBR-
C'IgG) was investigated for pp60^{src} specificity in comparison to antibodies from a rabbit serum which was prepared
directly against C'peptide by G. Walter (R-C'IgG). As shown
in Fig. 2, both IgG preparations precipitate a 60K and a
52K phosphoprotein from extracts of chick embryo cells (CEC)
transformed by SR-RSV-A and labeled with ^{32}P-orthophosphate.
This precipitation was completely inhibited by preincubation
of either of the IgG's with C'peptide (tracks 1 - 4). In

contrast, the immunoprecipitation of the 60K and 52K phosphoprotein by total TBR-IgG is barely competed by preincubation
with C'peptide (tracks 5, 6). Similar results were obtained
when extracts of ^{35}S-methionine-labeled RSV-transformed CEC
were used (data not shown). C'peptide-IgG's could not serve
as a phosphate acceptor in an immune complex protein kinase
reaction.

Therefore, in order to ascertain whether the immuno-
precipitated 60K phosphoprotein is indeed the phosphokinase-
associated pp60^{src}, we checked in a competition assay whether
C'peptide-specific IgG could remove pp60^{src} kinase activity
from cell extracts. For this purpose, lysates from CEC transformed by B77-ASV-C and lysates of normal primary CEC were
incubated with total TBR-IgG for kinase reaction after having
been pretreated as indicated in the legend to Fig. 3a which
shows the results obtained with R-C'IgG. R-C'IgG removed
kinase activity from virus-transformed cells as well as did
whole TBR-IgG, and the absorption capacity was blocked by
preincubation of R-C'IgG with C'peptide.

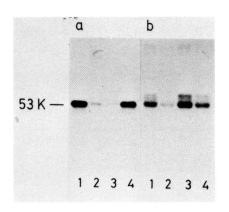

Figure 3. Kinase absorption
assay. Lysates from B77-ASV-
C (a) transformed CEC and
from normal primary CEC (b)
were pretreated with
1) Staph. aur.; 2) Total
TBR-IgG (50 µg) adsorbed to
Staph. aur.; 3) R-C'IgG (5
µg) adsorbed to Staph. aur.;
4) IgG as in 3) but after
preabsorption with C'peptide,
centrifuged and the super-
natants tested with total
TBR-IgG for kinase reaction.

Similar results were obtained with SR-RSV-A and Pr-RSV-A-
transformed cells. It can, therefore, be concluded that C'-
peptide-specific IgG indeed react with pp60^{src}. These results further show, that the carboxy terminal end of pp60^{src}
of these three sarcoma virus strains are antigenically related, and that this antigenic site is not detected in cellular pp60src as is evident from Fig. 3b.

About 5 % of pp60^{src} molecules have been found to be

complexed with a 50,000 molecular weight phosphotyrosine containing protein and a phosphoserine-containing 90,000 molecular weight protein (Hunter and Sefton, 1980; Brugge et al.,
1981; Oppermann et al., 1981). The amounts of phosphotyrosine and the IgG phosphorylating activity are greatly reduced
in the complexed pp60^{src} molecules (Brugge et al., 1981),
and we wished to determine, whether this function of pp60^{src}
may be the result of an altered configuration with the consequence of a different antigenicity. We have, therefore,
tested, whether complexed pp60^{src} could be detected by C'
peptide-IgG. As this could not be decided from the experiments with SR-RSV-A transformed cells, owing to the small
fraction of complexed pp60^{src} with this virus (Fig. 2),we examined cells infected by the ts-NY68 mutant of RSV which have
been shown to contain higher proportions of complexed pp60^{src}
as compared to wild type virus infected cells (Brugge et al.,
1981). As is shown in Fig. 4, total TBR-IgG indeed copreci-
pitates more pp50 and pp90 from ts-NY68-transformed cells
(track 1) than from wild-type SR-RSV-A-transformed cells
(Fig. 2, track 5). Although, the bands obtained with TBR-C'IgG
are weaker than with total TBR-IgG it is clear that C'IgG co-
precipitates pp50 and pp90 (Fig. 4, track 2).

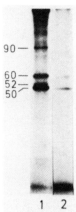

Figure 4. Immunoprecipitation by two
IgG preparation of ^{32}P-orthophosphate-
labelled CEC infected by the ts-NY68
mutant of SR-RSV at permissive 35° C
temperature.
a) Total TBR-IgG (30 µg);
2) TBR-C'IgG (3 µg);

Preparation of monoclonal antibody against C'peptide.
As we have had failed to obtain monoclonal antibodies
after immunization with native pp60^{src}, we tested whether
pp60^{src} reactive monoclonal antibodies could be prepared
against the C'peptide. Spleen cells from a BALB/c mouse which
was immunized with BSA-C'peptide were hybridized to X-63-Ag8-
653 myeloma cells, and a hybridoma culture was obtained which
produced C'peptide-specific IgG (mouse C'peptide-IgG). For
further studies, IgG was prepared from ascites of hybridoma

injected mice.

When the mouse C'peptide-IgG's were reacted with non-ionic detergent extracts from ^{32}P-orthophosphate-labeled SR-RSV-A transformed CEC,three major bands in the molecular weight range between 52K and 60K were detected (Fig. 5). A partial hydrolysis of these isolated bands with the V8-protease showed that the 60K band represents pp60^{src} and the lower molecular weight bands both represent cleavage products of pp60^{src} (data not shown). As increased amounts of mouse-IgG did not precipitate pp60^{src} quantitatively as compared to total TBR-IgG, one can assume, that the C'peptide-specific antibodies do not react with all pp60^{src} molecules that can be detected by TBR-serum.

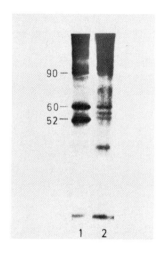

Figure 5. Protein immuno-precipitated from ^{32}P-ortho-phosphate-labeled SR-RSV-A transformed CEC
1) Total TBR-IgG (50 μg);
2) Monoclonal C'peptide-IgG (5 μg).

As no phosphorylated mouse-IgG could be observed upon reaction in a kinase assay, we tested as a further proof for the specificity of the mouse-C'peptide-IgG whether these antibodies could bind and remove pp60^{src}-associated kinase activity in a competition assay. As shown in Fig. 6, track 4, the monoclonal antibodies removed about 60-70 % kinase activity. This effect, however, was only observed when extraction buffer was used but not with RIPA-buffer. In contrast, TBR-IgG adsorbed almost 100 % of kinase activity under both conditions.

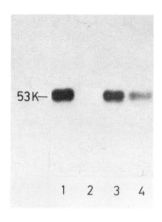

Figure 6. Kinase absorption test of a lysate from SR-RSV-A transformed CEC prepared with extraction buffer.
Before incubation of the extracts with TBR-serum, they were pretreated for 1 hour at 0° C as follows with:
1) Staph. aureus only;
2) Staph. aureus loaded with total TBR-IgG (50 μg);
3) Staph. aureus loaded with myeloma ascites IgG (5 μg);
4) Staph. aureus loaded with mouse C'peptide-IgG (5 μg).

The intracellular localization of pp60^{src} by immune electron microscopy.

Previous attempts to establish the localization of the viral pp60^{src} within the host cell have been handicapped by two technical limitations. Firstly, the localization methods used (immunofluorescence or conventional electron microscopy) were subject to artefactual relocation of the protein during preparation. Secondly, the immune reagents were partially purified multivalent TBR-antisera which may have recognized a number of antigens besides pp60^{src}. In addition, the localization was performed on equilibrium populations of transformed cells and provided no information on the distribution of the molecule during the transformation process.

To alleviate these difficulties we have attempted the localization of pp60^{src} using two novel techniques: C'peptide-specific antibodies with a high specificity for pp60^{src} were applied to frozen thin sections which have been shown by numerous control experiments to be virtually free of "relocation artefacts". In order to establish the localization during transformation we performed these studies on transformation-defective, temperature-sensitive (td-ts) mutant RSV (NY68) infected CEC. Localization experiments were performed at the nonpermissive temperature and at the permissive temperature 2 and 24 hours after downshift. For comparison, the same methods were performed on CEC infected with a wild-type RSV, a non-transforming virus (RAV-5) as well as on uninfected CEC. The following data must be considered preliminary since they represent a summary of limited number of preparations (2 or 3 fixations of each cell type).

In the first such experiments described here, we used R-C'peptide-IgG isolated by affinity cholumn chromatography over a column made of C'peptide coupled to CH-Sepharose 4B (Deutsche Pharmacia). R-C'peptide-IgG was used at a concentration of 50 µg/ml for labeling of frozen thin sections. For purpose of comparison, IgG from preabsorbed TBR-serum was used at 20 µg/ml. Freezing of cells and ultracryotomy was performed essentially as described by Tokuyasu (1978). Sections of 60 to 80 nm were incubated with immune reagents and consequently labeled with protein A coloidal Au. Average numbers of gold particles per cell cross section were obtained by counting a number of cells directly in the electron microscope.

Both immune reagents used labeled pp60^{src} in the cytoplasm and on the plasma membrane in wild-type RSV-transformed CEC. Roughly half the particles are on or very near the plasma membrane, and the label can be seen on both leaflets of the lipid bilayer (Fig. 7a, b). There appeared to be some association of pp60^{src} with the Golgi stacks (not shown) and endoplasmic reticulum (Fig. 7b). Control experiments on normal CEC (data not shown) and RAV-5-infected CEC with both TBR-IgG (Fig. 7c) and R-C'peptide-IgG (data not shown) showed negligeable background labeling. As we were interested in comparing the localization of pp60^{src} in typically transformed and nontransformed cells, we examined cells infected by a td-ts mutant at non-permissive temperature with 2 hours and 24 hours after downshift to the permissive temperature. CEC-infected with ts-NY68 at the permissive temperature show similar total numbers and distribution of gold particles to cells transformed by wild-type virus. At the non-permissive temperature, however, more than 80 % of pp60^{src} is located in the cytoplasm (table 1). First accumulations of the transforming protein at the plasma membrane are found within the "flowers" at the dorsal cell surface (data not shown). The distribution and average number of gold particles per cell cross-section in cells under various conditions is summarized in table 1. Thus, about half of the pp60^{src} in a transformed cell is bound to both the inner and outer leaflets of the plasma membrane. In contrast, at the non-permissive temperature cells infected with td-ts mutant virus show labeling of this molecule primarily in the cytoplasm. The reason for this is not clear, and it will be interesting to investigate this further by monospecific antibodies against different epitopes of pp60^{src}, to see whether this difference may be due to a conformational change of pp60^{src} detectable by a specific antigenic make up.

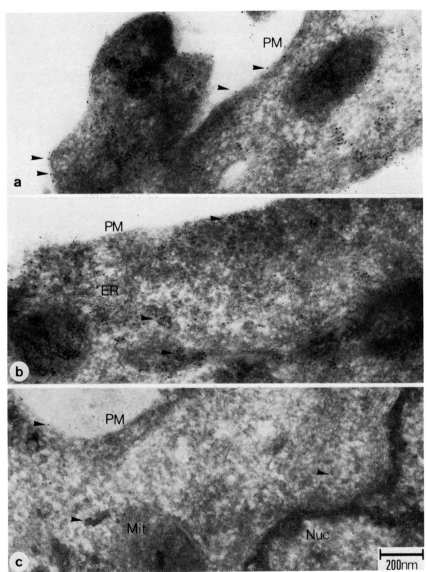

Fig. 7. Electron micrographs of colloidal gold-labelled, frozen thin sections of CEC infected with SR-RSV-a (a,b) and RAV-5 (c); a,c) TBR-serum, b,) C'peptide antibody.(Mit) mitochonria, (Nuc)nucleus,(PM)plasma membrane,(ER)endoplasmic reticulum. A few gold particles have been randomly accentuated by arrowheads.

Table 1

Distribution and Average Number of Gold Particles per Cell Cross Section

Cell Type	Total Number of Cells Counted		Average Number of Gold Particles per Cell Cross Section		Average Number of Gold Particles on Plasma Membrane		Average Number of Gold Particles over Cytoplasm per Cell Cross Section	
	TBR	CTP	TBR	CTP	TBR	CTP	TBR	CTP
Uninfected	43	38	16±5	<3	<1	<1	15±5	<2
Infected with: RAV-5	40	29	21±7	<3	4±2	<1	17±5	<2
ts 68 42°C	36	24	126±22	64±12	21±5	12±3	105±17	52±10
ts 68 2hrs at 35°C	32	33	119±21	63±13	43±8	21±5	77±13	42±8
ts 68 24hrs at 35°C	35	34	96±20	61±13	46±11	31±7	50±9	29±6
SR-RSV-A	42	35	114±25	61±10	59±14	33±6	55±11	28±5

CONCLUSIONS

Our experiments show that oligopeptides consisting of short linear amino acid sequences of $pp60^{src}$ induce antibodies which are reactive with a native protein, and thus can be used for the study of structure and function of $pp60^{src}$. The peptides which induced the most reactive antibody against $pp60^{src}$ correspond to regions which are also immunogenic in the native protein. This stems from the finding that above 10 % of individual TBR-sera contained antibody against these two peptides. All 6 peptides chosen according to a hydrophilicity value (Hopp and Woods, 1981) were immunogenic in a complex with carrier protein, but three induced no detectable $pp60^{src}$ reactive antibody, and two induced only weakly reactive antibody. This was paralleled by a similar pattern of antibody in TBR-sera against these peptides, thus suggesting that in such an appraoch one should not limit the protocol to few peptides only.

This study of $pp60^{src}$ with the C'peptide antibody allowed several conclusions: 1.) monoclonal antibodies can be produced against $pp60^{src}$ by the use of oligopeptides. 2.) Antibodies binding to the site of $pp60^{src}$ are not phosphorylated. 3.) The C'terminal antigenic site is group-specific for the $pp60^{src}$ molecules of the three sarcoma virus strains tested, but obviously different in endogenous $pp60^{src}$. 4.) $pp60^{src}$ as complexed with pp50 and pp90 and having a reduced kinase activity is also detected by C'peptide-IgG. 5.) The antibodies can be used for study of the intracellular localization of $pp60^{src}$ and show that roughly half the $pp60^{src}$

is located on both leaflets of the plasma membrane, the remainder is in the cytoplasm. 6.) Cells infected with a td-ts mutant virus contain similar amounts of the transforming protein at both the permissive and the non-permissive temperature, whereby the cell phenotype is normal. In such cells, however, the pp60^{src} is primarily in the cytoplasm. Downshift to the permissive temperature results in a translocation of the molecule to the plasma membrane and subsequent transformation of the cells.

ACKNOWLEDGEMENTS

We thank G. Walter for the generous gift of the carboxy terminal peptide and respective rabbit-antibody. Thanks are due to Heike Tributh and Ruth Back for competent technical assistance.

This work was supported by the Deutsche Forschungsgemeinschaft (SFB 47, Virologie).

REFERENCES

Bauer H (1982). The transforming protein of Rous sarcoma virus pp60^{src}: Growth and cell proliferation inducing properties. In Dumont JE, Nunez J, Schultz G (eds). "Hormone and Cell Regulation" Vol. 6, pp.187-205. Elsevier Biomedical Press.

Barnekow A, Boschek CB, Ziemiecki A, Bauer H (1980). Detection of the src-gene product pp60^{src} and its associated kinase on the surface of Rous sarcoma virus transformed cells. Biochem. Society Transactions 8:735-736.

Becker D, Kurth R, Critchley D, Friis RR, Bauer H (1977). Distinguishable transformation defective phenotype among temperature sensitive mutants of Rous sarcoma virus. J. Virol. 21:1042.

Boschek CB, Jockusch BM, FRIIS RR, Back R, Grundmann E, Bauer H (1981). Early changes in the distribution and organization of microfilament proteins during cell transformation. Cell 24:175.

Brugge JS, Steinbaugh PJ, Erikson RL (1978). Characterization of the avian sarcoma virus protein p60^{src}. Virology 91: 130.

Brugge JS, Erikson E, Erikson RL (1981). The specific interaction of the Rous sarcoma virus transforming protein, pp60^{src} with two cellular proteins. Cell 25:363.

Calothy G, Pessac B (1976). Growth stimulation of chick embryo neuro-retinal cells infected with RSV; relationship to viral replication and morphological transformation. Virology 71:336.

Czernilofsky AP, Levinson AD, Varmus HE, Bishop JM, Tischer, E, Goodman HM (1980). Nucleotide sequence of an avian sarcoma virus oncogene (src) and proposed amino acid sequence for gene product. Nature 287:198.

Erikson RL (1·981). The transforming protein of avian sarcoma viruses and its homologue in normal cells. Curr. Top. Microbiol. Immunol. 91:41.

Friis RR, Schwarz RT, Schmidt MFG (1977). Phenotype of Rous sarcoma virus-transformed fibroblasts. An argument for a multifunctional src gene product. Med. Microbiol. Immunol. 164:155.

Hopp TP, Woods KR (1981). Prediction of protein antigenic determinants from amino acid sequences Proc. Natl. Acad. Sci.USA 78:3824.

Hunter T, Sefton BM (1980). Transforming gene product of Rous sarcoma viruses phosphorylates tyrosine. Proc. Natl. Acad.Sci.USA 77:1311.

Köhler G, Milstein C (1975). Continuous cultures of fused cells secreting antibody of predifined specificity. Nature 256:495.

Oppermann H, Levinson W, Bishop JM (1981): A cellular protein that is associated with the transforming protein of Rous sarcoma virus is also a heat-shock protein. Proc.Natl.Acad.Sci.USA 78:1067.

Radke K, Gilmore T, Martin GS (1980). Transformation by Rous sarcoma virus: a cellular substrate for transformation-specific protein phosphorylation contains phosphotyrosine. Cell 21:821.

Rohrschneider LR (1979). Immunofluorescence on avian sarcoma virus-transformed cells: Localization of the src gene product. Cell 16:11.

Rohrschneider LR (1980). Adhesion plaques of Rous sarcoma virus-transformed cells contain the src gene product. Proc.Natl.Acad.Sci.USA 77:3514.

Rübsamen H, Friis RR, Bauer H (1979). Src-gene product from different strains of avian sarcoma virus: Kinetics and possible mechanism of heat inactivation of protein kinase activity from cells infected by transformation-defective, temperature-sensitive mutant and wild-type virus. Proc. Natl.Acad.Sci.USA 76:967.

Rübsamen H, Saltenberger K., Friis RR, Eigenbrodt E (1982). Cytosolig malic dehydrogenase activity is associated with a putative substrate for the transforming gene product of Rous sarcoma virus. Proc.Natl.Acad.Sci.USA 79:228.

Sefton BM, Hunter T, Ball EH, Singer SJ (1981). Vinculin: a cytoskeletal target of the transforming protein of Rous

sarcoma virus. Cell 24:165.
Sefton BM, Hunter T, Beemon K, Eckhart W. (1980). Evidence that the phosphorylation of tyrosine is essential for cellular transformation by Rous sarcoma virus. Cell 20:807.
Sutcliffe, JG, Shinnick, TM, Green N, Liu FT, Niman HL, Lerner RA (1980). Chemical synthesis of a polypeptide predicted from nucleotide sequence allows detection of a new retroviral gene product. Nature 287:801.
Tokuyasu KT (1978). A study of positive staining of ultrathin frozen sections. J. Ultrastruct. Res. 63:287.
Walter G, Scheidtmann KH., Carbone A, Laudano AP, Doolittle, RF (1980). Antibodies specific for the carboxy- and aminoterminal regions of simian virus 40 large tumor antigens. Proc.Natl.Acad.Sci.USA 77:5197.
Walter G, Hutchinson MA, Hunter T, Eckhart W (1981). Antibodies specific for the polyoma virus middle-size tumor antigen. Proc.Natl.Acad.Sci.USA 78:4882.
Weber M, Friis RR (1979). Dissociation of transformation parameter using temperature conditional mutants of Rous sarcoma virus. Cell 16:25.
Willingham MC, Jay G, Pastan I (1979). Localization of the ASV src gene product to the plasma membrane of transformed cells by electron microscopy immunocytochemistry. Cell 18:125.
Wong TW, Goldberg AR (1981). Synthetic peptide fragment of src gene product inhibits the src protein kinase and crossreacts immunoligically with avian onc kinases and cellular phosphoproteins. Proc. Natl. Acad. Sci. USA 78: 7412.

CONGRESS SYMPOSIA

EPSTEIN-BARR VIRUS AND OTHER LYMPHOTROPHIC HERPES
VIRUSES Epstein, M., A., UK, Chairman; Aurelian, L.,
USA, Co-Chairman; Arena

Nasopharyngeal Carcinoma: Can Antiviral Interventions
be Contemplated to Prevent this Cancer?
*de-Thé, G. and Zeng, Y., Lyon, France and
Beijing, People's Republic of China.

The Association of Epstein-Barr Virus with
Nasopharyngeal Carcinoma. *Glaser, R.,
Stoerker, J. and Cheng, Y. C., Columbus, OH USA
and Chapel Hill, NC USA.

Vaccine Control of Malignancies Induced by
Lymphotropic Herpesviruses. *Epstein, M. A.,
North, J. R. and Morgan, A. J., Bristol, England.

Marek's Disease Virus and Herpesvirus of
Turkeys: Antigenic Aspects. *Kato, S., Ikuta, K.
and Hirai, K., Osaka, Japan.

Lymphotropic Non-Human Primate Herpes Viruses.
*Lapin, B. A., Sukhumi, USSR. (By Title Only)

Please note: Papers that are listed as "By Title
Only" were presented at the 13th International
Cancer Congress, but are not included in these
volumes.

13th International Cancer Congress, Part B
Biology of Cancer (1), pages 37–47
© 1983 Alan R. Liss, Inc., 150 Fifth Avenue, New York, NY 10011

NASOPHARYNGEAL CARCINOMA: CAN ANTIVIRAL INTERVENTIONS BE
CONTEMPLATED TO PREVENT THIS CANCER ?

Guy de-Thé[1] and Yi Zeng[2]

1. Laboratory of Epidemiology and Immunovirology
of Tumors, Faculty of Medicine A. Carrel, Lyon,
France
2. Institute of Virology, Chinese Academy of
Medical Sciences, Beijing, People's Rep. of China

INTRODUCTION

Undifferentiated nasopharyngeal carcinoma (NPC) is a
leading cause of cancer death for large populations in
Southeast Asia, Africa and around the Mediterranea. The
question therefore arises as to whether the association with
the Epstein-Barr virus (EBV) can be utilized for the control
of this disease through early diagnosis and ultimately in
preventing the disease.

The existence of pre-neoplastic conditions characterized
by increasing IgA/VCA antibody titers and cytological changes
in the nasopharyngeal mucosa gives an opportunity to evaluate
the feasibility of conducting intervention trials aimed at
reducting or eliminating EBV reactivation and cytological
abnormalities with the ultimate goal of reducing NPC incidence.
The purpose of the present review is not to describe the
epidemiology of NPC as this has been repeatedly and recently
done (de-Thé, Ho, Muir, 1976 ; Hirayama, 1978), but rather
to assess the feasibility of implementing preventive and
antiviral interventions as a mean to try and prevent NPC and
to clarify the role of EBV in NPC development.

The situation of EBV vaccination in relation to NPC
will be quite different when EBV vaccine becomes available.
The ethical problem of EBV vaccination will be quite critical
as there is no known deadly disease associated with primary
EBV infection worth preventing in the large populations at
high risk for NPC.

These difficulties should not prevent considering the use of an EBV vaccine when available, but points out the need of evaluating other avenues to try and prevent NPC.

EBV/IgA ANTIBODIES ALLOW EARLY DIAGNOSIS OF NPC AND REPRESENT A CRITICAL RISK FACTOR FOR NPC DEVELOPMENT

Sero-epidemiological surveys of large population groups in the People's Republic of China by Zeng and collaborators have demonstrated the practical value of the IgA/VCA test in early detection of NPC in the highly endemic areas of South China (Zeng et al, 1980, 1982). This was achieved by the development of an immunoenzymatic test (Pi et al, 1981) more adapted to the field conditions than the classic immunofluorescence test as developed by Henle and Henle (1966).

The routine use of this test in certain areas of the Guang-Xi Autonomous Region of the People's Republic of China allowed to substantially improve the detection rate of NPC (Zeng et al, 1980) and to uncover most of the NPC cases at a very early stage of the disease. In the first study (Zeng et al, 1980), about 50 % of the diagnosed NPC were at stages I and II, while in a more recent survey, all cases were discovered at stage I and II (Zeng et al, 1982).

The impact of early diagnosis of NPC by a simple serological test is in itself a major achievement for better control of the disease, as up to 85 % of NPC at stage I can be cured (five years survival disease free in Hongkong (Ho, 1972).

To try and estimate the Incidence Rate (IR) of NPC among IgA positive individuals, two pieces of information were available :

a) out of 99 persons found to have IgA antibodies in 1977 and reexamined ten months later, two were found to have developed NPC in the meantime (Zeng et al, 1980).

b) the follow-up of the 3,350 individuals, found to have IgA/VCA antibodies in the Zangwu county survey, led to the uncovering of 33 new cases within 8-30 months of follow-up (estimated mean: 24 months) (Zeng et al, unpublished data). From these data, a yearly rate of 10/1,000 persons can be estimated for males aged 40 to 50 years and having IgA/VCA antibodies.

The Relative Risk (RR) to develop NPC for IgA/VCA positive individuals was found to be 50 to 80 times higher than that of the general population. Furthermore, the NPC prevalence among individuals having IgA/VCA antibodies was found to be related to the antibody titers: 1 % for individuals with IgA/VCA titers between 20 and 40, 3 % for individuals with IgA/VCA titers 80/160 and 9 % when IgA/VCA titers reached 320/640 (calculated from Zeng et al, 1982).

EPIDEMIOLOGICAL CHARACTERISTICS OF THIS IgA/VCA SUBPOPULATION GROUP

The first question coming to mind is : How long before clinical onset of NPC do IgA/VCA antibodies develop ? From the data of Ho et al (1978), Lanier et al (1980) and Zeng et al (1980, 1982, unpublished data), it can be estimated that IgA/VCA antibodies can be detected up to five years prior to diagnosis of late NPC cases and up to 15 to 18 months prior to the diagnosis of early NPC cases. These estimations are based on small numbers and only a prospective population study will enable to establish the mean duration of the IgA/VCA positive period preceeding NPC development. This point is critical since the clinical onset of the disease may be much delayed from the time of appearance of epithelial tumorous cells in nasopharyngeal mucosa. Subclinical disease may last for years for certain carcinomas.

The second question relates to the proportion of persons entering or leaving the IgA/VCA positive subpopulation group. The IgA/VCA positive individuals as tested by IE represent 2.5 to 5.5 % of the population aged 35 years and above. This proportion was shown to increase with age (Pi et al, 1981) and the age-specific prevalence curve of IgA antibodies paralleled that of the NPC age-specific incidence. The population based study, as implemented in Wuchow (Zeng et al, 1982) should give precise data on the rate of sero-conversion from IgA negative to IgA positive. The type of test used to detect IgA/VCA antibodies will indeed influence directly such rate. For all practical purposes, an overly sensitive test is to be avoided as this increases the proportion of false positive, as compared to a less sensitive test. In this context, it is of interest to note that Ho in Hongkong detected only 1 % of the population above 30 years of age as IgA/VCA positive, by immunofluorescence, versus

5 % for Zeng by the immunoenzymatic test.

The term "retroversion" is proposed to describe the loss of detectable IgA/VCA antibodies in an individual. The retroversion rate has been estimated to be around 9 % yearly by Zeng in his survey in the Zangwu county (1980 and unpublished data). It is of critical importance to establish firmly such retroversion rates in the study population where intervention trials are being contemplated.

In summary, the on-going sero-epidemiological survey of Wuchow city with its yearly follow-up of 1,000 IgA positive and 500 IgA negative individuals aged 40 to 50 years should establish firmly the annual rates of sero"conversion" and of "retroversion".

PRE-NEOPLASTIC CYTOLOGICAL CHANGES IN THE NASOPHARYNGEAL MUCOSA

In the sero-epidemiological surveys referred to above, the IgA/VCA positive individuals were clinically examined and a series of macroscopical abnormalities were noted in their nasopharynx: mostly hyperplasia, metaplasia, but also chronic nasopharyngitis, enlarged adenoids, polyps, etc.. In the Zangwu survey of Zeng et al (1980), 207 individuals with the above described macroscopic lesions were biopsied: besides 47 NPC, histopathology showed metaplasia in 32% of the non-tumorous biopsies and hyperplasia in 7 %. Up to 22 % of persons in the latter group noted as having "chronic inflammation" had IgA/EA antibodies. In the Wuchow survey (Zeng et al, 1982), biopsies were taken from 38 persons with such abnormalities and 21 were diagnosed histopathologically as NPC, 13 being at stage I.

When 17 persons exhibiting severe hyperplasia or meta-plasia in the nasopharynx and 38 individuals with minor hyperplasia or normal nasopharynx were followed up for 8 to 33 months, it was found that 5 of the 17 (28 %) metaplastic or hyperplastic cases developed NPC (and were detected either at stage I or II), whereas only 1 of the 38 controls was detected at stage I, 8 months after the first biopsy was taken (Li et al, submitted for publi-cation).

Serological and cytological anomalies can increase the risk for NPC from 1 to 60 times, or even up to 1,500 times as compared to that of the general population. It is of paramount importance that the Wuchow on-going population study verifies these estimations since they were made on relatively small numbers. These data will form the basis on which intervention trials will be designed.

DETECTION OF VIRAL MARKERS IN NASOPHARYNGEAL MUCOSA

In order to see whether the secretion of EBV/IgA antibodies corresponded to an EBV activity in the nasopharyngeal mucosa, 56 symptomless individuals having serum IgA/VCA antibodies for 15 to 18 months were carefully clinically examined and biopsied (de-Thé et al, 1981). Four early NPC were discovered and 14 further individuals, for whom no histopathological nor clinical evidence of NPC could be noted, were found to have detectable EBV/DNA sequences and/ or EBNA in their nasopharyngeal mucosa (Desgranges et al, 1982). In the remaining 38 biopsies of IgA positive individuals, no EBV markers were detected. 7 biopsies done on IgA/VCA negative individuals at the same time showed no detectable viral markers in their NP mucosa.

With these results in hand, it seemed that another critical and immediate NPC risk marker could be the presence of EB viral markers in the nasopharyngeal mucosa. As it was not possible to biopsy NP mucosa of normal, IgA/VCA negative individuals, it was difficult to establish the absence of EBV infection in normal NP mucosa. This possibility came about with the use of a negative pressure apparatus allowing to collect exfoliated cells from the nasopharynx. Enough cells could be obtained to make smears for cytological examination and EBNA studies, and to extract DNA for search of EBV/DNA sequences. Exfoliated cells, collected from the nasopharynx of 62 IgA/VCA positive and of 39 IgA/VCA negative individuals in Wuchow city were investigated. DNA was extracted from these cells and tested by spot and then by blot hybridization techniques using the cloned internal repeat of B 95-8 virus DNA as probe. Unexpected findings were observed. Both IgA positive and IgA negative groups exhibited a similar proportion of EBV/ DNA positive specimens (Desgranges et al, in preparation). Spot hybridization is known to yield some false positive results and thus all the spot positive specimens were reevaluated by blot hybridization halving the proportion of

positive. In this context, it is to be noted that the 3
individuals positive by spot and negative by blot also
lack IgG antibodies to EA. Is EBV present in non-tumorous
NP epithelial cells ? The anticomplement immunoenzymatic
test (ACIE) as developed by Pi et al (1981) was used to
detect EBNA in exfoliated cells. The study of 79 NPC
patients exhibited EBNA in tumor cells but also in inflammatory or hyperplastic part of their nasopharynx. Furthermore,
4 % of patients with ENT diseases other than NPC similarly
exhibited EBNA in their NP cells (Zeng et al, in preparation).
Similar observations were obtained by Chen et al (1982)
and Ho (personal communication).

The above data, which need confirmation by other
technics, suggest that EBV might be present in non-tumorous
nasopharynx but the extent of such a presence, in acute,
chronic or latent EBV infection, the cell type involved and
the variations to be observed between geographical areas
and ethnic groups, remain to be better determined. The
relatively easy access to exfoliated NP cells should promote
the implementation of such studies aimed at identifying
the risk factor associated with the presence of EBV markers
either in epithelial cells columnar or in the basal layer
or in the submucosal lymphoid cells.

PRELIMINARY STEPS TO BE IMPLEMENTED BEFORE INTERVENTION
TRIALS CAN BE CONTEMPLATED

As mentioned above, it is critical to clarify
certain characteristics of the natural history of EBV
reactivation in relation to risk of NPC before implementing
any intervention trial. Within the ongoing population
study of Wuchow, the following will have to be characterized :

      - the age/sex specific prevalence of IgA/VCA positive
and IgG/EA positive individuals,

      - the annual age/sex specific rate of retroversion
(from IgA+ to IgA-),

      - the annual age/sex specific rate of conversion
(from IgA- to IgA+),

      - the annual age/sex specific rate of significant
increases and decreases in IgA/VCA and IgG/EA antibodies,

      - the annual NPC incidence among IgA+ and IgA-
subpopulation groups.

The registration, initial bleeding, proper follow-up and cancer registration for ideally 40,000 persons 35 years of age and above in Wuchow, should give the necessary demographic and epidemiological base lines. The ongoing serological surveillance of 1,000 IgA+ and 500 IgA- individuals is minimal to obtain reliable figures concerning the rate of conversion, retroversion and antibody changes. The doubling of these figures would be desirable.

a) a better serological and cytological characterization of pre-NPC conditions are needed before contemplating interventions. Serologically, the parameters to involve will be the ADCC titers, anti-EBV/DNAse antibodies and the IgG/EA antibodies of individuals with high or low NPC risk.

b) the characteristic atypic, metaplastic cytological changes will have to be agreed upon by an international group.

c) which individuals will benifit most from intervention ? Epidemiologically, individuals at the borderline of IgA positivity would be eligible for studying the rate of negative connection from IgA+ to IgA-. But this would be difficult to achieve ethically and technically because of the variations at the laboratory tests. Motivation will be best for individuals with higher IgA/VCA titers and at higher risk for NPC (5 % prevalence of NPC in individuals with IgA/VCA titers around 160/320 as tested by the immuno-enzymatic test in China). This group should yield a large proportion of cooperative individuals after proper information on NPC is given.

WHAT TYPE OF INTERVENTION CAN BE CONTEMPLATED ?

This question remains wide open as there is yet no EBV specific proposal to make. However a few possibilities merit discussion :

a) non-specific anti-promoting agent such as beta-caroten

Peto et al (1981) recently reviewed the epidemiological data suggesting a two fold decrease in carcinoma risk for individuals having a high beta-caroten diet. A large intervention study involving 20,000 American physicians is being implemented by the Harvard School of Medicine (Hennekens, personal communication) to assess the role of beta-caroten intake and blood retinol in prevention of common carcinomas. In the on-going prospective serological

survey in Wuchow, one could contemplate to intervene by
distributing beta-caroten or placebo to randomized individuals
at high risk for NPC (IgA+ with cytological atypia or
metaplasia).

b) immunological modifiers, such as interferon and
gammaglobulin therapy

Experimentally, interferon was shown to be most effective
when the tumor burden was low but to be relatively inefficient
on large tumors (Gresser and Tovey, 1978). A similar situation
might prevail for human tumors and up to now mostly terminal
cancers were treated by interferon with deceiving results.

Alpha interferon treatment (3.10^6 IU daily for 5 weeks,
followed by 3.10^6 IU thrice weekly, for 5 weeks) was given
to 15 Chinese patients at early stages of NPC (stage II of
Ho). The results were encouraging but no regression of more
than 50 % was observed (Wang et al, submitted for publication).

ADCC titers of NPC patients prior to radiotherapy
appeared to be of high pronostic value, according to Pearson
et al (1978) and Mathew et al (1981). These authors have
initiated at the Mayo Clinic serotherapy of terminal NPC
cases, using semi-purified gamma-globulins having high ADCC
activity. They observed clinical and serological effects of
such a serotherapy on IgG/EA and IgA/VCA titers (Pearson,
personal communication). If this is confirmed, gammaglobulin
therapy possibly together with interferon therapy might be
of use to try, as complementary to radiotherapy. The
source of immunoglobulins remains an open question, as one
must have standardized batches of sera with high ADCC
activity. Preliminary investigations have shown that gamma-
globulins from blood donors were a better source for high
ADCC activity than placental extracts.

c) antiviral drugs

Very few compounds have yet shown major clinical effect
on herpesviruses in general and on EBV in particular. It
is hoped however that both pharmaceutical and public research
laboratories will progressively come up with clinically
useful compounds and it would be important to be epidemiologically ready to test them when needed. The aim would be
to try and inhibit EBV reactivation and to prevent NPC
clinical onset.

It is too early to judge whether Acyclovir[R] might be useful in this context, since its effectiveness on EBV-related diseases, such as severe infectious mononucleosis (IM) has not yet been completed in vivo. A clinical trial is actually in progress in the USA and once the results are available, consideration will be given in the present context.

The preliminary studies described above should imply small groups of patients (for example 15 to 20 males aged 40 to 50 years with IgA/VCA titers ranging from 80 to 320) to test the feasibility and possible effects of such interventions.

POPULATION INTERVENTIONS

To test the validity of the preliminary studies, to select the best drug combination to assess the feasibility of a major population intervention, several hundred persons with appropriate pre-malignant conditions will have to be identified with relatively homogenous risk for the disease.

It appears that randomized intervention groups (40 to 50 persons each) would be appropriate with a 100 person placebo group, to detect an effect on EBV (significant change in IgA titers i.e. 2 dilutions) and on exfoliated NP cytology, but not on NPC incidence. The number of group depends indeed on the results of the preliminary studies and on the decision to combine certain drugs.

If the pilot study were to be successful, an intervention at a population level might be decided with the aim to reduce the incidence of NPC. The study design will be very similar to the pilot study involving randomization of participants into intervention or placebo group. A vigorous follow-up for 3 to 5 years of all individuals concerned would be required.

ACKNOWLEDGEMENTS

The substantial help of Dr. N. Gutensohn, Harvard School of Public Health, Boston, for reanalyzing and assessing the data from China, was greatly appreciated during Dr. de Thé's stay at the Harvard School of Public Health.

REFERENCES

Chen SK, Tan SW, Liu B, Lu TS, Li WJ, Zhong F, Lo HL, Li SW,
    Li MJ and Siao JD (1982). Detection of EBNA antibody and
    localization of EBNA from patients with NPC. Cancer 1:40-42
    (in Chinese)
Desgranges C, Bornkamm GW, Zeng Y, Wang PC, Zhu JS, Shang M,
    and de-Thé G (1982). Detection of Epstein-Barr viral DNA
    internal repeats in the nasopharyngeal mucosa of Chinese
    with IgA/EBV-specific antibodies. Int. J. Cancer 29:87-91
De-Thé G, Desgranges C, Zeng Y, Wang PC, Bornkamm GW, Zhu JS
    and Shang M (1981). Search for pre-cancerous lesions and
    EBV markers in the nasopharynx of IgA positive individuals.
    In: Cancer Campaign, vol. 5, Nasopharyngeal Carcinoma,
    Grundmann, Krueger and Ablashi (eds), Gustav Fischer
    Verlag, Stuttgart, pp. 111-117.
De-Thé G, Ho JHC and Muir CS (1976). Nasopharyngeal Carcinoma.
    In: Epidemiology and Control, AS Evans (ed), Plenum Press,
    New-York, pp. 539-563, 2nd edition, 1981, pp. 621-652
Gresser I and Tovey G (1978). Antitumor effects of interferon.
    Bioch. Bioph. Acta, 516:231-247
Henle G and Henle W (1966). Immunofluorescence in cells
    derived from Burkitt's lymphoma. J. Bacteriol. 91:1248-
    1256.
Hirayama T (1978). Descriptive and analytical epidemiology
    of nasopharyngeal cancer. In: Nasopharyngeal Carcinoma
    Etiology and Control, de-Thé G and Ito Y (eds). IARC
    scientific publication 20, pp. 167-189.
Ho JHC (1972). Nasopharyngeal Carcinoma (NPC). In: Advances
    in Cancer Research, vol. 15, Klein G and Weinhouse S
    (eds), Academic Press, New-York, pp. 57-92.
Ho JHC, Kwan HC, Ng MH and de-Thé G (1978). Serum IgA
    antibodies to EBV capsid antigens preceeding symptoms of
    nasopharyngeal carcinoma. Lancet 1:436-347.
Lanier AP, Henle W, Bender TR, Henle G and Talbot ML (1980).
    Epstein-Barr virus-specific antibody titers in seven
    Alaskan natives before and after diagnosis of nasopharyngeal
    carcinoma. Int. J. Cancer 26:133-137
Li EJ, Tan BF, Zeng Y, Wang PZ, Zhong JM, Deng H, Zhu CS,
    Wei JN and Pan WJ (submitted for publication). Some
    changes observed on nasopharyngeal mucosa of persons
    showing EBV-VCA IgA antibodies.
Maupas P, Goudeau A, Coursaget P, Chiron JP, Drucker J,
    Barin F, Perrin J, Denis F, Diop Mar I and Summers J
    (1980). Hepatitis B virus infection and primary hepato
    cellular carcinoma: Epidemiological, clinical and

virological studies in Senegal from the perspective of prevention by active immunization. In: Cold Spring Harbor Conferences on Cell Proliferation, 7: 481–506.

Mathew GD, Qualtière LF, Bryan Neel III H and Pearson GR (1981). IgA antibody, antibody-dependent cellular cytotoxicity and prognosis in patients with nasopharyngeal carcinoma. Int. J. Cancer 27, 175–180

Pearson GR, Johansson B and Klein G (1978). Antibody-dependent cellular cytotoxicity against Epstein–Barr virus–associated antigens in African patients with nasopharyngeal carcinoma. Int. J. Cancer 22: 120–125.

Peto R, Doll R, Buckley JD and Sporn MB (1981). Can dietary beta–carotene materially reduce human cancer rates? Nature, vol 290 (March 19).

Pi GH, Zeng Y, Zhao WP and Zhang Q (1981). Development of an anticomplement immunoenzyme test for detection of EBNA and antibody to EBNA. J. Immunol. Method. 44, 73–78.

Wang PZ, Zeng Y, Dan H, Ma ER, Li EJ, Gresser, I, Cantell K and de-Thé G (submitted for publication). Progress report of alpha interferon therapeutic trial of early cases of nasopharyngeal carcinoma in south China. Interferon Scientific Memoranda (USA).

Zeng Y, Liu UX, Liu CR, Chen SW, Wei JN, Zhu JS and Zai HJ (1980). Application of an immunoenzymatic method and immuno-autoradiographic method for the mass survey of nasopharyngeal carcinoma. Intervirology 13: 162–168

Zeng Y, Zhang LG, Li HY, Jan MG, Zhang Q, Wu YC, Wang YS and Su GR (1982). Serological mass survey for early detection of nasopharyngeal carcinoma in Wuzhou city, China. Int. J. Cancer 29: 139–141.

13th International Cancer Congress, Part B
Biology of Cancer (1), pages 49–59
© 1983 Alan R. Liss, Inc., 150 Fifth Avenue, New York, NY 10011

THE ASSOCIATION OF EPSTEIN-BARR VIRUS WITH NASOPHARYNGEAL
CARCINOMA

Ronald Glaser, Ph.D.*, Jay Stoerker, M.S.*,
and Y.C. Cheng, Ph.D.**

*Department of Medical Microbiology and Immunology
 College of Medicine and Comprehensive Cancer
 Center, The Ohio State University, Columbus, Ohio 43210
**Department of Pharmacology, University of North
 Carolina, Chapel Hill, North Carolina 27514

Nasopharyngeal carcinoma (NPC) is a tumor that arises
from the squamous or respiratory epithelium of the nasopharynx. It is a relatively rare neoplasm in most part of the
world, including North America, with an age-adjusted rate
of less than 1 per 100,000 (Clifford, 1970; Hirayama, 1978).
However, NPC accounts for approximately 18% of all malignant
cancers among Chinese (Snow, 1975).

The Epstein-Barr virus is a human herpes virus with oncogenic properties. In addition to being associated with
the self-limiting lymphoproliferative disease, infectious
mononucleosis (IM)(Henle et al., 1968), EBV has been implicated in the etiology of NPC and Burkitt's lymphoma (BL)(Epstein et al., 1964). Nasopharyngeal carcinoma patients
from various geographic areas of the world, including North
America, Africa and Europe, have been shown to have EBV DNA
associated with the tumor cells (zur Hausen et al., 1970;
Nonoyama et al., 1973; Glaser et al., 1980) and the carcinoma cells express EBV associated nuclear antigen (EBNA)(Wolf
et al., 1973; Huang et al., 1974). As indicated earlier,
it is clear that Chinese are at high risk to NPC (Clifford,
1970) and that a very consistent association between EBV and
Chinese patients with NPC has been established by finding
high antibody titers against EBV early antigen (EA) and
virus capsid antigen (VCA) in such patients (Henle et al.,
1970; Henle et al., 1973). Patients beyond the initial stage
of this disease generally show high titers of IgG and IgA
antibodies to the EBV VCA and to the diffuse (D) component

of the EA complex (de-The et al., 1975; Henle and Henle, 1976; Henle et al., 1977). The antibody spectrum and titers increase with the stage of the disease (Henle et al., 1970; Henle et al., 1973; Henle et al., 1977; Glaser et al., 1980). Correspondingly, the antibody titers decline gradually after effective therapy of NPC so that the EBV specific serologic test may serve to monitor the success of treatment. Relapses or metastases are associated with rising antibody titers months before they become clinically evident.

In a recent study, IgA positive individuals without symptoms of NPC were examined for the presence of EBV DNA and EBNA in naspharyngeal biopsies. EBV DNA and/or EBNA were detected in biopsies of 14 of 52 symptomless IgA positive individuals, while none of 7 biopsies from IgA negative individuals were positive (Desgranges et al., 1982). Thus, the use of assays to determine VCA IgA antibody titers could be important in diagnosing high risk patients.

Studies from our laboratories have shown that EBV is capable of inducing a virus-specific DNase during its replicative cycle (Cheng et al., 1980a), and that NPC patients, when compared to normal EBV positive individuals, IM, BL, and other cancer patients, show a high frequency of strong anti-EBV DNase antibody reactivity (Cheng et al., 1980b). These studies have continued and we have now examined sera from four groups of adult Chinese for antibody (IgG and IgA) against EBV EA, VCA, and the EBV specific DNase. Specimens were obtained from normal Chinese individuals, NPC patients at diagnosis, NPC patients in remission, and NPC patients with recurrent disease. The geometric mean antibody titers against EBV antigens and mean titers of antibody to EBV DNase were determined and statistical analysis was performed comparing the groups. We found that the antibody titers against all the EBV antigens and EBV DNase were much higher in the three NPC groups studied when compared to normal individuals, and that of the three patient groups studied, NPC patients at diagnosis had the highest antibody titers including antibody to the EBV DNase. Consistent with the literature, we found that EBV VCA IgA and EA IgA (when present) were good markers for diagnosed NPC patients, as compared to normal controls. The fact that antibody titers to the EBV DNase are the highest in NPC patients at diagnosis is encouraging and studies are underway to determine if this assay could be used for screening patients prior to the onset of clinical symptoms to identify patients at risk for NPC (Glaser et al., unpublished data).

In a more recent study, antibody titers to EBV DNase in juvenile patients with NPC were assayed. Of 11 NPC patients examined at the time of diagnosis, 8 of these had high titers against EBV DNase (> 6 units/ml). Data obtained in the study show that those patients who had low titers of EBV DNase at time of diagnosis had good prognosis for survival. Every patient that was examined who was a long-term survivor had serum that neutralized less than 6 units of enzyme at diagnosis or, in one case, the long-term survivor had serum that neutralized greater than 6 units of enzyme at diagnosis, but dropped to a neturalizing titer of 1.3 units of antibody 36 months after diagnosis and is a long-term survivor. One patient who relapsed had high antibody titers to EBV DNase at diagnosis and after relapse. Every patient who died of NPC-associated disease showed high antibody titers against EBV DNase at diagnosis and prior to death. Data obtained suggests that antibody titers to EBV DNase may be useful in predicting the course of disease after therapy (Tan et al., unpublished data).

Since EBV has been associated with IM and BL, two diseases involving B-lymphocytes, it was surprising that when NPC biopsies were examined by in situ hybridization for the presence of the EBV genome, the localization of the EBV DNA was in the epithelial cells of the tumor (Wolf et al. 1973). If one assays touch preparations of biopsy specimens from NPC tumors tumors by the anticomplementary immunofluorescence (IF) test for EBNA, one can detect the antigen in the nuclei of the epithelial cells of the tumor. When epithelial explant cell cultures prepared from NPC tumors are exposed to iododeoxyuridine (IUdR), EBV can be induced to replicate in the NPC epithelial cells as determined by the synthesis of virus specific antigens detected by IF (Glaser et al., 1976; Trumper et al., 1977). More recently, using anticomplement immunoenzymatic assays, EBNA was found not only in NPC tumor cells, but also in hyperplastic cells and ciliated columnar epithelial cells from NPC patients. The EBNA was detected with less frequency in squamous epithelial cells from normal individuals (Zeng et al., 1981). It is possible that EBV may infect and transform normal epithelial cells, for example, ciliated columnar epithelial cells, or the virus may become latently associated with the ciliated columnar cells and then eventually move by infection or direct cell to cell contact to squamous epithelial cells. How EBV becomes associated with and transforms the epithelial cells of the nasopharynx is still not clear.

Thus far, it has not been possible to establish an EBV genome positive NPC tumor cell line, though many attempts have been made by workers in many laboratories. It is known that growth properties of primary epithelial cells can change very rapidly when grown in vitro (Stampfer et al., 1980). Cell culture techniques currently available may be hampered by the tendency of explanted material to keratinize and terminally differentiate.

Any investigation of the association between EBV and NPC faces a second difficulty; the "laboratory host range" of the virus. Even though EBV DNA is regularly found in the epithelial cells of NPC, as already discussed, and these cells can be induced to express virus antigens (Glaser et al., 1976; Trumper et al., 1977) it is not yet clear if it is possible to infect cultures of human nasopharyngeal epithelium under laboratory conditions, though there is one unconfirmed report (Huang et al., 1977) In fact, for many years the virus had been categorized as a B-lymphocyte-tropic virus.

Although the narrow host range under laboratory conditions for EBV has been a frustration studying the association of EBV with epithelial cells, data from several studies show that epithelial cells can occasionally support the replication of EBV after direct infection. We had previously shown that certain NPC epithelial explants could be directly infected with HR-1 EBV (Glaser et al, 1976). Huang et al. (1977) presented data suggesting that it was possible to infect human nasopharyngeal epithelial cell explants with B95 virus as measured by enhanced growth. Attempts to infect non-malignant nasopharyngeal epithelial cells from squirrel monkeys in our laboratory showed that these cells had virus receptors and could be induced to express at least EA, which is associated with viral replication (Glaser et al.; 1980b). However, we were not able to demonstrate EBNA or morphologic transformation using HR-1 or B95 derived virus stocks. In a more recent study, a human epithelial cell line (designated U) was infected with EBV (Ben-Bassat et al., 1982). The EBNA was expressed in cells infected with B95-8 EBV but not HR-1. A stimulation of cellular DNA synthesis was also observed after virus infection (Ben-Bassat et al., 1982). The EA and VCA, however, were not expressed. Preliminary data from Dr. Joseph Pagano's laboratory suggest that EA and VCA were detected in primary human cervical epithelial cells infected with EBV and that EBV DNA could be detected by hybridization (personal communication), and preliminary data from our laboratory suggest that at least EA can be expressed in BGM-70 monkey epithelial cells after infection with HR-1 EBV, but not B95-8. The susceptibility of epithelial cells to EBV now shown in several studies strongly support the hypothesis that nasopharyngeal epithelial cells could be directly infected with EBV and eventually, in certain individuals, these cells probably become malignantly transformed to produce NPC.

The suggestion has been made that EBV may enter epithelial cells by virus mediated cell fusion, between epithelial cells of the nasopharynx and EBV infected lymphoid cells in close proximity (Bayliss and Wolf, 1980). Formation of multinucleated cells resulting from the fusion of superinfected and uninfected Raji cells immobilized as a monolayer has been observed. These experiments show that EBV can induce fusion between lymphoblastoid cells having receptors for EBV and other cell types. It is of interest that EBV can be induced to replicate when EBV genome positive cells are treated with certain drugs, such as IUdR or tumor promoting plant diterpine esters (zur Hausen et al., 1978; Kawanishi et al.; 1981). It may be possible that EBV can become associated with epithelial cells by infection by in vivo cell fusion resulting from virus replication after exposure to a chemical inducer (Kawanishi et al., 1981), or by both mechanisms.

Somatic cell hybridization has been used as a means to study the EBV replicative cycle in epithelial cells. Human epithelial/Burkitt cells have been prepared by fusing human D98 epithelial cells to HR-1 cells (Glaser and O'Neill, 1972; Glaser and Rapp, 1972). When coverslip cultures of D98/HR-1 cells were fixed in acetone and assayed for EBV specific antigens by the direct and indirect IF test, no evidence of EBV-EA or VCA was found though the cells are EBNA positive (Glaser et al., 1973). However, when the cells were treated with 60 µg/ml IUdR, EA and VCA were synthesized and EBV particles were synthesized (Glaser and Rapp, 1972; Glaser Glaser et al., 1973). The conditions and time of appearance of virus specific markers are shown in Table 1. Results

TABLE 1

Appearance of EBV specific markers in D98/HR-1 epithelial hybrid cells after treatment with IUdR.

Virus Marker

Time (Days)	Treat-ment	EA	VCA	DNA	Virus Parti-cles[a]	DNA Poly-merase[b]	DNase[c]	Ribo-nucleo-tide Reduc-tase
1	+ IUdR	+	-	-	-	NT	+	NT
2		+	-	-	-	NT	+	+
3		+	-	-	-	+	+	+
1	- IUdR	+	+	+	-	NT	NT	NT
2		+	+	+	-	NT	NT	NT
3		+	+	+	-	+	NT	+
7		+	+	+	+	NT	NT	NT

[a] Observed in thin sections of cells by electron micro-scopy.

NT= Not tested

[b] (Miller et al., 1977)

[c] (Cheng et al., 1980)

[d] (Henry et al., 1978)

from these studies have shown that 1) EBV can remain latent or repressed in human epithelial-like cells for long periods of time, 2) the host cell in which the EBV genome resides is not only affected by the presence of the EBV genome, but the degree of repression of the virus genome is dependent on the host cell, and 3) data obtained from studies using epithelial somatic cell hybrids have been directly applicable to studying EBV and NPC.

Studies of the interaction of the EBV genome with epithe-lial cells have been pursued by DNA transfection procedures. One advantage of this technique as a model for NPC is the

lack of dependence on either cell fusion or infection for
entry into the cells. While the use of epithelial hybrid
cells yielded important information on the association
between EBV and epithelial cells, the introduction of chromosomes from lymphoid cells makes interpretation somewhat
difficult. Transfection introduces specific virus DNA into
the cells, and simulates direct infection. In addition, the
use of DNA transfection allows the introduction of subgenomic
fragments of EBV into epithelial cells, and should ultimately
lead to the delineation of the precise genetic information
responsible for EBV products and transformation.

Grogan et al. (1981) demonstrated infectivity of EBV by
a calcium phosphate technique, showing that DNA from transforming virus also synthesizes EA after introduction into
human placental cells. The epithelial cells did not show
biological changes associated with morphological transformation. Infectious virus has apparently been recovered
using transfection techniques with the human placental cells
(Grogan et al., 1981; Miller et al., 1981). The surprising
finding that DNA from transforming strains of EBV, as well
as HR-1 (lytic) EBV DNA, gave rise to lytic infection in
human placental cells, suggests that the regulation of
genome expression toward cell transformation vs. lytic
replication may be host regulated, at least in part. This
is similar to results shown for Simian Virus 40 (SV-40)
which transforms human cells after infection but replicates,
kills and produces virus progeny in infected monkey kidney
cells. In transfection experiments using DNA from transforming AG876, and nontransforming HR-1 cell lines, we
noted host cell restriction of the expression of EBV antigens at different levels in two transfected epithelial cell
lines (Stoerker et al, 1981). In a cell line derived from
a squamous cell carcinoma of the nasal septum, CCL-30, both
AG-876 and HR-1 DNAs induced EA and VCA, while transfected
cells derived from a Chinese NPC (EBV genome negative)
restricted the HR-1 DNA to the expression of EA.

Cloning of EBV DNA in recombinant plasmids has allowed
the process to functional mapping to begin. Grogan et al.
(1981) have demonstrated the activity of the EcoRl B fragment
in the induction of at least part of the EA complex in primary human placental cells. In our laboratory, we have seen
the induction of EBV antigens at a higher level of efficiency than other cell types using D98/HR-1 hybrid cells transfected with EBV DNA. The use of genome positive D98/HR-1

cells is providing us the means to use a marker rescue approach to the functional mapping of the EBV genome. We have been able to induce the synthesis of at least EA by introducing the Bam HI H and ligated H, F, X fragments into the D98/HR-1 cells. In addition, using ligated fragments, we have rescued transforming virus from the D98/HR-1 cells by transfection after inducing the endogenous HR-1 virus DNA to replicate with IUdR. These cells cannot be induced to produce biologically active virus using IUdR alone (Stoerker and Glaser, 1982). The significance of this observation is still under study.

The association of EBV with NPC is well established. Study of the interaction between EBV and epithelial cells in vitro and in vivo has been hampered by the narrow and apparently selective host range of the virus. However, data from several laboratories now show that EBV can infect certain epithelial cells directly. Studies with somatic cell hybrids between EBV genome positive lymphoblastoid cells and cells of epithelial origin have shown that the virus may be expressed in epithelial cells, and that the virus cycle is host modified, at least in part. The EBV genome positive hybrid cells also show enhanced tumorigenicity and cloning efficiency. This suggests that introduction of EBV DNA into epithelial cells can cause morphological and biological changes in vitro resembling transformation.

Transfection of infectious EBV DNA from transforming and nontransforming EBV into epithelial cells has verified EBV DNA activity in epithelial cells, although morphologic transformation has not been demonstrated.

REFERENCES

Bayliss, GJ, Wolf, H (1980). Epstein-Barr virus-induced cell fusion. Nature 287:164.

Ben-Bassat, H, Mitrani-Rosenbaum, S, Goldblum, N (1982). Induction of Epstein-Barr virus nuclear antigen and DNA synthesis in a human epithelial cell line after Epstein-Barr virus infection. J Virol. 41:703.

Cheng, YC, Chen, JY, Hoffmann, PJ, Glaser, R (1980). Studies on the activity of DNase associated with the replication of the Epstein-Barr virus. Virology 100:334.

Cheng, YC, Chen, JY, Glaser, R, Henle, W (1980). Frequency and levels of antibodies to Epstein-Barr virus-specific DNase are elevated in patients with nasopharyngeal carcinoma. Proc Natl Acad Sci USA 77:6162.

Clifford, P (1970). A review on the epidemiology of nasopharyngeal carcinoma. Int J Cancer 5:287.

Desgranges, C, Bornkamm, GW, Zeng, Y, Wang, PC, Zhu, JS,
Shang, M, de-The (1982). Detection of EB viral DNA inter-
nal repeats in the nasopharyngeal mucosa of Chinese with
IgA/EBV specific antibodies. Int J Cancer 29:87.

de-The, G, Ho, JHC, Ablashi, DV, Day, NE, Macario, AJL,
Martin-Berthelon, MC, Pearson, G, Sohier, R (1975b). Nasopharyngeal carcinoma. IX. Antibodies to EBNA and correlation with response to other EBV antigens in Chinese patients. Int J Cancer 16:713.

Epstein, MA, Achong, BG, Barr, YM (1964). Virus particles
in cultured lymphoblasts from Burkitt's lymphoma. Lancet
1:702.

Glaser, R, O'Neil, FJ (1972). Hybridization of Burkitt
lymphoblastoid cells. Science 176:1245.

Glaser, R, Rapp, F (1972) Rescue of Epstein-Barr virus from
somatic cell hybrid of Burkitt lymphoma lymphoblastoid
cells. J Virol 10:288.

Glaser, R, Nonoyama, M, Decker, B, Rapp, F (1973). Synthesis of Epstein-Barr virus antigens and DNA in activated
Burkitt somatic cell hybrids. Virology 55:62.

Glaser, R, de-The, G, Lenoir, G, Ho, JHC (1976). Superinfection of epithelial nasopharyngeal carcinoma cells with
Epstein-Barr virus. Proc Natl Acad Sci USA 73:960.

Glaser, R, Lang, CM, Lee, KJ, Jacobs, D, McQuattie, C (1980).
Attempt to infect normal nasopharyngeal epithelial cells
with the Epstein-Barr virus. J Natl Cancer Inst 64:1085.

Glaser, G, Nonoyama, M, Szymanowski, RT, and Graham, W.
(1980). Human nasopharyngeal carcinomas positive for
Epstein-Barr virus DNA in North America. J Natl Cancer
Inst 64:1317.

Grogan, E, Miller, G, Henle, W, Rabson, M, Shedd, D, Nieder-
man, JO (1981). Expression of EBV early antigen after
transfection with viral DNA and DNA fragments. J Virol.
40:861.

Henle, G, Henle, W, Diehl, V (1968). Relation of Burkitt
tumor associated Herpes-type virus to infectious mononucleosis. Proc Natl Acad Sci, USA 59:94.

Henle, W, Henle, G, Ho, HC, et al (1970). Antibodies to
EB virus in nasopharyngeal carcinoma, other head and neck
neoplasms and control groups. J Natl Cancer Inst 44:225.

Henle, W, Ho, HC, Henle, G, Kwan, HC (1973b) Antibodies to
Epstein-Barr virus related antigens in nasopharyngeal carcinoma. Comparison of active cases and long term survivors. J Natl Cancer Inst 51:361.

Henle, G, Henle, W (1976b). Epstein-Garr virus-specific serum antibodies as an outstanding feature of nasopharyngeal carcinoma. Int J Cancer 17:1.

Henle, W, Ho, HC, Henle, G, Chau, JCW, Kwan, HC (1977) Nasopharyngeal carcinoma: Significance of changes in Epstein-Barr virus related antibody patterns following therapy. Int J Cancer 20:663.

Hirayama, T (1978). Nasopharyngeal Carcinoma: Etiology and Control. G de-The, Y Ito (eds) Lyon (IARC Scientific Pubs No 20), Kyoto, Japan, p. 167.

Huang, DP, Ho, JHC, Henle, W, Henle, G (1974). Demonstration of EBV-associated nuclear antigen in NPC cells from fresh biopsies. Int J Cancer 14:580.

Huang, DP, HO, HC, Ng, MH, Lui, M (1977). Possible transformation of nasopharyngeal epithelial cells in culture with Epstein-Barr virus from B95-8 cells. Brit J. Cancer 35:630.

Kawanishi, M., Sugawara, K, Ito, Y (1981). Epstein-Barr virus-induced early polypeptides in Raji and NC37 cells activated by diterpene ester TPA in combination with n-butyrate. Virology 115:406.

Miller, G, Grogan, E, Heston, L, Robinson, J, Smith, D (1981). Epstein-Barr viral DNA: infectivity for human placental cell. Science 212:452.

Nonoyama, M, Huang, CH, Pagano, JS, Klein, G, Singh, S (1973). DNA of Epstein-Barr virus detected in tissues of Burkitt's lymophoma and nasopharyngeal carcinoma. Proc Natl Acad Sci USA 70:3265.

Snow, J Jr (1975). Carcinoma of the nasopharynx in children. Ann Otol Rhinol Laryngol 84:817.

Stampfer, M, Hallowes, RC, Hackett, AJ (1980). Growth of normal human mammary cells in culture. In Vitro 16:415.

Stoerker, J, Parris, DS, Yajima, Y, Glaser R (1981). Pleiotropic expression of EBV DNA in epithelial cells. Proc Natl Acad Sci USA 78:5882.

Stoerker, J, Glaser, R (1982). Rescue of transforming Epstein-Barr virus from IUdR induced D98/HR-1 epithelial hybrid cells after transfection with cloned subgenomic fragments of B95-8 virus. Sixth Herpesvirus Workshop, Cold Spring Harbor, New York (in press).

Trumper, PA, Epstein, MA, Giovanella, BC, Finerty, S (1977). Isolation of Infectious EB virus from the epithelial tumor cells of nasopharyngeal carcinoma. Int J Cancer 20:655.

Wolf, H, zur Hausen, H, Becker (1973). EB virus genomes in epithelial nasopharyngeal carcinoma cells. Nature 244:245.

Zeng, Y, Shen, SJ, Pi, GH, Ma, JL, Zhang, Q, Zhao, ML, Dong, HJ (1981). Application of anticomplement immunoenzymatic method for the detection of EBNA in carcinoma cells and normal epithelial cells from the nasopharynx. In Grundman et al. (eds): "Cancer Campaign" Vol. 5:237, Nasopharyngeal Carcinoma. Gustav Fischer Verlag:Stuttgart, New York.

zur Hausen, H, Schulte-Holthausen, H, Klein, G, Henle, W, Henle, G, Clifford, P, Santesson, L (1970). EB-virus DNA in biopsies of Burkitt tumors anaplastic carcinomas of the nasopharynx. Nature 228:1056.

zur Hausen, H, O'Neil, FJ, Fresen, KO (1978). Persisting oncogenic herpesvirus induced by tumour promoter TPA. Nature 272:373.

13th International Cancer Congress, Part B
Biology of Cancer (1), pages 61–70
© **1983 Alan R. Liss, Inc., 150 Fifth Avenue, New York, NY 10011**

VACCINE CONTROL OF MALIGNANCIES INDUCED BY LYMPHOTROPIC
HERPESVIRUSES

M.A. Epstein, J.R. North, A.J. Morgan

Department of Pathology
University of Bristol Medical School
University Walk
Bristol BS8 1TD, U.K.

Malignancies induced by or associated with lymphotropic
herpesviruses have been important in viral oncology for
several reasons:- (i) studies on the naturally occurring
lymphoma induced by Marek's disease herpesvirus in chickens
and on the experimental lymphomas which Herpesvirus saimiri
and Herpesvirus ateles cause in sub-human primates have given
important insights into tumour induction by viruses of this
family; (ii) the lymphomas of Marek's disease provide the
first instance of a naturally occurring malignancy to have
been controlled by an anti-viral vaccine (Churchill, Payne,
Chubb 1969) whilst H. saimiri lymphomas have likewise been
prevented by a killed viral vaccine (Laufs, Steinke 1975);
(iii) endemic Burkitt's lymphoma (BL) and Epstein-Barr (EB)
virus with which it is associated have provided a system in
human oncology which mirrors relationships in animal lymphomas
with a herpesvirus aetiology (Epstein, Achong 1979).

Although endemic BL does not present a significant
problem in terms of world cancer incidence, undifferentiated
nasopharyngeal carcinoma (NPC), the other important EB virus-
associated malignancy, is the commonest tumour of men and
the second most common tumour of women of Southern Chinese
origin (Shanmugaratnam 1967).   There is also a medium high
incidence in North and East Africa, and amongst South East
Asian populations related to Southern Chinese (Clifford 1970;
Shanmugaratnam 1971).   In world health terms undifferentiated NPC is a very substantial human cancer problem.
Because of this, it has been urged that a vaccine against
EB virus should be developed with high priority in the hope
that prevention of infection might reduce the incidence of

the tumour (Epstein 1976). Antibodies to the EB virus-
determined membrane antigen (MA) are known to have virus
neutralising activity (Pearson, Dewey, Klein, Henle, Henle
1970; de Schryver, Klein, Hewetson, Rocchi, Henle, Henle,
Moss, Pope 1974) and any vaccine for administration to human
populations should be based on EB virus MA components free
of viral nucleic acid (Epstein 1976). Antigen-containing
membranes from cells infected with Marek's disease herpesvirus have been used as an experimental vaccine in chickens
and have substantially reduced lymphoma incidence following
challenge with virulent virus (Kaaden, Deitschold 1974),
whilst cell membrane preparations from H. saimiri infected
cells have been shown to induce neutralising antibodies on
inoculation into marmosets (Pearson, Scott 1977).

EB virus MA contains two high molecular weight molecules of 340,000 and 270,000 daltons (gp340/270) (Qualtière,
Pearson 1979; Strnad, Neubauer, Rabin, Mazur 1979; Thorley-
Lawson, Edson 1979; North, Morgan, Epstein 1980) and the
present paper describes studies on them to evaluate their
use as an experimental vaccine.

EXPERIMENTAL

The molecular explanation for the concordance between
naturally occurring human antibodies to MA and those which
neutralise EB virus has been provided by the demonstration
that the same glycoproteins are present in the cell membrane
MA complex as are in the virus envelope (North, Morgan,
Epstein 1980). Furthermore, monoclonal antibodies and a
monospecific conventional antiserum which exclusively recognise gp340 and gp270 are virus-neutralising (Hoffman,
Lazarowitz, Hayward 1980; North, Morgan, Epstein 1980);
this indicates the importance of these particular molecules
for use in a vaccine. Recent results have also shown that
antigenic determinants are shared between the two high molecular weight components (Hoffman, Lazarowitz, Hayward 1980;
Franklin, North, Morgan, Epstein 1981). As regards sources
of gp340 and gp270, most EB virus-carrying, virion-producing
lymphoblastoid cell lines synthesise roughly equal amounts
of the two molecules. However, the B95-8 marmoset lymphoblastoid line (Miller, Shope, Lisco, Stitt, Lipman 1972) is
anomalous in this connection in that it expresses almost
exclusively gp340, thus providing an important advantage for
molecular weight-based purification procedures.

Radioimmunoassay for Gp340

Any purification procedure requires a sensitive assay
to quantify the product in order to permit modifications
designed to maximise yields. For the purification of MA
from B95-8 cells, a quantitative radioimmunoassay has been
developed based on the use of small amounts of highly purified radioiodinated gp340 (North, Morgan, Thompson, Epstein
1982a). This crucial radioiodinated material was prepared
by the following steps:- (i) B95-8 cell membrane preparations were fractionated on Ultrogel AcA 22 in 0.5% deoxy-
cholate (DOC); (ii) the fractions containing gp340 were
purified further by affinity chromatography on Ricinus
communis agglutinin-II-agarose (Ricin-agarose); (iii) the
eluate from Ricin-agarose was either radio-iodinated at this
stage for final purification (see iv below), or applied to
columns of Sepharose CL-6B for chromatography in 8M urea
under reducing conditions and then radioiodinated for final
purification; (iv) Radioiodination was achieved using
Chloramine T, and the final purification step was carried
out by sodium dodecyl sulphate polyacrylamide gel electrophoresis (SDS-PAGE). The ^{125}I-gp340 was located by autoradiography and the appropriate region was excised, SDS was
removed, and the antigen renatured. Full details are given
in North, Morgan, Thompson, Epstein (1982a).

The antigenicity of ^{125}I-gp340 prepared in this way
was established by the finding that up to 75% was precipitated specifically by antisera to MA from normal EB virus-
positive human donors and the radiolabelled material was
used thereafter in a conventional competition-radioimmuno-
assay to quantify unlabelled gp340 in test samples (North,
Morgan, Thompson, Epstein 1982a). One unit of the antigen
was arbitrarily defined as that amount which caused a 50%
reduction in ^{125}I-gp340 binding to a standard reference
serum.

Preparation of Immunogenic Gp340

A preparative SDS-PAGE procedure has been elaborated
for the isolation of gp340 from B95-8 cell membranes.
Successful renaturation of the antigen was achieved in two
steps:- (i) SDS was removed under conditions where protein
refolding was prevented by urea, which appeared to enhance
SDS-protein dissociation; (ii) Final renaturation of the
protein with good recovery of antigenic determinants was

brought about by removal of the urea during dialysis against buffer containing non-ionic detergent (either 0.1% Triton X100 or 0.87% octylglucoside).

The yield of antigen was monitored by the radioimmuno-assay and the final procedure described above was found to give a fifty fold increase in recovery as compared to conventional techniques. SDS-PAGE analysis of the purified material demonstrated its homogeneity (**Fig. 1**).

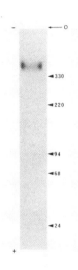

Fig. 1. Autoradiograph of SDS-PAGE showing purified ^{125}I-gp340. Numbers indicate the positions of unlabelled marker proteins of known molecular weights.

During the development of these methods, gel filtration studies on the MA complex from a variety of EB virus-carrying cells demons-trated that the two high molecular weight glycoproteins (gp340 and gp270) do not associate in detergent solution indicating that the recognition of both molecules by individual monoclonal antibodies is through common antigenic determinants and is not the result of aggregation as has been suggested. Furthermore, the sensitivity of the antigenic determinants of gp340 to reversible denatura-tion by SDS has demonstrated that the majority of the epitopes recognised by human anti-MA sera do not reside in the carbohydrate moiety of the mole-cule. A full account of this work has been published (Morgan, North, Epstein 1982).

Immunogenicity of Purified Gp340

The immunogenicity of gp340, purified as described, has been assessed in various species of laboratory animals, and the efficacy of several different immunisation procedures has also been evaluated.

Gp340 and Freund's Adjuvant - Detergent solutions of the purified glycoprotein were emulsified in complete Freund's adjuvant and were inoculated into Balb/c mice and Sandy Lop rabbits. Thereafter the animals were boosted several times at 6 to 8 week intervals with the antigen in incomplete Freund's adjuvant and were bled 4 weeks following each

injection. Mice gave some antibody responses after the
second immunisation with 80 units of antigen while excellent
responses were obtained in rabbits by about the fourth
injection of 300 units of antigen. Such antisera reacted
only with the gp340 component of MA and did not recognise
any other molecules either from the surface or the interior
of B95-8 cells (Fig. 2). However, these successful antibody
responses were rather slow, and it was considered that the
use of Freund's adjuvant was less than ideal since it cannot
be contemplated in the human context.

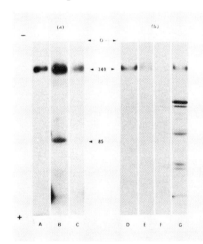

Fig. 2. Autoradiograph (a),
and fluorograph (b) of SDS-
PAGE showing molecules immuno-
precipitated from lysates of
B95-8 cells which had been
radiolabelled using ^{125}I and
lactoperoxidase (a), or by
the biosynthetic incorporation
of ^{3}H-leucine (b). Immune
precipiations were performed
using sera from rabbits
immunised with purified gp340
in complete Freund's adjuvant
(tracks A & D) or from mice
immunised with purified gp340
in liposomes with B. pertussis
(tracks C & E). Control
precipitations were performed with human anti MA +ve serum
(tracks B & G) or human anti MA -ve serum (track F). Numbers
indicate apparent molecular weights estimated by comparison
with marker proteins run on each gel. All the experimental
sera bound monospecifically to gp340.

Incorporation of Gp340 in Liposomes – Gp340 was eluted from
SDS-PAGE and renatured in buffers containing the dialysable
detergent, octylglucoside. This mixture was used to dissolve
L-α-phosphatidyl choline from the walls of a glass container
and the solution was then exhaustively dialysed to remove the
detergent. When antigen which had formed liposomes was
isolated by floatation in discontinuous sucrose density
gradients, more than 50% was found in the low density fractions, indicating a very acceptable level of incorporation.
Full details of this technique have already been described
(North, Morgan, Thompson, Epstein 1982b). A single intra-
peritoneal inoculation of Balb/c mice with 80 units of

antigen in liposomes with B. pertussis (2×10^9 organisms per mouse) as adjuvant induced the formation of high levels of specific antibody to gp340 within 4 weeks. Subsequent booster doses without adjuvant enhanced antibody levels and these antibodies were virus-neutralising.

It is well known that B. pertussis is not a satisfactory adjuvant in rabbits. Accordingly, the immunogenicity of gp340-liposomes was investigated in mice and rabbits without B. pertussis. Although the responses in mice to intravenous injections of 80 units of liposomal antigen were somewhat retarded compared to those obtained with B. pertussis, nevertheless good levels of specific antibody were obtained within weeks. The incorporation of lipid A (from the lipopolysaccharide component of E. Coli cell walls) in liposomes has been reported to give excellent adjuvant effects with liposomal antigens (Schuster, Neidig, Alving, Alving 1979). It has now been found in the present system that 50 µg of lipid A per 250 µg phospholipid of gp340-liposomes gave substantial enhancement of antibody responses to gp340 in rabbits after intravenous inoculation.

Induction of Antibodies to gp340 in Cotton-top Marmosets

EB virus is known to cause fatal lymphoproliferative disease in owl monkeys (Aotus trivirgatus) and cotton-top marmosets (Saguinus oedipus oedipus) (see Miller, 1979) and with the latter species there is some evidence that the tumours are monoclonal and that a dose response has been demonstrated. Although S. o. oedipus is an endangered species, methods are available for successful breeding in captivity (Kirkwood, Epstein, Terlecki 1983) and it would appear that this is the animal of choice for the evaluation of any vaccine designed to prevent EB virus infection and subsequent tumours in man. It was therefore important to determine whether EB virus-neutralising antibodies could be induced in cotton-top marmosets by live virus, or, more importantly, by the administration of purified gp340. Animals inoculated with sub-tumour inducing doses of EB virus particles have indeed been found to produce high levels of antibody to both virus capsid antigen and MA.

DISCUSSION

The foregoing results make clear the crucial contribution of the radioimmunoassay (North, Morgan, Thompson,

Epstein 1982a) to the monitoring and development of an
efficient preparative procedure giving good yields of gp340
(Morgan, North, Epstein 1982). The success of this procedure depended on a two-step method for antigen renaturation
after SDS-PAGE and the present findings emphasise the importance of these advances which have provided the gp340 in a
form retaining both its antigenic and its immunogenic
properties.

Although the original experiments demonstrating the
immunogenicity of gp340 involved the use of complete Freund's
adjuvant, the well-known deleterious effects of the adjuvant
render such preparations quite unsuitable for human use and
it was for this reason that alternative methods were sought
for presenting gp340. Reports of successful immunisations
using artificial liposomes containing Semliki Forest virus
spike protein (Morein, Helenius, Simons, Pettersson,
Kääriäinen, Schirrmacher 1978) or hepatitis B virus surface
antigen (Manesis, Cameron, Gregoriadis 1979) suggested a way
forward and the experiments described have shown clearly
that this form of presentation is also highly effective with
the gp340 component of EB virus MA. Furthermore, a significant improvement in immunogenicity was obtained without
the addition of exogenous adjuvant when the liposomes also
included the lipid A fraction of E. coli lipopolysaccharide.

The progress reported here now points the way to key
experiments to investigate the protective effects of
immunisation with the gp340 subunit of MA against EB virus
infection in marmosets, as a preliminary to the evaluation
of liposomal gp340 as a possible vaccine in man. Prevention
of infection by vaccination against the herpesvirus of
Marek's disease profoundly influences the subsequent incidence of lymphomas induced by this virus (Churchill, Payne,
Chubb 1969; Kaaden, Dietzschold 1974), and if EB virus
infection could be prevented in a similar way, it might be
that consequential EB virus-related disease could be avoided.

The efficacy of subunit antiviral vaccines has been
demonstrated in both human and veterinary diseases (Szmuness,
Stevens, Zang, Harley, Kellner 1981; Bittle, Houghten,
Alexander, Shinnick, Sutcliffe, Lerner, Rowlands, Brown 1982)
and it would seem sensible for development of an EB virus
vaccine to proceed in this direction. It has already been
pointed out that if such a vaccine can be shown experimentally to protect susceptible South American sub-human

primates, the most satisfactory test for it in a human EB virus-related disease would be in the context of young adults known to be at risk for infectious mononucleosis (Epstein 1976). Information on such protection could readily be accumulated amongst young people in Western countries and thereafter the effect of vaccination and consequential prevention of disease could likewise rather easily be assessed in relation to BL; the various advantages of field trials against BL in an area of high endemicity have already been pointed out (Epstein 1976). If these hurdles can be overcome, and an efficient EB virus subunit vaccine can be developed for man, the much more difficult problem of intervention against NPC becomes a very high priority. The peak age incidence of BL is around the age of 7, and it is not unreasonable to suppose that maintenance of immunity until this stage of life could well influence the development of this disease; in the highest incidence areas NPC is usually a disease of middle age and later, and the problems of prevention of EB virus infection for many decades are considerable. However, if investigations such as those presented here are pressed forward with the utmost vigour, answers to these difficult questions will be obtained sooner rather than later.

Bittle JL, Houghten RA, Alexander H, Shinnick TM, Sutcliffe JG, Lerner RA, Rowlands DJ, Brown F (1982). Protection against foot and mouth disease by immunization with a chemically synthesized peptide predicted from the viral nucleotide sequence. Nature 298: 30.

Churchill AE, Payne LN, Chubb RC (1969). Immunization against Marek's disease using a live attenuated virus. Nature 221: 744.

Clifford P (1970). A review: on the epidemiology of nasopharyngeal carcinoma. Int. J. Cancer 5: 287.

De Schryver A, Klein G, Hewetson J, Rocchi G, Henle W, Henle G, Moss DJ, Pope JH (1974). Comparison of EBV neutralization tests based on abortive infection or transformation of lymphoid cells and their relation to membrane reactive antibodies (anti-MA). Int. J. Cancer 13: 353.

Epstein MA (1976). Epstein-Barr virus - is it time to develop a vaccine program? J. Nat. Cancer Inst. 56: 697.

Epstein MA, Achong BG (1979). The relationship of the virus to Burkitt's lymphoma. In Epstein MA, Achong BG (eds): "The Epstein-Barr Virus" Berlin, Heidelberg & New York, Springer-Verlag, p 321.

Franklin SM, North JR, Morgan AJ, Epstein MA (1981). Antigenic differences between the membrane antigen polypeptides determined by different EB virus isolates. J. Gen. Virol. 53: 371.

Hoffman GJ, Lazarowitz SG, Hayward SD (1980). Monoclonal antibody against a 250,000 dalton glycoprotein of Epstein-Barr virus identifies a membrane antigen and a neutralising antigen. Proc. Nat. Acad. Sci. 77: 2979.

Kaaden OR, Dietzschold B (1974). Alterations of the immunological specificity of plasma membranes of cells infected with Marek's disease and turkey herpes viruses. J. Gen. Virol. 25: 1.

Kirkwood JK, Epstein MA, Terlecki AJ (1983). Factors influencing population growth of a colony of cotton-topped tamarins. Laboratory Animals - in press.

Laufs R, Steinke H (1975). Vaccination of non-human primates against malignant lymphoma. Nature 253: 71.

Manesis EK, Cameron CH, Gregoriadis G (1979). Hepatitis B surface antigen-containing liposomes enhance humoral and cell-mediated immunity to the antigen. FEBS Lett. 102: 107.

Miller G (1979). Experimental carcinogenicity by the virus in vivo. In Epstein MA, Achong BG (eds): "The Epstein-Barr Virus" Berlin, Heidelberg & New York, Springer-Verlag, p 351.

Miller G, Shope T, Lisco H, Stitt D, Lipman M (1972). Epstein-Barr virus: transformation, cytopathic changes, and viral antigens in squirrel monkey and marmoset leukocytes. Proc. Nat. Acad. Sci. 69: 383.

Morein B, Helenius A, Simons K, Pettersson R, Kääriäinen L, Schirrmacher V (1978). Effective subunit vaccines against an enveloped animal virus. Nature 276: 715.

Morgan AJ, North JR, Epstein MA (1982). Purification and properties of the gp340 component of Epstein-Barr (EB) virus membrane antigen (MA) in an immunogenic form. Submitted to press.

North JR, Morgan AJ, Epstein MA (1980). Observations on the EB virus envelope and virus-determined membrane antigen (MA) polypeptides. Int. J. Cancer 26: 231.

North JR, Morgan AJ, Thompson JL, Epstein MA (1982a). Quantification of an EB virus-associated membrane antigen (MA) component. J. Virol. Methods - in press.

North JR, Morgan AJ, Thompson JL, Epstein MA (1982b). Purified EB virus gp340 induces potent virus-neutralising antibodies when incorporated in liposomes. Submitted to press.

Pearson G, Dewey F, Klein G, Henle G, Henle W (1970).

Relation between neutralization of Epstein-Barr virus and antibodies to cell-membrane antigens induced by the virus. J. Nat. Cancer Inst. 45: 989.

Pearson GR, Scott RE (1977). Isolation of virus-free Herpesvirus saimiri antigen-positive plasma membrane vesicles. Proc. Nat. Acad. Sci. 74: 2546.

Qualtière LF, Pearson GR (1979). Epstein-Barr virus-induced membrane antigens: immunochemical characterisation of Triton X100 solubilized viral membrane antigens from EBV-superinfected Raji cells. Int. J. Cancer 23: 808.

Schuster BG, Neidig M, Alving BM, Alving CR (1979). Production of antibodies against phosphocholine, phosphatidyl-choline, sphyngomyelin and lipid A by injection of liposomes containing lipid A. J. Immunol. 122: 900.

Shanmugaratnam K (1967). Nasopharyngeal carcinoma in Asia. In Shivas AA (ed):"Racial and Geographical Factors in Tumour Incidence" University of Edinburgh Press, p 169.

Shanmugaratnam K (1971) Studies on the etiology of nasopharyngeal carcinoma. In Richter GW, Epstein MA (eds): "International Review of Experimental Pathology" New York & London, Academic Press Inc, 10, p 361.

Strnad BC, Neubauer RH, Rabin H, Mazur RA (1979). Correlation between Epstein-Barr virus membrane antigen and three large cell surface glycoproteins. J. Virol. 32: 885.

Szmuness W, Stevens CE, Zang EA, Harley EJ, Kellner A (1981). A controlled clinical trial of the efficacy of the Hepatitis B vaccine (Heptavax B): a final report. Hepatology 1: 377.

Thorley-Lawson DA, Edson CM (1979). The polypeptides of the Epstein-Barr virus membrane antigen complex. J. Virol. 32: 458.

13th International Cancer Congress, Part B
Biology of Cancer (1), pages 71–80
© **1983 Alan R. Liss, Inc., 150 Fifth Avenue, New York, NY 10011**

MAREK'S DISEASE VIRUS AND HERPESVIRUS OF TURKEYS:
ANTIGENIC ASPECTS

Shiro Kato, M.D.[1], Kazuyoshi Ikuta, PhD.[2],
Kanji Hirai, PhD.[3]
[1]Director, Prof.; [2]Res. Assoc., Res. Inst. for
Microb. Dis., Osaka Univ., Osaka, Japan. [3]Assist.
Prof., Med. Sch. Tokai Univ., Isehara, Japan.

Marek's disease virus (MDV) is the etiological agent of
Marek's disease (MD), a highly contagious malignant lymphoma
of chickens. Studies on transformation and oncogenicity
with MDV have been far behind those with the other herpesviruses. The reasons are probably the following: (1) No
one has yet isolated any transformed cell lines in vitro in
culture. (2) Although several lymphoid cell lines were
established from MD tumors (Akiyama et al. 1973; Powell et
al. 1974), there has been no reports on the virus specific
tumor antigens. In addition, very little is known about the
biochemical properties of the proteins specified by MDV,
possibly because of the cell-associated nature of this virus.
However, there are several advantages to study on oncogenicity by MDV. Firstly, MDV becomes attenuated during serial
passage in cultured cells and the attenuated MDV does not
produce MD tumors in chickens (Churchill et al. 1969;
Nazerian 1970; Purchase et al. 1971). Although the cleavage
patterns with restriction endonuclease of DNA from MDV at
different passage levels were very similar, some fragments
were lost at higher passage levels with loss of oncogenicity
(Hirai et al. 1981b). Therefore, the studies on the structure of MDV DNA and virus-specific proteins at different
passage levels in culture may lead to an understanding of
the oncogenicity. Secondly, herpesvirus of turkey (HVT) was
shown to be serologically related to MDV (Witter et al. 1970)
and has been used to protect chickens from MD (Okazaki et al.
1970). At present, this is an only available vaccine against
tumor formation. Thus, analysis of serological cross-
reactive proteins of MDV and HVT is important to understand
of vaccinal immunity of HVT. Both EBV and MDV share much

similar lymphotropic biology. Both viruses infect and
trasform lymphocytes. The cells transformed by EBV or MDV
harbor the viral genomes in a latent form which are present
as a plasmid-like circular DNA molecules (Adams and Lindale
1975; Tanaka et al. 1978; Hirai et al. 1981c). Both latent
EBV and MDV genomes possess a nucleosomal structures (Shaw
et al. 1979; Hirai et al. 1981c). The rate of transcription
of latent viral genomes is restricted in both EBV and MDV
transformed cells (Hayward and Kieff 1976; Silver et al.
1979; Hirai et al. 1981c). It was also demonstrated that
the heterophile antigens was associated with the surface of
both EBV and MDV-transformed cells (Maeda et al. 1979; Ikuta
et al. 1981b). Therefore much of works on MDV could contribute to studies on EBV because of the similarity of MDV
system in relation to oncogenicity.

I. THE STRUCTURES OF DNAS OF VIRULENT AND AVIRULENT STRAINS
OF MDV

For identification of the specific portions of MDV
genomes that might be responsible for oncogenicity by MDV,
two virulent strains, BC-1 and JM, of MDV were serially
passaged in cultured chick embryo fibroblasts (CEF). The
purified viral DNA at different passage levels were compared
by restriction endonuclease digestion followed by 0.5%
agarose gel electrophoresis as described previously (Hirai
et al. 1979). Some fragments, Bam HI D and H, Sal I E and
F, and Sma I G, were lost at higher passage levels with loss
of oncogenicity. These fragments were not found in the
restriction endonuclease digestion products of the DNAs of
attenuated, avirulent MDV strains, C2(A) and GA(A) (Hirai et
al. 1981a and b) and termed as virulent strain-specific
fragments. However, experiments with Southern's blot
hybridization (Southern 1975) showed that ^{32}P-labeled DNA of
either BC-1 or JM strains at higher passage levels hybridized
with all the DNA fragments of the strains at low passage
levels, and vice versa. The reciprocal DNA-DNA reassociation
kinetics also indicated that the DNAs of virulent and avirulent MDV strain shared more than 95% of their nucleotide
sequences. To examine more directly whether the MDV strains
at higher passages lost the sequences of the DNA fragments
specific for virulent strains, ^{32}P-labeled virulent strain-
specific DNA fragments were hybridized to Southern's blots
of the DNA fragments obtained from high-passaged virus.
The virulent strain-specific fragments hybridized to the

DNA fragments of higher passaged avirulent virus with heterogeneous electrophoretic mobilities. These fragment specific
for avirulent strains were Bam HI D1, D2 and het, Sal I het,
and Sma I het. The reassociation kinetics of ^{32}P-labeled
virulent strain-specific fragments in the presence of
unlabeled DNA extracted from avirulent strains at higher
passage levels contains most of the nucleotide sequences
of the virulent strain-specific DNA fragments.

To examine whether the DNAs of chicken lymphoid cell
lines isolated from MD tumors contain the virulent strain-
specific fragment in their Bam HI digests, we digested the
DNAs of lymphoid cell lines MDCC-MSB1 and BMCL1 with Bam HI
and hybridized to Southern's blots containing the Bam HI
fragments with ^{32}P-labeled virulent BC-1 or Bam HI fragments.
The Bam HI-cleavage patterns of MDV DNA in the MD lymphoid
cells were very similar with those of virulent BC-1 DNA.
In addition, these cell lines contained the virulent strain-
specific fragments, Bam HI D and H, but not Bam HI D1, D2
and het. These results suggest that the virulent strain-
specific fragments are responsible for the oncogenicity of
MDV and that the altered structure could result in loss of
oncogenicity.

To locate the virulent strain-specific fragments on the
MDV genomes, we attempted to construct linkage maps of Bam
HI, Sal I and Sma I fragments of MDV DNA by Southern's
hybridization. The tentative linkage maps are shown in
Fig. 1. Nucleotide sequence homology was found not only
between Bam HI D and H and between Sal I E and F, but also

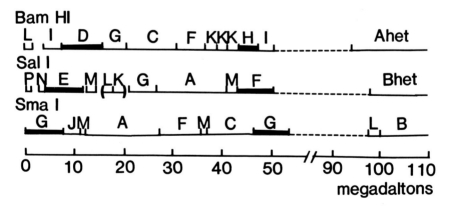

Fig. 1. Partial linkage map of Bam HI, Sal I and Sma I
fragments of MDV DNA. The solid blocks indicate the virulent strain-specific fragments.

among these fragments, indicating the presence of repeated
sequences in MDV DNA. Recently, Cébrian et al. (1982)
reported the presence of inverted repeated sequences both at
the end and in internal portions of MDV DNA as found in the
structure of herpes simplex virus (Scheldrick and Berthelot
1974). Their results suggest that the virulent strain-
specific fragments, Bam HI D and H, Sal I E and F, and Sma I
G, contain inverted repeated sequences. The important point
of linkage maps of MDV DNA is that the virulent strain-
specific fragments are separated by non-repeated sequences.
In addition, Bam HI fragments that hybridize with Sal I E
and F were isolated from cloned recombinant plasmids with
an inserted Bam HI fragment and the fragments were found to
share homology. Therefore, the region located between Bam
HI D and H might correspond to a long (U_L) or small (U_S)
region on non-repeated sequences, each flanked by inverted
repeated sequences. The altered forms of avirulent MDV DNA
might occur as a consequence of recombination between these
distant regions of virulent viral DNA. The size of the
common sequences to Bam HI D, Sal I E and Sma I G or to Bam
HI H, Sal I F and Sma I G is found to be 1.2×10^6 daltons,
about 2 K base pairs. These portions could be responsible
for oncogenicity of MDV.

II. IDENTIFICATION OF IMMUNOLOGICALLY CROSS-REACTIVE
PROTEINS SPECIFIC FOR MDV AND HVT.

In spite of antigenic similarities between MDV and HVT,
previous studies on the extent of DNA homology between these
viruses revealed that the two viruses have very little
homology (Hirai et al. 1979; Lee et al. 1979; Kaschka-Dierich
et al. 1979). However, much of studies on the serological
similarities between MDV and HVT are based on the techniques
of immunofluorescence and immunodiffusion (Chubb and churchill
1968; Purchase 1969; Witter et al. 1970). Recently, we have
identified more than 40 distinct MDV and HVT-specific polypeptides in cells infected with MDV and HVT, respectively,
by purified antibodies by affinity chromatography (Ikuta et
al. 1981). These methods allowed us to analyze systemati-
cally the biochemical nature and extent of the antigenic
cross-reactive polypeptides. When MDV and HVT-specific
polypeptides labeled with ^{35}S-methionine were immunoprecipitated with heterologous HVT and MDV antibodies, respectively,
almost all of the MDV and HVT-specific polypeptides possessed
cross-reactive determinants, except for small MDV or HVT-

specific polypeptides of less than 28K as shown in Fig. 2.

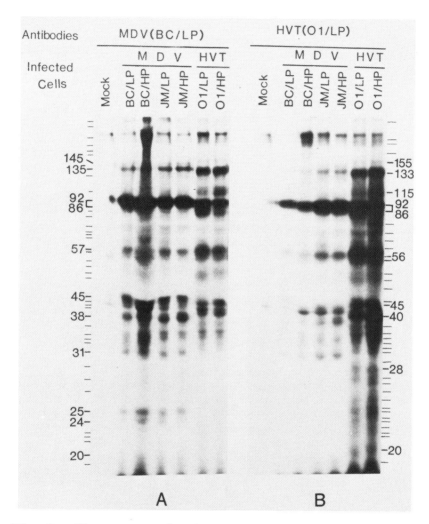

Fig. 2. Fluorograms of polypeptides immunoprecipitated from MDV or HVT-infected cells labeled with ^{35}S-methionine and separated by SDS-polyacrylamide gel electrophoresis. Monolayers of CEF were mock-infected or infected with the BC-1 and JM strains of MDV and 01 strain of HVT at the low and high passages (BC/LP, BC/HP, JM/LP, JM/HP, 01/LP and 01/HP, respectively). Antibodies used: (A), MDV (BC/LP) antibody; (B), HVT (01/LP) antibody.

Next we have focused our attention on the virus-specific glycoproteins that appear to be serologically cross-reactive between MDV and HVT. Since the exact mechanism of HVT-vaccinal immunity in MD is not known, analysis of serological cross-reactions between glycoproteins of MDV and HVT is a prerequisite for studies on the vaccinal immunity of HVT. However, little is known about the biochemical natures of MDV and HVT-specific glycoproteins. We have identified twelve and sixteen virus-specific glycoproteins labeled with ^{3}H-glucosamine in cells infected with MDV and HVT, respectively. Most of MDV and HVT-specific glycoproteins appeared to cross-react with their heterologous antibodies. It was also found that serial passages of MDV and HVT in culture result in change in size and number of virus-specific glycoproteins, simultaneously with loss of oncogenicity and vaccigenicity, respectively. Among these cross-reactive glycoproteins, MDV-gp64 (MW 64,000) and HVT-gp56 (MW 56,000) were clearly detectable in immunoprecipitates of culture fluids of MDV and HVT-infected cells, respectively. Both gp64 and gp56 may correspond to the A antigen (Churchill et al. 1969).

It is difficult for us using polyvalent sera to determine the number of virus-specific and cross-reactive determinants in MDV and HVT-specific proteins. For identification of the antigenic determinants of both virus-specific proteins, we have isolated the mouse hybridoma cells which secrete the monoclonal antibodies to MDV and HVT-specific antigens. These monoclonal antibodies were screened by immunofluorescence techniques. Table 1 shows the results of immunoprecipitation, using MDV and HVT-positive monoclonal antibodies, of ^{35}S-methionine-labeled polypeptides from virus-infected cells. It is noteworthy that a considerable number of monoclonal antibodies recognize the antigenic sites which are common between MDV and HVT. The monoclonal antibodies to MDV-gp64 and HVT-gp56 reacted common antigenic determinants. It was also found by immunofluorescence technique that the monoclonal antibodies reacted with the membrane antigens on both MDV and HVT-infected cells. Pulse-chase experiments showed that HVT-gp56 existes in a precursor and product forms in the infected cells. The precursor protein was pulse-labeled with ^{35}S-methionine for 10 min and the label was chased. This size of precursor protein was found to be 50,000 (pr50K) daltons. The precursor protein was glycosylated in the cells and then transferred to the culture medium. The precursor molecule appeared to be converted directly to the product form within 30 min-chase.

Table 1. Cross-reactivity of monoclonal antibodies to MDV and HVT antigens.

Identified antigenic polypeptides	Number of isolated hybridoma clones				
	Immunogen Cross-reaction	MDV		HVT	
		S^1	C^2	S^1	C^2
145K, 155K		2	3	0	0
115K, 56K, 50K, 46K		0	4	2	3
92/86K		12	2	1	0
64K, 56K		0	2	0	1
36K, 40K		4	0	0	0

[1]S;MDV or HVT-specific. [2]C;Cross-reactive between MDV and HVT.

III. DEMONSTRATION OF HETEROPHILE ANTIGENS EXPRESSED ON THE SURFACE OF MD LYMPHOBLASTOID CELL LINES.

All MD tumor-derived lymphoblastoid cell lines expressed MD tumor-associated surface antigen (MATSA) (Witter et al. 1975). We have previously shown that chicken antisera to MSB1, which is one of MD cell lines, with anti-MATSA specificity also contained a heterophile antibody with Hanganutziu-Deicher (H-D)-like antibody specificity (Ikuta et al. 1980; 1981b), but not a heterophile antibody with Forssman specificity (Ikuta et al. 1981a). We have examined the presence of hete- rophile antigens, H-D and Forssman antigens, on the surface of MD lymphoblastoid cell lines by membrane immunofluorescence test (MIF). The results were shown in Table 2. All MD lym- phoma-derived cell lines, except trasplantable MD tumor-

Table 2. Demonstration of heterophile antigen on avian lym- phoblastoid cell lines by MIF.

Derived from	Cell lines	T or B determi- nant	MATSA	Heterophile antigen	
				H-D[1]	Forssman[2]
MD lymphoma	MSB1, HP1, BMCL1, JP1, JP4, BO1(T), BP8,	T	+	+	−
	RP1 (transplant)	T	+	±	++
LL[3] lymphoma	1104B1, 1104X5	B	−	±	++
NCSL[4]			−	−	+

[1]Chicken anti-equine hematoside serum was used as anti-H-D.
[2]Rabbit anti-Forssman glycolipid serum was used as anti-Forss- man. [3]Lymphoid leukosis. [4]Normal chicken spleen lymphocytes.

derived cell line RP1, expressed H-D antigen on their cell surfaces. These results suggest that H-D and Forssman antigens appear to be unrelated to MATSA.

Although we have attempted to identify the portions of MDV genome that might be responsible for oncogenicity of MDV, more direct evidence are required for identification of MDV oncogene. For example, we have to show the ability to transformation by transfection of the virulent strain-specific fragments. It will be also necessary to show the presence of MDV-specific RNA in MD lymphoblastoid cell lines, which hybridizes to the virulent strain-specific fragments. For identification of MDV oncogene products, further studies on the possible functions of MDV-specific proteins are in progress. We have shown that most of virus-specific polypeptides in cells productively infected with MDV or HVT possess cross-reactive determinants, although the two viruses have very little DNA homology. This discrepancy could be explained by supposing that, although the cross-reactive polypeptides of MDV and HVT show a high degree of homology in their amino acid sequences, the genetic code words for each amino acids of MDV and HVT cross-reactive polypeptides are different, or that only a slight portion of the amino acid sequences responsible for the antigenicity of the cross-reactive determinants is common in MDV and HVT cross-reactive polypeptides. These possibilities could be tested by comparison of the nucleotide sequences of both viral DNAs. Very little is known about the roles of the MDV and HVT cross-reactive proteins in immunoprotection against MD. Since the MDV-gp64 and HVT-gp56 are expressed on the surfaces of infected cells, they can be targets of various immune cytolytic reactions.

ACKNOWDGMENT
     This work was supported by a Grant-in-Aid for Scientific Research from the Ministry of Education, Science and Culture of Japan.

REFERENCES
Adams A, Lindale T (1975). Intracellular forms of Epstein-Barr virus DNA in Raji cells. In:Oncogenesis and Herpesviruses, Vol II. pp125. IARC, Ryon.
Akiyama Y, Kato S, Iwa N (1973). Continuous cell culture from lymphoma of Marek's disease. Biken J 16:177.

Cébrian J, Kaschka-Dierich C, Berthelot N, Schelrick P (1982). Inverted repeat nucleotide sequences in the genomes of Marek's disease virus and the herpesvirus of turkey. Proc Natl Acad Sci USA 79:555.

Chubb RC, Churchill AE (1968). Precipitating antibodies associated with Marek's disease. Vet Rec 83:4.

Churchill AE, Chubb RC, Baxendale W (1969). The attenuation, with loss of oncogenicity, of the herpes-type virus of Marek's disease (strain HPRS-16) on passage in cell culture. J Gen Virol 4:557.

Hayward D, Kieff ED (1976). Epstein-Barr virus specific RNA in cellular extracts and in the polyribosomal fraction of permissive and nonpermissive lymphoblastoid cell lines. J Virol 18:518.

Hirai K, Ikuta K, Kato S (1979). Comparative studies on Marek's disease virus and herpesvirus of turkey DNAs. J Gen Virol 45:119.

Hirai K, Ikuta K, Kato S (1981a). Restriction endonuclease analysis of the genomes of virulent and avirulent Marek's disease viruses. Microbiol Immunol 25:671.

Hirai K, Ikuta K, Kato S (1981b). Structural changes of the DNA of Marek's disease virus during serial passages in cultured cells. Virology 115:385.

Hirai K, Ikuta K, Kitamoto N, Kato S (1981c). Latency of herpesvirus of turkey and Marek's disease virus genomes in a chicken T-lymphoblastoid cell line. J Gen Virol 53:133.

Ikuta K, Kitamoto N, Saito C, Kato S (1980). Demonstration of heterophile antibody in chicken antisera against Marek's disease tumor-derived cell line, MSB-1. Biken J 23:57.

Ikuta K, Kitamoto N, Shoji H, Kato S, Naiki M (1981a). Expression of Forssman antigen of avian lymphoblastoid cell lines transformed by Marek's disease virus or avian leukosis virus. J Gen Virol 52:145.

Ikuta K, Kitamoto N, Shoji H, Kato S (1981b). Hanganutziu and Deicher type heterophile antigen expressed on the cell surface of Marek's disease lymphoma-derived cell lines. Biken J 24:23.

Ikuta K, Nishi Y, Kato S, Hirai K (1981c). Immunoprecipitation of Marek's disease virus-specific polypeptides with chicken antibodies purified by affinity chromatography. Virology 114:277.

Kaschka-Dierich C, Bornkamm GW, Thomssen R (1979). No homology detectable between Marek's disease virus (MDV) DNA and herpesvirus of turkey (HVT) DNA. Med Microbial Immunol 165:223.

Lee Y-S, Tanaka A, Silver S, Smith M, Nonoyama M (1979). Minor DNA homology between herpesvirus of turkey and Marek's disease virus ? Virology 93:277.

Maeda M, Sairenji T, Hinuma Y (1979). Reactivity of Paul-Bunnell type heterophile antibody in sera from infectious mononucleosis patients with the surface of lymphoid cells carrying Epstein-Barr virus genomes. Microbiol Immunol 23:1189.

Nazerian K (1970). Attenuation of Marek's disease virus and study of its properties in two different cell cultures. J Natl Cancer Inst 44:1257.

Okazaki W, Purchase HG, Burmester BR (1970). Protection against Marek's disease by vaccination with a herpesvirus of turkeys. Avian Dis 14:113.

Powell PC, Payne LN, Frazier JA, Rennie M (1974). T lympho-blastoid cell lines from Marek's disease lymphomas. Nature 251:79.

Purchase HG (1969). Immunofluorescence in the study of Marek's disease. I. Detection of antigen in cell culture and an antigenic comparison of eight isolates. J Virol 3:557.

Purchase HG, Burmester BR, Cunningham CH (1971). Pathogenicity and antigenicity of clones from strains of Marek's disease virus and the herpesvirus of turkeys. Infect Immun 3:295.

Shaw JE, Levinger LF, Carter CWJr (1979). Nucleosomal structure of Epstein-Barr virus DNA in transformed cell lines. J Virol 29:657.

Sheldrick P, Berthelot N (1974). Inverted repetitions in the chromosome of herpes simplex virus. Cold Spring Harbor Symp Quant Biol 39:667.

Silver S, Tanaka A, Nonoyama M (1979). Transcription of the Marek's disease virus genomes in a nonproductive chicken lymphoblastoid cell line. Virology 93:127.

Southern EM (1975). Detection of specific sequences among DNA fragments separated by gel electrophoresis. J Mol Biol 98:508.

Tanaka A, Silver S, Nonoyama M (1978). Biochemical evidence of the non-integrated status of Marek's disease virus DNA in virus-transformed cells of chicken. Virology 88:19.

Witter RL, Nazerian K, Purchase HG, Burgoyne GH (1970). Isolation from turkeys of a cell-associated herpesvirus antigenically related to Marek's disease virus. Amer J Vet Res 31:525.

Witter RL, Stephens EA, Sharma JM, Nazerian K (1975). Demonstration of a tumor-associated surface antigen in Marek's disease. J Immunol 115:177.

CONGRESS SYMPOSIA

TRANSFORMATION OF CELLS IN CULTURE BY CHEMICAL
CARCINOGENS/RADIATIONS Kuroki, T., Japan, Chairman;
DiPaolo, J., USA, Co-Chairman; Arena

Initiation, Promotion, Transformation, and
Mutagenesis of Mouse Embryo Cell Lines.
*Heidelberger, C., Los Angeles, CA USA.

Malignant Transformation of Epithelial Cells in
Culture. *Fusenig, N. E., Heidelberg, W. Germany.

Environment Cancer Hazards: In Vitro Studies on
Risk, Protection and Potentiation. *Borek, C.,
New York, NY USA.

Cellular and Molecular Mechanisms of Neoplastic
Transformation of Human Cells, *Kakunaga, T.,
Crow, J. D., Leavitt, J. and Hamada, H., Bethesda, MD
USA and Palo Alto, CA USA.

Analysis of Cellular Transforming Genes by Trans-
fection. *Cooper, G., Shih, C., McCoy, M.,
Cunningham, J., Toole, J. J., Shilo, B-Z. and
Weinberg, R. A., Cambridge, MA USA. (By Title Only)

Factors that Modify In Vitro Transformation.
DiPaolo, J., USA.

Please note: Papers that are listed as "By Title
Only" were presented at the 13th International
Cancer Congress, but are not included in these
volumes.

81

13th International Cancer Congress, Part B
Biology of Cancer (1), pages 83–89
© 1983 Alan R. Liss, Inc., 150 Fifth Avenue, New York, NY 10011

INITIATION, PROMOTION, TRANSFORMATION, AND MUTAGENESIS OF
MOUSE EMBRYO CELL LINES

Charles Heidelberger, Ph.D.

Director For Basic Research
University of Southern California Comprehensive
Cancer Center, Los Angeles, CA 90031 USA

In recent years, the complexities of studying cellular
and molecular mechanisms of chemical carcinogenesis in whole
animals have precluded the use of such systems to obtain
definitive information on mechanisms. Hence, we and others
have developed some systems in which normal or near-normal
rodent cells grown in culture in relatively well-defined media and conditions are treated with chemical, physical, or
viral oncogens. In suitable systems the "normal" cells lose
their growth controls and take on some of the phenotypes
associated with oncogenic transformation. These include
loss of cell density-dependent growth inhibition, acquisition of the ability of the cells to grow on top of each
other in a disoriented fashion, and the ability of these
cells to give rise to tumors on inoculation into suitably
prepared syngeneic animals. In general, two types of cell
cultures have been used: 1) Primary or secondary cultures
of Syrian hamster embryonic cells (SHE cells) (Berwald and
Sachs 1965; DiPaolo, Donovan and Nelson 1969a; Huberman and
Sachs 1966; Barrett and Ts'o 1978b. 2) Permanent cloned
cell lines derived from mouse cells (Chen and Heidelberger
1969a; Chen and Heidelberger 1969b; Chen and Heidelberger
1969c; Kakunaga 1973; DiPaolo, Takano and Popescu 1972;
Heidelberger and Iype 1967; Reznikoff, et al. 1973a,
1973b).

In all these systems transformation can be quantitated
usually by scoring for piled-up original colonies (SHE
cells) (Berwald and Sachs 1965) or for piled-up foci on top
of a confluent monolayer (Chen and Heidelberger 1969;
Reznikoff et al. 1973a&b). The colony assay can usually be

scored about two weeks after carcinogen treatment (Berwald and Sachs 1965), whereas the cell lines are generally scored 6 weeks after treatment (Reznikoff et al. 1973a&b). The cell lines are usually cloned and have fairly uniform properties, whereas the SHE cultures are usually mixed cell populations with a variety of behaviors. It should be noted that the permanent cell lines are generally immortal, and are very seldom, if ever, diploid. Because of these differences, it is now generally considered that both types of systems are useful models for the study of chemical carcinogenesis. A "Gene-Tox" program has recently evaluated the published literature obtained with the cell transformation systems, and a manuscript has been prepared and will be submitted for publication for Mutation Research, but has not yet been approved for general distribution. The topic of cell transformation has been frequently reviewed by many authors (Barrett and Ts'o 1978b, Heidelberger 1980; Reznikoff, Bertram, Brankow, and Heidelberger 1973; Heidelberger 1980; Heidelberger 1981; Heidelberger 1981).

The phenomenon of subdividing mouse-skin carcinogenesis into the phases of initiation (irreversible) and promotion (reversible) by Berenblum and his colleagues (Berenblum 1941), has had a profound impact on the field. In cell culture systems, as well, initiation and promotion have been repeatedly demonstrated and described (Mondal et al. 1976; Kennedy et al. 1978; Mondal and Heidelberger 1976; Mondal 1978), and are being utilized to study the mechanisms of these two phenomena. Incidentally, the tumor epidemiologists are now recognizing the importance of late stages (promotion) in the induction and hopefully in the prevention of human cancers (Peto 1981). There has also been recent progress reported on the quantitation of transformation of human diploid fibroblasts with chemical and physical carcinogens (Maher, Rowan, Silinskas, McCormick 1982; Yang, Maher, McCormick 1980).

Barrett JC, Ts'o POP (1978). Evidence for the progressive nature of neoplastic transformation in vitro. Proc. Natl. Acad. Sci. USA 75. 3761-3765.
Berenblum I (1941). The carcinogenic action of croton resin. Cancer Res. 1: 44-48.
Bertram JS, Heidelberger C (1974). Cell Cycle Dependency of Oncogenic Transformation Induced by N-Methyl-N'-Nitro-N-Nitrosoguanidine in Culture. Cancer Res. 34, 526-537.
Berwald Y, Sachs L (1965). In Vitro transformation of

normal cells to tumor cells by carcinogenic hydrocarbons. J. Natl. Cancer Inst. 35, 641-661.

Billings PC, Heidelberger C (1982). Effects of Praziquantel, a New Antischistosomal Drug, on the Mutation and Transformation of Mammalian Cells, Cancer Res., 42., 2692-2696.

Boreiko C, Heidelberger C (1980). Isolation of mutants temperature-sensitive for expression of the transformed state from chemically transformed C3H/10T1/2 cells. Carcinogenesis, 1: 1059-1073.

Chen TT, Heidelberger C (1969a). Cultivation In Vitro of Cells Derived from Adult C3H Mouse Ventral Prostate. J. Natl. Cancer Inst. 42, 903-914.

Chen TT, Heidelberger C (1969b). In Vitro Malignant Transformation of Cells Derived from Mouse Prostate in the Presence of 3-Methylcholanthrene. J. Natl. Cancer Inst. 42, 915-925.

Chen TT, Heidelberger C (1969c). Quantitative Studies on the Malignant Transformation of Mouse Prostate Cells by Carcinogenic Hydrocarbons in vitro. Internat. J. Cancer 4, 166-178.

Corbett TH, Heidelberger C, Dove WF (1970). Determination of the Mutagenic Activity to Bacteriophage T4 of Carcinogenic and Noncarcinogenic Compounds. Mol. Pharmacol. 6, 667-679.

DiPaolo JA, Donovan PJ, Nelson RL (1969). Quantitative studies of in vitro transformation by chemical carcinogens. J. Natl. Cancer. Inst. 42: 867-874.

DiPaolo JA, Takano K, Popescu NC (1972). Quantitation of chemically induced neoplastic transformation of BALB/3T3 cloned cell lines. Cancer Res. 32: 2686-2695.

Embleton MJ, Heidelberger C (1972). Antigenicity of Clones of Mouse Prostate Cells Transformed In Vitro. Intern. J. Cancer 9, 8-18.

Embleton MJ, Heidelberger C (1975). Neoantigens on Chemically Transformed Cloned C3H Mouse Embryo Cells. Cancer Research 35, 2049-2055.

Fernandez A, Mondal S, Heidelberger C (1980). Probabilistic view of the transformation of cultured C3H/10T1/2 mouse embryo fibroblasts by 3-methylcholanthrene. Proc. Natl. Acad. Sci. USA, 77: 7272-7276.

Gehly EB, Fahl WE, Jefcoate CR, Heidelberger C (1979). The Metabolism of Benzo(a)pyrene by Cytochrome P-450 in Transformable and Nontransformable C3H Mouse Fibroblasts. J. Biol. Chem. 254, 5041-5048.

Gehly EB, Heidelberger C (1982). Metabolic Activation of

Benzo(a)pyrene by Transformable and Nontransformable C3H Mouse Fibroblasts in Culture, Cancer Res., 42: 2697-2704.

Gehly EB, Landolph JR, Heidelberger C, Nagasawa H, Little, JB (1982). Induction of Cytotoxicity, Mutation, Cytogenetic Changes, and Neoplastic Transformation by Benzo(a)pyrene and Derivatives in C3H/10T1/2 Clone 8 Mouse Fibroblasts, Cancer Res., 42: 1866-1875.

Grover PL, Sims P, Huberman E, Marquardt H, Kuroki T, Heidelberger C (1971). In Vitro Transformation of Rodent Cells by K-region Derivatives of Polycyclic Hydrocarbons. Proc. Natl. Acad. Sci. USA 68, 1089-1101.

Heidelberger C (1973). Current Trends in Chemical Carcinogenesis. Fed. Proc. 32, 2154-2161.

Heidelberger C (1973). Chemical Oncogenesis in Culture. Advances in Cancer Res. 18, 317-366.

Heidelberger C (1974). Cell Culture Studies on the Mechanisms of Hydrocarbon Oncogenesis. In Ts'o POP, DiPaolo (eds): "Chemical Carcinogenesis," Part B, New York: Marcel Dekker, Inc., pps. 457-462.

Heidelberger C (1975). Chemical Carcinogenesis. Ann. Rev. Biochem. 44, 79-121.

Heidelberger C (1975). Studies on the Cellular Mechanisms of Chemical Oncogenesis in Culture. In Gottlieb AA, Plescia OJ, and Bishop DHL (eds): "Fundamental Aspects of Neoplasia," New York: Springer-Verlag, pps. 357-363.

Heidelberger C (1976). Chemically and Metabolically Induced DNA Adducts: Relationship to Chemical Carcinogenesis. In Smith KC (ed): "Aging, Carcinogenesis, and Radiation Biology. The Role of Nucleic Acid Addition Reactions," New York: Plenum Press, pps. 341-371.

Heidelberger C (1977). Chemical Carcinogenesis. Cancer Res. 40, 430-433.

Heidelberger C (1980). Assays for In Vitro Carcinogenesis, Initiation, and Promotion. In Witschi H (ed): "The Scientific Basis of Toxicity Assessment," Elsevier/North-Holland Biomedical Press, pps. 61-67.

Heidelberger C (1980). Mammalian Cell Transformation and Mammalian Cell Mutagenesis In Vitro. J. of Environmental Pathology and Toxicology, 3-, No. 4, 69-87.

Heidelberger C (1981). Cellular Transformation as a Basic Tool for Chemical Carcinogenesis. In Mishra N, Dunkel V, and Mehlman M (eds): "Advances in Modern Environmental Toxicology Vol. 1. Mammalian Cell Transformation by Chemical Carcinogens," New Jersey: Senate Press, Inc., pps. 1-28.

Heidelberger C (1981). Initiation and Promotion, Mutagenesis and Transformation of C3H/10T1/2 Mouse Embryo Fibroblasts. GANN Monograph Cancer Res., 27: 207-219.

Huberman E, Aspiras L, Heidelberger C, Grover PL, Sims P (1971). Mutagenicity to Mammalian Cells of Epoxides and Other Derivatives of Polycyclic Hydrocarbons. Proc. Natl. Acad. Sci. USA 68. 3195-3199.

Huberman E, Kuroki T, Marquardt H, Selkirk JK, Heidelberger C, Grover PL, and Sims P (1972). Transformation of Hamster Embryo Cells by Epoxides and Other Derivatives of Polycyclic Hydrocarbons. Cancer Res. 32, 1391-1396.

Huberman E, Sachs L (1966). Cell susceptibility to transformation and cytotoxicity by the carcinogenic hydrocarbon benzo(a)pyrene. Proc. Natl. Acad. Sci. USA 56: 1123-1129.

Kakunaga T (1973). A quantitative system for assay of malignant transformation by chemical carcinogens using a clone derived from BALB/3T3. Int. J. Cancer. 12: 463-473.

Kennedy AR, Mondal S, Heidelberger C, Little JB (1978). Enhancement of X-ray Transformation by 12-0-Tetradecanoyl-phorbol-13-acetate in a Cloned Line of C3H Mouse Embryo Cells. Cancer Res. 38, 439-443.

Kuroki T, Huberman E, Marquardt H, Selkirk JK, Heidelberger C, Grover PL, and Sims P (1971/72). Binding of K-Region Epoxides and Other Derivatives of Benz(a)anthracene and Dibenz(a,h)anthracene to DNA, RNA, and Proteins of Transformable Cells. Chem.-Biol. Interactions 4, 389-397.

Landolph JR, Bhatt RS, Telfer N, Heidelberger C (1980). Comparison of Adriamycin-and Ouabain-induced Cytotoxicity and Inhibition of Rubidium Transport in Wild-Type and Ouabain-resistant C3H/10T1/2 Mouse Fibroblasts, Cancer Res. 40, 4581-4588.

Landolph JR, Heidelberger C (1979). Chemical Carcinogens Produce Mutations to Ouabain Resistance in Transformable C3H/10T1/2 Cl 8 Mouse Fibroblasts. Proc. Natl. Acad. Sci. USA, 76, 930-934.

Landolph JR, Telfer N, Heidelberger C (1980). Further Evidence that Ouabain-Resistant Variants Induced by Chemical Carcinogens in Transformable C3H/10T1/2 Cl 8 Mouse Fibroblasts are Mutants, Mutation Res. 72, 295-310.

Maher VM, Rowan LA, Silinskas KC, Kateley SA, McCormick JJ (1982). Frequency of UV-induced neoplastic transformation of diploid human fibroblasts is higher in xeroderma pigmentosum cells than in normal cells. Proc. Natl. Acad. Sci. USA 79: 2613-2617.

Marquardt H, Heidelberger C (1972). Influence of "Feeder

Cells" and Inducers and Inhibitors of Microsomal Mixed-Function Oxidases on Hydrocarbon-induced Malignant Transformation of Cells Derived from C3H Mouse Prostate. Cancer Res. 32, 721-725.

Marquardt H, Kuroki T, Huberman E, Selkirk JK, Heidelberger C, Grover Pl, and Sims P, (1972). Malignant Transformation of Cells Derived from Mouse Prostate by Epoxides and Other Derivatives of Polycyclic Hydrocarbons. Cancer Res. 32, 716-720.

Mondal S, Brankow DW, Heidelberger C (1976). Two-Stage Chemical Oncogenesis in Cultures of C3H/10T1/2 Cells. Cancer Res. 36, 2254-2260.

Mondal S, Brankow DW, Heidelberger C (1978). Enhancement of Oncogenesis in C3H/10T1/2 Mouse Embryo Cell Cultures by Saccharin. Science 201, 1141-1142.

Mondal S, Embleton MJ, Marquardt H, Heidelberger C (1971). Production of Variants of Decreased Malignancy and Antigenicity from Clones Transformed In Vitro by Methylcholanthrene. Internat. J. Cancer 8, 410-420.

Mondal S, Heidelberger C (1976). Transformation of C3H/10T1/2 Cl 8 Mouse Embryo Fibroblasts by Ultraviolet Irradiation and a Phorbol Ester. Nature, 260, 710-711.

Mondal S, Iype PT, Griesbach LM, Heidelberger C (1970). Antigenicity of Cells Derived from Mouse Prostate Cells after Malignant Transformation In Vitro by Carcinogenic Hydrocarbons. Cancer Research 30, 1593-1597.

Peterson AR, Bertram JS, Heidelberger C (1974). DNA Damage and its Repair in Transformable Mouse Fibroblasts Treated with N-Methyl-N'-Nitro-N-Nitrosoguanidine. Cancer Res. 34, 1592-1599.

Peterson AR, Bertram JS, Heidelberger C (1974). Cell Cycle Dependency of DNA Damage and Repair in Transformable Mouse Fibroblasts Treated with N-Methyl-N'-Nitro-N-Nitrosoguanidine. Cancer Research 34, 1600-1607.

Peto R, Doll R, Buckley JD, Sporn MB (1981). Can dietary beta-kerotine materially reduce human cancer rates? Nature 290: 201-203.

Rapp UR, Nowinski RC, Reznikoff CA, Heidelberger C (1975). Endogenous Oncornaviruses in Chemically-Induced Transformation. 1. Transformation Independent of Virus Production. Virology 65, 392-409.

Reznikoff CA, Brankow DW, Heidelberger C (1973). Establishment and characterization of a cloned line of C3H mouse em bryo cells sensitive to postconfluence inhibition of division. Cancer Res. 33: 3231-3238.

Reznikoff CA, Bertram JS, Brankow DW, Heidelberger C (1973).

Quantitative and Qualitative Studies of Chemical Transformation of Cloned C3H Mouse Embryo Cells Sensitive to Postconfluence Inhibition of Cell Division. Cancer Res. 33, 3239-3249.

Selkirk JK, Huberman E, Heidelberger C (1971). An Epoxide is an Intermediate in the Microsomal Metabolism of the Chemical Carcinogen, Dibenz(a,h)anthracene. Biochem. Biophys. Res. Commun. 43, 1010-1016.

Sims P, Grover PL, Kuroki T, Huberman E, Marquardt H, Selkirk JK, and Heidelberger C (1973). The Metabolism of Benz(a)anthracene and Dibenz(a,h)anthracene and their related "K-region" epoxides, cis-dihydrodiols and phenols by Hamster Embryo Cells. Biochem. Pharmacol. 22, 1-8.

Yang LL, Maher VM, and McCormick JJ (1980). Error-free excision of the cytotoxic, mutagenic N^2-deoxyguanosine DNA adduct formed in human fibroblasts by ($\pm$)-7β,8α-dihydroxy-9α,10α-epoxy-7,8,9,10-tetrahydrobenzo(a)pyrene. Proc. Natl. Acad. Sci. USA, 77, pps. 5933-5937.

13th International Cancer Congress, Part B
Biology of Cancer (1), pages 91–104
© 1983 Alan R. Liss, Inc., 150 Fifth Avenue, New York, NY 10011

MALIGNANT TRANSFORMATION OF EPlTHELIAL CELLS IN CULTURE

Norbert E. Fusenig, M.D., Ph.D.

Division of Differentiation and Carcinogenesis
in vitro, Institute for Biochemistry,
German Cancer Research Center, D-6900 Heidelberg

The use of cell culture systems for the study of neoplastic transformation by chemicals has provided important
information on the mechanism of chemical carcinogenesis. In
vitro carcinogenesis studies have usually been performed
on cells of stromal origin due to their ease of culture.
Although it is to be expected that certain characteristics
will be common to malignant conversion of all mammalian
cells, the development of neoplasia exhibits unique characteristics in each tissue. Moreover, most tumors arise in
epithelial tissues and the phenotypic expression of neoplastic states are clearly different for stromal and epithelial cells and differ among epithelia from specific
organs. Thus, there is increasing interest in epithelial in
vitro systems, preferably in those derived from tissues
being most frequent targets for the development of tumors
in man or for experimental carcinogenesis studies in animals.

During the last decade a number of culture systems
have been developed from different epithelial target tissues
preferably from "lining" epithelia such as trachea,
bronchus, bladder, and epidermis, but also from other epithelial organs (Steele et al., 1980; Harris et al., 1978;
Summerhayes et al., 1981; Yuspa et al., 1980a; Fusenig et
al., 1979; Milo et al., 1980; Williams, 1976; Montesano et
al., 1977; Autrup et al., 1978; Parsa et al., 1980; for
further references see Franks and Wigley, 1979).

Malignant conversion has been observed in epithelial
cell and organ cultures, but until recently transformation

events induced by chemicals or occurring spontaneously have been rare and non-quantitative. The problem with epithelial cell transformation in vitro is mainly due to difficulties in maintaining growth and differentiation of pure cell populations over periods long enough to allow malignant conversion. Due to their strict dependency on mesenchymal influences many epithelia could only be grown when cultured with mesenchymal elements. Unbalanced terminal differentiation leads to the early dilution of the proliferative compartment and to altered functional behaviour of such cells. In addition to the low transformation frequency in these systems altered foci were only recorded after long latency periods of up to several months. This may in part be related to the lack of characteristic morphologic changes associated with malignant transformation of epithelial cells as compared to mesenchymal cells. Finally, due to their tendency to grow as coherent sheets, it is very difficult to establish clonal growth of epithelial cells, a prerequisite for quantitative transformation assays.

The long latency periods required to induce epithelial transformation in vitro and the low transformation frequencies correlate with the late appearence of carcinomas in vivo (compared with mesenchymal tumors), but these problems may also reflect a reduced sensitivity of cultured epithelial cells to the transforming activity of chemical carcinogens. Several studies could demonstrate, however, that epithelial cells in culture are able to metabolize chemical carcinogens, such as polycyclic hydrocarbons, to their reactive intermediates at a similar or even higher rate as compared to mesenchymal cells (Irmscher and Fusenig, 1980; Theall et al., 1981; Kuroki et al., 1981). These metabolites bind to epithelial cell DNA and the lesions induced by bound carcinogens, or other carcinogenic factors such as UV-light, can be effectively repaired in epithelial cells in culture (Parkinson and Newbold, 1980; Bowden et al., 1977). Where tested, cultured epithelia also exhibited sensitivity to most known effects of tumor promoters (for references see Hecker et al., 1982). The transformed phenotypes of in vitro induced malignant epithelia were also indistinguishable or very similar to cancer cells isolated from in vivo induced carcinomas.(Fusenig et al., 1978; Breitkreutz et al., 1981; Montesano et al., 1977; Yuspa et al., 1980b)

From these findings it was concluded that the low

transformation frequency of epithelial cells in culture was most probably due to the inadequate culture conditions preventing sufficient proliferative activity, a prerequisite for the expression of transformation. This has been further substantiated by recent observations that chemical carcinogens may induce transformation at a higher frequency in epithelial cell cultures grown under improved culture conditions. This is particularly true for epidermal cell cultures derived from murine skin, a model system which has been used extensively to study correlations between cell differentiation and transformation in vitro (Yuspa et al., 1980a; Fusenig et al., 1979, 1982; Slaga et al., 1978; Indo and Miyayi, 1979).

I shall concentrate here on discussing two aspects of epidermal cell transformation in vitro; firstly, the consequences of improving culture conditions to allow long-term growth of mouse keratinocytes and secondly, alterations associated with early and later stages of malignant conversion of these cells. For several years my laboratory has been engaged in establishing a culture system for epidermal cells derived from newborn mouse skin and in characterizing the functional abilities of isolated keratinocytes under different growth conditions (Fusenig and Worst, 1975; Fusenig et al., 1979, 1981; Breitkreutz et al., 1981). The cultured cells maintain proliferation over limited periods and express many features of epidermal differentiation in vitro. Due to terminal differentiation and decrease in proliferation cultures usually degenerate within the first three weeks after plating. Within this rather short growth period only exceptionally could transformation be induced by chemicals (Fusenig et al., 1973). We therefore modified the culture conditions in order to prolong the growth phase of these cells in vitro.

Reducing the culture temperature to about $30^{o}C$ proved advantageous for continued growth of rodent epidermal as well as other epithelial cells (see Fusenig et al., 1979, 1982). Continued growth and stratification in primary epidermal cultures under these conditions was mainly confined to areas of high cell density often when only limited areas of the dish were covered by cells. The best results were obtained when about 1×10^{6} freshly isolated cells were plated on a space of $1\ cm^{2}$ in the center of a dish (central plating (Fusenig et al., 1982) (Fig. 1).

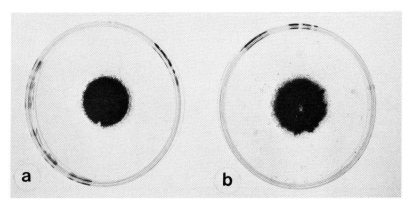

Fig. 1. Stratified primary epidermal cultures one (a) and
three (b) weeks after central plating in 35 mm petri dishes
(taken from Fusenig et al., 1982).

Proliferation of primary-plated keratinocytes is positively
dependent on cell concentrations and was maximal at 2 - 3
x 10^5 attached cells/cm^2 demonstrating a density dependent
stimulation in contrast to the known inhibition in fibroblast cultures (Fusenig et al., 1982). Although high cell
density at plating is important, long-term epidermal cultures developed if only part of the culture dish surface
was covered by keratinocytes. Due to better diffusion
of nutrients or because of the dilution of factors inhibitory to cell proliferation (higher medium to cell ratio),
these cell areas contindued to proliferate over months
forming stratified colonies.

Long-term growth of primary mouse epidermal cells can
further be improved when cells are plated "centrally" at
high density on a gas permeable substrate (Petriperm dishes,
Heräus, Hanau, FRG). Attachment and spreading of cells is
poorer as compared to plastic, but once epidermal colonies
become established they will develop into longterm cultures at a higher efficiency than on plastic.

Keratinocytes plated at low density will only lead to
longterm cultures when supported either by irradiated mesenchymal feeder layers (Rheinwald and Green, 1975; Fusenig
et al., 1979) or in low calcium medium conditioned from
fibroblast cultures (Kulesz-Martin et al., 1981).

All these conditions lead to continued proliferation
of mouse keratinocytes in primary cultures - and eventually
to their adaptation to permanent growth in culture. As
soon as cultures had survived more than 4 months they
usually became subculturable without need for further
conditioning growth substitutes. This altered state of
growth was usually first noted in foci exhibiting increased proliferation, altered cell morphology and reduced
differentiation. At this stage cells would form colonies
when plated at low cell densities on solid substrates.
Passages were usually successful after 6 months, (earlier
if the cells were grown with irradiated 3T3 cells) and
cell lines could be developed from these cultures (Tab. 1).
When treated with chemical carcinogens (DMBA) or promoters
(TPA) the frequency of transformation could not be increased
under these culture conditions.

CULTURE CON-DITIONS 30°C	NO. EXP.	TOTAL NO. OF PLATED DISHES	CONTINUED PRO-LIFERATION AFTER 4 MONTHS[++]	I. PASSAGE	CELL TYPES	NO. OF CELL LINES[+++]	
						INITIATED	PRESERVED
CENTRAL PLATING	3	28	12/19	6 MO.	2 AND 3	5	3 HEL III TO V
CENTRAL PLATING ON PETRIPERM DISHES	3	9	6/7	6-7 MO.	2 AND 3	4	4 HELP I TO IV
PEC ON 3T3 5 x 10^4 PLATED CELLS	7	53	26/31	2-4 MO.	2 AND 3	16	6 H3L I TO VI

[+]CULTURES WERE UNTREATED OR SOLVENT CONTROLS (ACETON OR DMSO 0.05 %) OF TRANSFORMATION EXPERIMENTS

[++]DISHES WITH PROLIFERATING EPIDERMAL FOCI OUT OF TOTAL NUMBER OF DISHES LEFT

[+++]MANY INITIATED LINES WERE LOST IN THE FIRST PASSAGES DUE TO FUNGAL INFECTION (AT 30°C)

Tab. 1. Mouse keratinocyte cell lines originated spontaneously from primary cultures grown under different conditions
(modified from Fusenig et al., 1982).

Keratinocyte lines developed spontaneously or after carcinogen or promoter treatment did not differ significantly
in their morphology. The passaged cell cultures still expressed a variety of keratinocyte characteristics although
individual variations among different lines were obvious,

and often more than one pattern was seen in different regions of the same line. Phenotypic changes in mouse keratinocyte lines comprised slight variations from the normal
appearance of stratifying primary cultures to a rather undifferentiated morphology with considerable cellular and
nuclear polymorphism. These phenotypic alterations were
rather stable but could not be associated with sequential
stages in cell transformation. They probably reflect more
varying degrees in differentiation than different degrees
of transformation (Fusenig et al., 1982; Yuspa et al., 1980b).

These cell lines which had aquired the potency to
continued growth in culture still expressed keratin peptides and filaments, which could be decorated by specific
antibodies, and still expressed an epidermis-specific antigen (Fusenig et al., 1982; Breitkreutz et al., 1981). Some
cell lines also coexpressed the cytoskeletal protein vimentin and related filaments, but the expression varied in frequency from line to line with a tendency to increase with
higher passages (Franke et al., 1979; Summerhayes et al.,
1981). The expression of vimentin, however, is obviously
more related to cell growth in vitro than characteristic
for the transformed phenotype. Increased levels of plasminogen activator activity could be determined but activity
was higher in keratinized squames (Isseroff et al., 1982).
Thus, there are so far no early and specific changes available to clearly identify transformed epidermal foci.

The earliest changes which we could observe in primary
cultures were cytogenetic alterations. Primary epidermal
cultures grown at high cell densities at 37° or 30°C (in
normal medium or with reduced Ca^{++} concentration) or cocul-
tured with 3T3 feeder cells, exhibited early and progressive
numerical and structural chromosome alterations (Tab. 2).
The percentage of diploid cells decreased with culture time
while the hypodiploid fraction increased up to 25 % and
tetraploidy reached similar values. Remarkably, structural
chromosome alterations including gaps, breaks, fragments
and metacentric chromosomes raised significantly within the
first two or three weeks in culture. Cell cultures analyzed
during early passages all had severe chromosomal alterations
(Fusenig et al., 1982)

	Diploid cells	Hypodiploid fraction (34-39)	Tetraploid fraction (80)	Structural chromosome aberrations	Metacentric chromosomes
PEC-37 2 D	82	2	11	6	2
PEC-37 4 D	80	2	18	4	3
PEC-37 8 D	65	19	16	8	3
PEC-30 3 D	78	6	16	4	0
PEC-30 8 D	60	22	18	8	5
PEC-30 14 D	48	26	26	12	6
PEC-CA 30 3 D	80	6	14	5	2
PEC-CA 30 8 D	62	17	21	15	5
PEC-CA 30 14 D	58	20	22	13	14
PEC-CA 30 21 D	44	26	30	14	13
PEC-3T3 30 4 Mo	52	11	37	12	8

Tab. 2. Numerical and structural chromosomal alterations
analyzed in banded metaphases in primary epidermal cultures
grown for 2 - 21 days (D) or 4 months (Mo) under different
conditions (from Fusenig et al., 1982).

Although the tumor promoter TPA did not significantly
enhance spontaneous or DMBA initiated transformation frequency, TPA itself considerably enhanced both numerical
and structural chromosome alterations. This was observed
as early as two cell cycles after treatment and chromosomal loss leading to hypodiploidy was again predominant.
Rearrangements of chromosomes forming tetraradials, rings
and dicentric chromosomes, never observed in untreated
cultures, were particularly impressive after TPA treatment
(Dzarlieva and Fusenig, 1982). Similar findings were
reported for a mouse keratinocyte line and human lymphocytes following short term TPA treatment (Fusenig and
Dzarlieva, 1982; Emeritt and Cerutti, 1981).

There is now overwhelming evidence that the initiation
of neoplasia by chemical carcinogens involves a direct
alteration of the genetic material, but it is still debated
whether this invariably results in malignant neoplasia
(for references see Pitot, 1981; Bouck and DiMayorca, 1982).
In tumor cells, visible chromosomal alterations have proved
to be more the rule than the exception and the obvious
conclusion is that large genomic rearrangements may be
crucial steps in carcinogenesis (Cairns, 1981).

Our observations indicate that chromosomal alterations are associated with epidermal cell adaptation to continuous growth in culture. This acquisition of the potentiality to grow in unusual locations and under artificial conditions of nourishment may be considered as an early step in malignant transformation. In skin carcinogenesis, similar alterations seem to occur early in the transformation process, which enable the cells to grow above the basal layer under conditions were normal keratinocytes can not proliferate but are obliged to differentiate. Similarly, Yuspa and coworkers (1980a) noted that the earliest alteration they could assess in epidermal cell transformation in vitro was the adaptation to growth under high Ca^{++} concentrations while normal cells stopped proliferating and differentiated.

Whether the phenotypic expression of autonomous cell growth in culture and early steps in malignant cell transformation are closely related or equal, can not yet be answered. The early phenotypic changes are very similar or indistinguishable in spontaneously developed and carcinogen-induced cell lines. Since both processes can be modulated by changing growth conditions the alterations associated with cell adaptation to growth in culture may well be studied as processed relevant for malignant cell transformation.

Whether these cell lines represent carcinoma cells or are premalignant states (in vitro equivalents of benign tumors e.g. papilloma) is still not settled. At early passages, cells often do not express the classical transformation criteria such as anchorage independent growth in vitro and tumorigenicity after injection into compatible hosts in vivo. Most cell lines acquire these characteristics with higher passage levels. This acquisition of more autonomous growth potential under even less favourable environmental conditions is often interpreted as a progression from preneoplastic (benign) to neoplastic (malignant) cells - a process which could be enhanced in one cell system by tumorpromoters (Colburn, 1980). One might, however, also question the adequacy of the test systems for detecting early stages of malignant epithelial cells. Both the ability to survive and multiply in agar, and at the various injection sites in vivo is more likely to be characteristic of metastatic cells with their higher degree of growth autonomy than for carcinoma cells eary in the development of a tumor. We were thus interested in finding other car-

cinoma-associated phenotypic expressions which might be
tested in vitro and in vivo as more sensitive criteria
for assessing the onset of malignant growth behaviour of
epithelial cells.

Altered morphogenesis and tissue architecture are the
earliest indicators for developing carcinomas in vivo, often
accompanied by metaplasia and atypical differentiation
features. Normal keratinocytes grow to stratified epidermal-
like structures in organotypical culture assays (attached
to lifted collagen layers). Transformed cell lines, however,
usually formed thick amorphous colonies when grown under
the same conditions, often resembling microtumors (Fusenig
et al., 1978, 1979; Fusenig and Dzarlieva, 1982). The diagnostic value of this test for detecting early stages of
epidermal cell transformation, however, has to be further
evaluated with more cell lines.

Invasive growth into the underlying normal stroma is
one of the first indications of malignancy in developing
carcinomas of lining epithelia in vivo. To test this growth
potentiality under conditions imitating the natural environment as closely as possible, we transplanted epidermal
cells onto a well vascularized granulation tissue induced
subdermally (Fusenig et al., 1978, 1980, 1982). On this
graft bed both normal (primary) and transformed epidermal
cells form a stratified, and often keratinizing epithelium,
within a few days. While normal cells strictly stayed at
the surface of the graft tissue (except when induced to
form skin appendages), all passaged keratinocyte cultures
tested so far formed invasive plugs which clearly in-
filtrated the underlying connective tissue within one to
two weeks (Fig. 2).

Thus, cells which had adapted to continuous growth in
culture, when tested at early passages, revealed typical growth behaviour of carcinoma cells and must be considered malignantly transformed. In most instances these
cells at the same or later passages also formed tumors
following injection into syngeneic or nude mice. The failure of some lines to form tumors in syngeneic animals may
be due to immunological incompatibilities since rejection
was sometimes noted in transplants of cells which formed
tumors in nude mice. Since rejection in the transplantation
assay occurred only 3 weeks following transplantation,
immunological problems obviously do not seriously influence

the diagnostic value of the test, so that also allogeneic cells (and even human carcinoma cells in preconditioned hosts) can be tested by this assay (Fusenig et al., 1980; Boukamp et al., 1982).

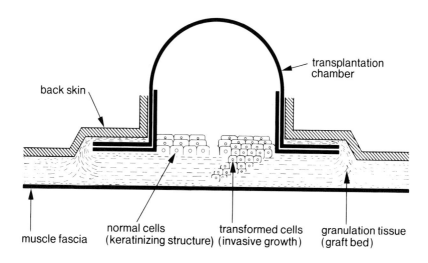

Fig. 2. Schematic cross section through a transplant of normal (left) or transformed (right) epidermal cells on an induced subdermal graft bed (taken from Fusenig et al., 1980).

CONCLUSIONS

    Spontaneous transformation of rodent cells in culture to continuous growth in vitro eventually followed by the acquisition of characteristics of tumor cells is a well known phenomenon both for mesenchymal and epithelial cells. One may speculate that the atypical in vitro environment applies strong selection pressure for the best adapted phenotypes which could be generated by large scale rear-rangements of the genome, which may result in visible chro-mosomal alterations. The demonstration of numerical and structural chromosomal alterations occurring early during, and increeasing with, culture time indicate a genetic lability of mouse keratinocytes in culture. This might be due to a lack of gene regulation mechanims in vitro or to the action of so far unknown factors (e.g. activated viruses or transfected DNA sequences). Whatever the mechanism of cell adaptation to growth under less favourable conditions may be, the phenomenon is genetically fixed, is dependent on a minimum number of cell replications and affords for its stable expression a latency period of several months.In order to prove that adaptation of mouse keratinocytes to routine culture conditions parallels the onset of malignant transformation, cells have to be tested more extensively before or just after the first passage.

REFERENCES

Autrup H, Stoner GD, Jackson F, Harris CC, Shamsuddin AKM, Barrett LA, Trump BF (1978). Explant culture of rat colon: a model system for studying metabolism of chemical carcinogens. In vitro 14:868-877.

Bouck N, DiMayorca G (1982). Chemical carcingens transform BHK cells by inducing a recessive mutation. Mol Cell Biol 2:97-105.

Boukamp P, Tilgen W, Dzarlieva RT, Breitkreutz D, Haag D, Riehl R, Bohnert A, Fusenig NE (1982). Phenotypic and genotypic characteristics of a cell line from a squamous cell carcinoma of human skin. J Natl Cancer Inst 68: 415-427.

Bowden GT, Hohneck G, Fusenig NE (1977). DNA excision repair in ultraviolet-irradiated normal and malignantly transformed mouse epidermal cell cultures. Cancer Res 37:1611-1617.

Breitkreutz D, Boukamp P, Lueder M, Fusenig NE (1981). Morphological and biochemical criteria for keratinization in primary and permanent mouse epidermal cell cultures. Front Matrix Biol 9:57-82.

Cairns J (1981). The origin of human cancer. Nature 289: 353-357.

Colburn NH (1980). Tumor promtion and preneoplastic progression. In Slaga TJ (ed): "Carcinogenesis", Vol 5, New York: Raven Press, pp 33-36.

Dzarlieva RT, Fusenig NE (1982). Tumorpromoter 12-O-tetradecanoyl-phorbol-13 acetate enhances sister chromatid exchanges and numerical and structural chromosome aberrations in primary mouse epidermal cell cultures. Cancer Letters 16:7-17.

Emeritt I, Cerutti RA (1981). The tumor promoter phorbol-12-myristate-13-acetate induces chromosomal damage via indirect action. Nature 293:144-146.

Franke WW, Schmid E, Breitkreutz D, Lueder M, Boukamp P, Fusenig NE, Osborn M, Weber K (1979). Simultaneous expression of two different types of intermediate sized filaments in mouse keratinocytes proliferating in vitro. Differentiation 14:35-50.

Franks LM, Wigley CB (1979) (eds): "Neoplastic transformation in differentiated epithelial cell systems in vitro", London: Academic press.

Fusenig NE, Samsel W, Thon W, Worst PKM (1976). Malignant transformation of epidermal cells in culture by DMBA. INSERM 19:219-228.

Fusenig NE, Amer SM, Boukamp P, Worst PKM (1978). Charaeterisics of chemically transformed mouse epidermal cells in vitro and in vivo. Bull Cancer 65:271-280.

Fusenig NE, Breitkreutz D, Boukamp P, Lueder M, Irmscher G, Worst PKM (1979). Chemical carcinogenesis in mouse epidermal cell cultures. In Franks LM, Wigley CB (eds): "Neoplastic transformation in differentiated epithelial cell systems in vitro", London: Academic Press, pp 37-98.

Fusenig NE, Valentine EA, Worst PKM (1980). Growth behaviour of normal and transformed mouse epidermal cells after reimplantation in vivo. In Richards RJ, Rajan KT (eds): "Tissue culture in medical research (II)", Oxford, New York: Pergamon Press, pp 87-95.

Fusenig NE, Breitkreutz D, Lueder M, Boukamp P, Worst PKM (1981). Keratinization and structural organization epidermal cell cultures. In Schweiger HG (ed): "International Cell Biology 1980-1981", Berlin, Heidelberg: Springer Verlag, pp 1004-1014.

Fusenig NE, Worst PKM (1982). Mouse epidermal cell cultures: II Isolation, characterization and cultivation of epidermal cells from perinatal mouse skin. Exp Cell Res 93:443-457.

Fusenig NE, Dzarlieva RT (1982). Phenotypic and chromosomoal alterations in cell cultures as indicators of tumor-promoting activity. In Hecker E (ed): "Carcinogenesis", Vol 7, New York: Raven Press, pp 201-216.

Fusenig NE, Breitkreutz D, Dzarlieva RT, Boukamp P, Herzmann E, Bohnert A, Pöhlmann J, Rausch Ch, Schütz S, Hornung J (1982). Epidermal cell differentiation and malignant transformation in culture. In Smith GJ, Stewart BW (eds): "In vitro epithelial cell differentiation and neoplasia", Sydney: in press.

Harris CC, Autrup H, Stoner GD (1978). Carcinogenesis studies in human respiratory epithelium. An experimental model system. In Harris CC (ed): "Pathogenesis and therapy of lining cancer", New York: Marcel Decker, pp 559-608.

Hecker E, Fusenig NE, Kunz W, Marks F, Thielmann HW (1982) (eds). Cocarcinogenesis and biological effects of tumor promoters. "Carcinogenesis", Vol 7, New York: Raven Press.

Indo K, Miyayi H (1979). Qualitative changes in the biologic characteristics of cultured fetal rat keratinizing epidermal cells during the process of malignant transformation after benz(a)pyrene treatment. J Natl Cancer Inst 63:1017-1027.

Irmscher G, Fusenig NE (1980). Metabolism of 7,12-dimethylbenzanthracene (DMBA) by mouse skin keratinocytes, fibroblasts and carcinoma cells in culture. Arch Toxicol 44:181-195.

Isseroff RR, Rifkin DB, Fusenig NE (1982). Plasminogen activator in differentiating normal and transformed mouse keratinocytes. J Invest Dermatol, in press.

Kulesz-Martin MF, Koehler B, Hennings H, Yuspa SH (1980). Quantitative assay for carcinogen altered differentiation in mouse epidermal cells. Carcinogenesis 1:995-1006.

Kuroki T, Nemoto N, Kitano Y (1981). Metabolism of benzo(a) pyrene in human epidermal keratinocytes in culture. Carcinogenesis 1:559-565.

Milo G, Ackermann GA, Voges J (1980). Growth and ultrastructural characterization of proliferating human keratinocytes in vitro without added extrinsic factors. In vitro 16:20-30.

Montesano R, Drevon C, Kuroki T, Saint-Vincent L, Handelman S, Sanford KK, deFeo D, Weinstein IB (1977). Tests for malignant transformation of liver cells in culture: cytology, growth in agar, and production of plasminogen activator. J Natl Cancer Inst 59:1651-1658.

Parkinson EK, Newbold RF (1980). Benzo(a)pyrene metabolism and DNA adduct formation in serially cultivated strains of human epidermal keratinocytes. Int J Cancer 26:289-299.

Parsa I, Marsh WH, Sutton AL (1980). An in vitro model of pancreas carcinogenesis. Am J Pathol 98:649-661.

Pitot AC, Goldsworthy T, Moran S (1981). The natural history of carcinogenesis: Implications of experimental carcinogenesis in the genesis of human cancer. J Supramol Struct Cell Biochem 17:133-146.

Rheinwald JG, Green H (1975). Serial cultivation of strains of human epidermal keratinocytes: the formation of keratinizing colonies from single cells. Cell 6:331-343.

Slaga TJ, Viaje A, Bracken WM, Buty SG, Miller DR, Fischer

SM, Richter CK, Dumont JN (1978). In vitro transformation of epidermal cells from newborn mice. Cancer
Res 38:2246-2252.

Summerhayes IC, Cheng YE, Sun TT, Chen LB (1981). Expression of keratin and vimentin intermediate filaments
in rabbit bladder epithelial cells at different stages
of benzo(a)pyrene-induced neoplastic progression.
J Cell Biol 90:63-69.

Steele VE, Marchok AC, Cohen GM (1980). Transformation
of rat tracheal epithelial cells by benzo(a)pyrene
and its metabolites. Cancer Letters 8:291-298.

Theall G, Eisinger M, Grünberger D (1981). Metabolism
of benzo(a)pyrene and DNA adduct formation in cultured
human epidermal keratinocytes. Carcinogenesis 2:581-
587.

Williams GM (1978). Primary and long-term culture of
adult rat liver epithelial cells. Methods Cell Biol 14:
357-364.

Yuspa SH, Lichti U, Morgan D, Hennings H (1980a). Chemical
carcinogenesis studies in mouse epidermal cell cultures.
In Bernstein IA, Seji M (eds): "Biochemistry of normal
and abnormal epidermal differentiation", Tokyo Press,
pp 171-191.

Yuspa SH, Hawley-Nelson P, Koehler B, Stanley JR (1980b).
A survey of transformation markers in differentiating
epidermal cell lines in culture. Cancer Res 40:4694-
4703.

ACKNOWLEDGEMENTS
The expert technical assistance in cell culture experiments
by Jutta Pöhlmann and Charlotte Rausch and the secretarial
help in preparing the manuscript by Monika Matejka is
gratefully acknowledged.

This work was supported by the Deutsche Forschungsgemeinschaft (SFB 136).

13th International Cancer Congress, Part B
Biology of Cancer (1), pages 105–125
© **1983 Alan R. Liss, Inc., 150 Fifth Avenue, New York, NY 10011**

ENVIRONMENTAL CANCER HAZARDS;   IN VITRO STUDIES ON RISK,
PROTECTION AND POTENTIATION.

Carmia Borek, Ph.D.,

Dept. of Radiology and Pathology
Columbia University College of Physicians &
Surgeons, New York, NY   10032

INTRODUCTION

     Radiation is a fact of life. It occurs in nature and
pervades the environment. Although both ionizing and non-
ionizing ultraviolet radiation are weak carcinogens compared
to some chemicals they are are the most ubiquitous oncogenic
agents, present in the environment and used in medical
practice, and are measurable at low doses.

     Cell culture systems of rodent and human origin where
in vitro oncogenic transformation can be studied offer
powerful tools for investigating both qualitative and
quantitative aspects of radiation carcinogenesis, over a
wide range of doses and under defined conditions free of host
mediated effects (Borek and Sachs 1966, Borek and Hall 1973,
1974, Borek et al., 1978, Borek 1982).

     These systems are useful in pragmatic studies where
dose response relationships and cancer risk estimates are
established with particular focus on the low dose range of
radiation where animal studies are limiting. These in vitro
systems serve well also in mechanistic studies where cellular
and molecular processes underlying transformation can be
assessed and where factors which modulate the frequency and
quality of these events can be identified and investigated.
(For review see Borek 1979, 1981, 1982).

RADIOGENIC TRANSFORMATION IN RODENT CELLS

A limited number of cell systems has been used in
studies of radiation induced transformation and these have
been reviewed in detail (see Borek 1979, 1981, 1982). The
present article will focus on 2 systems:

a) The hamster embryo cell system (Borek and Sachs 1966)
which has been used extensively for quantitative and
qualitative assessments of radiogenic transformation (Borek
and Sachs 1966, 1967, 1968, Borek and Hall 1973, 1974,
Borek et al., 1978). These embryonic cells are direct
descendants of the cells in situ, consist of diploid cells,
and have a finite life span. A cell suspension is prepared
by mincing and dissociating with trypsin a midterm embryo.
Cells are plated at low density and treated with radiation
or chemical agents after overnight attachment. The cells
are incubated for 10 days to allow colony formation before
they are fixed and stained, by which time transformed clones
can be distinguished by their altered morphology. Examples
of normal and transformed clones are shown in Fig. 1.

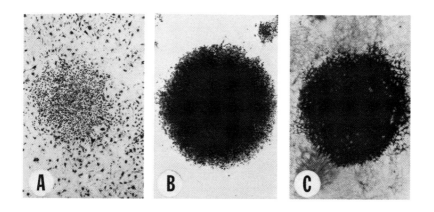

Fig 1. a) a colony of normal hamster embryo cells.
b) a colony of hamster embryo cells transformed by
x irradiation. Note dense multilayered cells.
c) A focus of 10T½ cells transformed by x irradiation.
Note the dense focus growing over the flat sheet of normal
cells.

By counting the number of normal and transformed clones in treated versus control dishes both the surviving and transformation frequency can be assessed from the same dishes. Under carefully controlled conditions, the spontaneous transformation incidence is below 10^{-6}.

The morphologically transformed cells are near diploid or diploid (Borek and Hall 1973). They possess a variety of newly acquired biochemical and morphological criteria and an unlimited life span. They grow in agar and form tumors in animals, properties which serve as the most important criteria for ascertaining the neoplastic nature of the cells (Borek et al., 1977, 1978, Borek 1979, 1981, 1982).

The hamster embryo cell system has been useful in assessing radiogenic transformation rates at very low doses. It has enabled us to establish that neutrons are much more effective than x rays in producing transformation (Borek et al., 1978) and that x rays can induce transformation at low doses (Borek and Hall 1973) as low as 0.1 rad as found recently (Borek 1982) (Fig. 2).

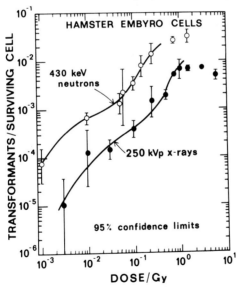

Fig. 2. Pooled data for the hamster embryo cells of the number of transformants per surviving cell following irradiation with 250 kVp x-rays (full symbols) or 430 keV monoenergetic neutrons (open symbols) (Borek et al. 1978, Borek 1982). The error bars indicate 95% confidence intervals for the estimated value.

The system has also contributed to our recent knowledge that x rays at low doses are twice as oncogenic as γ rays (Borek et al., 1982) (Fig. 3) and that at low

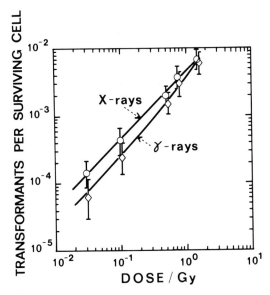

Figure. 4. Transformants per surviving cell as a function of dose for hamster embryo cells exposed to graded doses of 250 KV x-rays or Cobalt-60 gamma-rays. Data pooled from several experiments. The error bars represent 95% confidence limits.

doses splitting the dose of x rays leads to a higher transformation rate (70%) as compared to the induction following exposure to the same total dose given acutely (Borek and Hall 1974, Borek 1979a). This latter finding indicates that extrapolation of cancer risk estimates from high to low doses is neither conservative nor prudent depending on the distribution of dose in time.

b) The second rodent system used in our studies is the mouse C3H10T½ heteroploid line developed in Heidelberger's lab by(Reznikoff et al., 1973). The 10T½ cell line exhibits a low spontaneous transformation incidence, below 10^{-6} for cell passages up to 14. The way in which experiments are conducted with this cell line are as follows: Cells are seeded into $100\text{-}cm^2$ petri dishes. To assess the plating efficiency and cell surviving fraction, a sufficient number of cells are seeded so that an estimated number of

about 50 cells will grow into colonies after the subsequent
treatment; these are incubated for 2 weeks after which they
are fixed and stained and the number of colonies per dish
are scored. For the assessment of transformation, cells
are seeded so that estimated 400 reproductively viable cells
survive the subsequent treatment. Cells are allowed to
attach by overnight incubation at 37°C before growth
medium changed weekly. By 2 weeks the nontransformed cells
form a confluent layer and stop dividing, but additional
time is required for transformation to be expressed and for
cells to grow into visible foci. At the end of this period
the cells are fixed and stained and type II and III foci
are scored as transformed using the criteria described by
(Reznikoff et al., 1973) which include dense staining,
piled-up cells, and a crisscross pattern at the edge of the
clone. A typical type III transformed clone is shown in
Fig. 1.

Initiation and Phenotypic Expression of Transformation

One of the basic conundrums in cancer research evolves
from our inability at the present time to distinguish
unequivocally primary events associated with initiation of
neoplastic transformation from those that function as
secondary events. Although we aim to identify the process
of initiation and consequently hope to modulate it, we are
faced with the fact that at present we determine the
occurrence of iniation by its phenotypic expression. Thus
although radiation carcinogenesis was recognized some 85
years ago, we are still relatively ignorant of the mechanisms
involved and must judge the events determining neoplastic
transformation by a variety of phenomena associated with
the neoplastic phenotype. These phenomena appear to be
similar irrespective of the initiating oncogenic agent
whether it is a virus whose contribution is the introduction
of new genetic material, a chemical carcinogen forming
adducts with cellular DNA, or radiation, whose initiating
action on the cell is established and over within a fraction
of a second.

We therefore strive to define various steps within the
processes of transformation and try to associate cellular
and molecular events with each step.

Though we are relatively ignorant of the exact
processes underlying radiogenic transformation and to what

extent indirect reaction and specific genetic rearrangements
or cellular oncogenes are involved we can recognize early
and late events in the course of in vitro neoplastic
development (Borek, 1982). These can be put into a scheme
illustrated in Fig. 4.

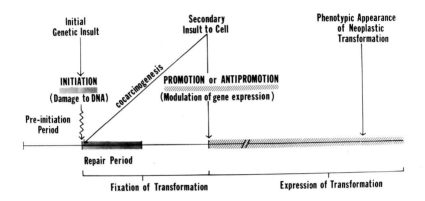

Fig. 4. Diagram of events which may occur at a cellular
level in the course of induction and development of
transformation.

Early events can be regarded as initiation and fixation
of the transformed state following exposure to radiation;
where cell division soon after exposure plays a crucial
role (Borek and Sachs 1967, 1968, Borek 1980, 1981, 1982);
and where cocarcinogens can interact and enhance transformation frequency (Fig. 2). For example a product of
pyrolysis of proteins foods,3 amino, 1 methyl, 5H pyrido
(4, 3-b) indol (Trp P-2) (Sugimura et al., 1977) interacts
synergistically with x rays to enhance radiogenic transformation in hamster embryo cells (Borek and Ong 1981).
Later events in radiogenic transformation are associated

with phenotypic expression of the induced events. This
expression requires several cell divisions (Borek and Sachs
1967) and is ultimately expressed in vitro in fibroblasts
by the appearence of morphologically identifiable transformed sites (Fig. 1) and by a variety of associated
phenotypic changes including malignancy (Borek et al., 1978)
(Fig. 4). Throughout the period of expression promotional
events and enhancement of transformation rate may take
place if the cells are exposed to the appropriate promoting
agent. One of the most studied promotors has been TPA, a
phorbol ester derivative 12-0 tetradecanoyl-phorbol
13-ecetate (Hecker 1971) (Carcinogenesis 1982) (Borek
1982, 1982a).

Inhibiting and Permissive Factors in Transformation

In the effort to find ways to inhibit neoplastic
development in vitro systems have been useful for assessing
a variety of compound for their inhibitory effect on transformation as well as for their activity as antipromotors
in antagonizing the enhancing effect of promoting agents
(Fig. 2). (Borek 1982, 1982a).

A number of retinoids e.g.. all trans-retinoic acid and
a trimethyl methoxy phenyl analog of N – ethyl retinamide
have been found effective in their ability to inhibit
the expression and progression of radiogenic and chemically
induced transformation as well as eliminate the promotional
effects of TPA, (Miller et al., 1981, Borek 1982a). This
inhibitory action is reflected in their ability to modify
gene expression and membrane related properties and e.g..
inhibition of Na^+/K^+ ATPase rather than alter genetic
parameters, such as sister chromatid exchanges (Borek
1982a). Selenium a micronutrient has also been found
effective in inhibiting the expression and progression of
radiogenic and chemically induced transformation (Borek
1982a).

Protease inhibitors such as antipain appear to have a
dual action ; able to inhibit radiogenic transformation when
added after radiation (Borek et al., 1979 , Geard et al.,
1981) but potentiate transformation when added prior to
irradiation · (Borek et al., 1979, Borek, 1980, Geard et al.,
1981). The enhancing or inhibiting actions are not
reflected in altered sister chromatid exchanges (Geard
et al., 1981) or in changes in DNA metabolism (Borek and

Cleaver 1981).

In the effort to modulate carcinogenesis a more critical aim in environmental cancer prevention is to find conditions or agents which would inhibit early events, namely initiation and thus prevent onset and progression of neoplastic development.

Our recent studies have shown that thyroid hormones play a crucial role in the process of initiation of radiation and chemically induced in vitro transformation and that in the absence of thyroid hormone cells are rendered incompetent to be transformed by radiation and chemical carcinogens. (Guernsey, Ong and Borek 1980, Borek 1982).

The Role of Thyroid Hormones in Neoplastic Transformation

The exposure of cells to oncogenic agents both in vivo and in vitro takes place under conditions whereby the cells are bathing in a complex milieux in which a variety of factors such as hormones could serve to modulate the ensuing events. Little is known about the role of hormones in transformation. Their levels vary in vivo with physiological changes and in vitro with different media and different batches of serum used in the experiments.

By removing a particular hormone from the serum used in culture media one can evaluate its role in the process of transformation providing the absence of this hormone does not modify cellular growth kinetics.

We have used this approach in our studies aimed at evaluating the role of thyroid hormones in neoplastic transformation. (Guernsey, Ong and Borek 1980, Guernsey, Borek and Edelman 1981, Borek et al., 1981, Borek 1982)

By selectively removing both triiodothyronine (T_3) and Thyroxine (T_4) from fetal bovine serum using a commercial resine (Samuels et al., 1979) we rendered the euthyroid serum (EU), hypothyroid ($-T3$). By adding to the hypothyroid serum a defined dose of 10^{-9} M of T_3 the reconstituted hypothyroid serum was defined as hyperthyroid ($+T_3$).

Experiments were carried out with the 10T½ cells and Syrian hamster embryo cells (SHE). We established that

neither growth kinetics (growth curves) nor sensitivity
to the toxic action of radiation (survival curves) were
affected by the absence of thyroid hormones (Borek 1982).
However, when cells are grown for 4 days under hypothyroid
conditions and exposed to 3 grays (Gy) (Gy = 100 rad)
under these conditions no transformation was observed,
in contrast to cells grown and irradiated under hyper and
euthyroid conditions (Figure 5).

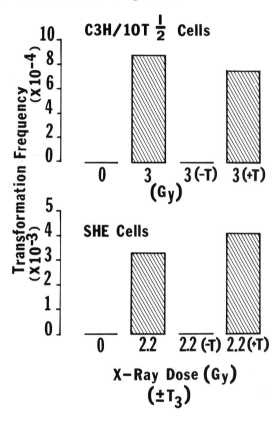

Fig. 5. X ray induced transfromation in cells grown and
maintained with various levels of thyroid hormones for 7 days
and exposed to x irradiation under these conditions. SHE
(Syrian hamster cells) were exposed to 2.2 Gy (1Gy = 100
rad) 10T½ cells were exposed to 3 Gy. Transformation was
observed under euthyroid conditions and hyperthyroid
conditions (+T$_3$) but not under hypothyroid conditions (-T$_3$)
(Data from Guernsey et al., 1981).

If T_3 was added to the hypothyroid cells prior to irradiation transformation was observed. A dose-related role of T_3 in the transformation process was illustrated by the fact that when T_3 was added to the hypothyroid milieu prior to irradiation at doses of 10^{-12}M to 10^{-7}M, transformation incidence was T_3 dose dependent (Fig. 6). The action of T_3 was specific to the active hormone and was not minicked by reverse T_3, an inactive isomer.

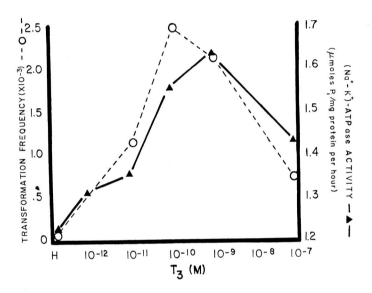

Fig. 6. Effects of varying concentrations of T_3 on transformation frequency (-0-) and on Na^+/K^+ ATPase activity (Δ) in 10T½ cells. For transformation experiments cells were pretreated in various doses of T_3 for 7 days prior to x-irradiation (4 Gy) and maintained in the same conditions for the remainder of the experiment.(Guernsey et al., 1981).

The involvement of thyroid hormone in initiation of transformation was further indicated by the fact that maximum transformation was achieved when T_3 was added at least 12 hr prior to irradiation (Fig.7). If added at the time of radiation, transformation was dramatically decreased, and if added after radiation no transformation was observed. The activity of T_3 when added prior to irradiation was exercised within 24 hr and its removal after radiation did not reduce transformation.

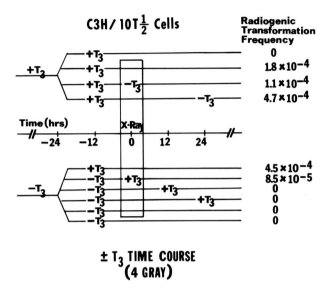

C3H/ 10T½ Cells

± T₃ TIME COURSE (4 GRAY)

Fig. 7. Time course study of 10T½ cells exposed to 4 Gy x rays under hypothyroid ($-T_3$) and hyperthyroid ($+T_3$) conditions. T_3 was removed or added at various times after exposure to radiation maximum transformation is seen when T_3 is added to the hypothyroid medium 12 hours before exposure to x rays. The addition of T_3 after irradiation results in no observed transformation indicating its required presence at exposure time. Removal of T_3 after irradiation does not alter transformation.

Exposure of the cells to cyclohexamide at 100 ng/ml concurrently with T_3 (i.e. added 12 hours before and removed 24 hours after irradiation), Inhibited transformation completely indicating a requirement for protein synthesis. We found a close similarity between the T_3 dose related induction of transformation and a T_3 dose related induction of Na^+/K^+ATPase an enzyme whose synthesis is regulated by thyroid hormones (Guernsey, Borek and Edelman 1981).(Fig. 6).

These results as well as the time course data and the inhibitory action cyclohexamide, raise the possibility that T_3 is involved in the induction of host proteins which are required for rendering cells competent to transformation.

The role of thyroid hormones in transformation is also seen in more experiments using chemical carcinogens. Both Benzo(a)Pyrene(B(a)P),which requires activation as well as N-methyl-N-nitro-N-nitroguanidine (MNNG) a direct carcinogen initiated their action and transformed the SHE and 10T½ cells only under conditions where thyroid hormones were present (Borek, Guernsey and Ong 1981, Borek et al., in preparation). Under hypothyroid conditions no transformation was observed. A dose response, relationship indicated that similar to radiogenic transformation chemically induced transformation was T_3 dose dependent, the maximum transformation being observed at T_3 doses of $(10^{-9}M)$. A time course study shows that for maximum transformation by the chemical carcinogen T_3 must be present 12 hours prior to exposure to the chemical carcinogens and when added simultaneously with B(a)P or MNNG transformation was lower. If added after removal of the chemical(Fig.8) no transformation was observed. The role of protein synthesis was indicated by the fact that 100 ng/ml cyclohexamide inhibited the T_3 mediated effect on chemically induced transformation (Borek et al., in preparation)

While the absence of thyroid hormone prevented the initiation of transformation by radiation and chemical carcinogens, the role of T_3 in virus transformation is less crucial. Exposure of rat cells to the Kirsten murine sarcoma virus under hypothyroid conditions reduced transformation frequency significantly but did not eliminate the appearence of transformed foci (Borek and Rhim in preparation).

A logical extention of studies indicating that a hormone modifies initiation is the assessment of the role of this hormone in promotion. If cells are not initiated it is unlikely that transformation rate will be enhanced by a promotor.

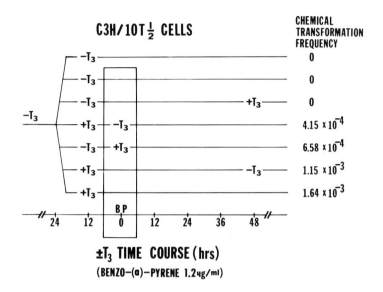

Fig. 8. Time course study of 10T½ cells grown under hypothyroid conditions and exposed to 1.2 µg/ml Benzo-(a)-pyrene under the same conditons, T_3 was added at 10^{-9}M at various periods before and after adding the carcinogen. No transformation was observed under hypothyroid conditions. Maximum transformation was seen when T_3 was added 12 hours before treatment with B(a)P. (Numerical data in part from Borek et al., 1981 and Borek et al., in preparation).

We have evaluated the effects of TPA and a new promotor teleocidine (Sugimura et al., 1982) on radiation induced transformation. Preliminary data indicate that in the absence of thyroid hormone no enhancement of transformation by the promotors is observed though under euthyroid and hyperthyroid condition, the enhancement of radiogenic transformation by the promotors was significant (Borek and Ong, in preparation). (Table 1).

Table 1.   The action of thyroid hormones in transformation
and promotion In Vitro*

C3H/10T½ Cells Treatment	Transformation Frequency/ Survival
$-T_3$ + XR	1.4×10^{-5}
$-T_3$ + XR + TPA	1.1×10^{-5}
$-T_3$ + XR + Teleocidin	1.5×10^{-5}
$+T_3$ + XR	3.8×10^{-4}
$+T_3$ + XR + TPA	8.7×10^{-4}
$+T_3$ + XR + Teleocidin	8.2×10^{-4}
Eu + XR	4.7×10^{-4}
Eu + XR + TPA	7.8×10^{-4}
Eu + XR + Teleocidin	1.2×10^{-3}

*TPA conc. = 0.1 ug/ml
XR = 4 Gray
Teleocidin conc. = 0.001 ug/ml
Eu - untreated serum, euthyroid
$-T_3$ - resin treated serum devoid of thyroid hormones
$+T_3$ - hyperthyroid serum (10^{-9}M T_3)

Our in vitro experiments clearly indicate that a
hypothyroid state may serve as a protective state and that
the hormone potentiates transformation. Animal data
seem to indicate similar trends. An inhibition of
hepatoma growth in rats was found after induction of
hypothyroidism (Mishkin et al., 1979). It is of
interest to note that in man following radiotherapy
a temporary hypothyroid state is observed. One
could speculate that this temporary state maybe in
fact beneficiary and protect from secondary
malignancies which arise in long term survivors of
cancer therapy.

Though the data suggest that the T_3 effect in
transformation is mediated via the synthesis of one
or more proteins one cannot exclude the possibility that
thyroid hormones which are involved in oxidative
processes may potentiate transformation partly by
affecting free radical mechanism. (Borek and Mehlman
in press, Borek and Troll 1983).

Enzymatic Factors

   The ability to inhibit neoplastic transformation by
modifying available free radicals is demonstrated in our
findings that superoxide dismutase, (SOD) a scavenger of
superoxide anions inhibits radiation induced transformation as well as the promotional action of TPA; (Borek
and Troll 1983) suggesting that both x rays induced
transformation may be initiated in part via the
generation of free radicals (Bacg and Alexander 1963)
similar to TPA (Troll et al., 1981).

Table 2.   The inhibiting effect of SOD on X-ray
            induced transformation and TPA
            enhancement in hamster embryo cells[+]

Treatment	S.F.	% Transformation
3 Gy x rays	0.75	0.70 + 0.14
3 Gy + TPA	0.69	1.82 + 0.09
3 Gy + SOD	0.91	0.17 + 0.06
3 Gy + TPA + SOD	0.89	0.51 +0.08

[+]SOD was added at 10 units/ml at seeding time cells were
   irradiated 24 hours later SOD was left in the medium
   throughout the experiment (14 days) TPA was added
   24 hours after irradiation at 0.1 ug/ml (in part
   from Borek and Troll 1983).

TRANSFORMATION OF HUMAN CELLS

   Animal cells have yielded important information for
assessing the oncogenic potential of environmental
agents including radiation, yet the ability to develop
parallel human cell cultures in which one could study
these effects in the closest system to man is of great
importance. True, one is confronted with a complex
genetic variability in man, both in seemingly non
diseased as well as diseased individuals but the uses
of human cells in studies on carcinogenesis would
afford the opportunity to evaluate the association
between genetic diseases and enhanced susceptibility
to the agents (Borek 1982).

Kakunaga (1978) was the first to demonstrate that
human cells derived from adult normal skin can be
directly transformed by chemicals into malignant cells.
Milo and DiPaolo (1978) and Silinskas et al.(1981) reported
the transformion of foreskin fibroblasts by chemical
carcinogens. Normal human skin fibroblasts have been
transformed by x irradiation (Borek 1980, 1980a)
(Fig. 9) by UVA (Sutherland et al., 1980, Maher et al.,
1982) and by UVB   (Andrews and Borek 1982). These
various studies have made it possible to assess the
similarities and differences in rates and in steps
of progression between animal and human cells.

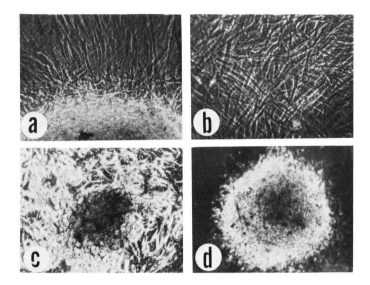

Fig. 9.   Human KD transformation by 4 Gy x irradiation.
          a) Transformed focus growing over normal cells.
          b) Transformed cells in culture.
          c) The same transformed cultures under conditions of
             low Ca^{++} medium.
          d) Transformed KD cells growing in agar.

Exposure of normal human fibroblasts of the KD strain
(Kakunaga 1978), in synchronized cultures to, 4 Gy
x rays resulted in oncogenic transformation. (Borek
1980) (Fig.9). The neoplastic cells were visible as
transformed foci which could be selected out in vitro
by using low calcium medium. Under these conditions the
transformed cells continued to grow though the normal
cells died, indicating an alteration in nutritional
requirements. The transformed cells were near diploid
or diploid and grew in agar though only some of the
cells which were capable of growing in agar induced
tumors in nude mice, indicating that growth in agar is
suggestive but not indicative of the malignant potential
of the cells (Borek 1980). In the KD cells, similar
to the hamster cells, (Borek and Sachs 1967), cell
division soon after exposure was essential for fixation
of the transformed state. When on dividing cells held
in liquid holding were exposed to x rays no transformation
was observed. Thus, DNA replication is involved in the
process of human cell transformation. The expression
of transformation was seen within 40 days and required
additional cell divisions (a total of $\sim$ 10-13) for focus
formation in culture. The ability to grow in agar was
acquired about the same time as the ability to form foci
in culture indicating that the diploid human cells
differed from diploid hamster cells in the pattern of
progression of neoplastic development. Hamster cells
showed morphological transformation within 10 days after
exposure to x rays but growth in agar was seen after
long term progressive culturing in vitro (Borek and
Hall 1973). Differences in frequency of radiogenic
transformation between hamster diploid cells and human
diploid cells are also striking. Transformation rate
of the human cells following exposure to 4 Gy was 100
fold lower (10^{-6}) compared to transformation rate in
the hamster cells (Borek 1980a, 1982).

The ability to transform human cells with UV light
has enabled us to assess differences in sensitivity of
genetically diseased cells to transformation by UVB,
the range of UV light relevant to human cancer.
Using cells from patients with xeroderma pigmentosum
(XP) and Bloom syndrome, diseases associated with high
cancer rates, we found that XP cells were more susceptible
to transformation than the Bloom cells, using growth

in agar as a quantitative assay. (Andrews and Borek,
1982 and in preparation). A total dose of 67.2 J/M^2
yielded 10^{-4} transformation in the XP cells. The ability
to grow in agar was acquired earlier than with x ray
transformed KD cells and was observed within 5 doublings.
XP cells are particularly susceptible to DNA damage by
UV (Cleaver 1980) and have also been shown to be more
sensitive than normal cells to transformation by UVA
light (Maher et al., 1982).

Thus, with available methods in vitro it is now
possible to approach cellular and molecular studies in
carcinogenesis using cultured human cells which are the
most relevant systems for estimating cancer risk for
evaluating effective ways to reduce it.

Andrews A, Borek C (1982). Neoplastic transformation of
human xeroderma pigmentosium and Bloom syndrome cells
by UVB. Clinical Res. 30: 574A.
Bacq ZM, Alexander P (1963). The role of oxygen in the
phenomena of chemical protection against ionizing
radiation. In Dickens F, Neil E (eds): "Oxygen on the
animal organism," London: Pergamon Press, p. 509.
Borek C (1979). Malignant transformation in vitro.
Criteria biological markers and application in
environmental screening of carcinogens. Radiat. Res.
79: 209.
Borek C (1980). X-ray induced transformation of human
diploid cells. Nature 283: 776.
Borek C (1980a). The induction, expression and modulation
of radiation induced oncogenesis in vitro in diploid
human and rodent cells. In Pullman B, Golbion H,
PT'so (eds): "Carcinogenesis Fundamental Mechanisms
and Environmental Effects," Holland: Reidel
Publishing Co., p. 509.
Borek C (1981). Cellular transformation by radiation.
Induction, promotion and inhibition. J Supramol.
Struct. 16: 311.
Borek C (1982). Radiation oncogenesis in culture. In
Klein G, Weinhouse S (eds): "Adv. Cancer Res.", Vol.
37, New York: Academic Press, p 159.
Borek C (1982a). Vitamins and micronutrients modify
carcinogenesis and tumor promotion in vitro. In
Arnott MS et al., (eds): "Molecular Interrelations of
Nutrition and Cancer," New York: Raven Press, p 337.
Borek C, Cleaver C (1981). Protease inhibitors neither
damage nor interfere with DNA repair in human cells.

Mutat. Res. 82: 373.

Borek C, Guernsey DL, Ong A (1981). Thyroid hormone modulates radiation and chemically induced neoplastic transformation in vitro. Proceedings of the American Association for Cancer Research 22: 139, and Borek C, Guernsey DL, Ong A, Edelman IS in preparation.

Borek C, Hall EJ (1973). Transformation of mammalian cells in vitro by low doses of x-rays. Nature 244: 450.

Borek C, Hall, EJ (1974). Split doses of x rays on neoplastic transformation of single cells. Nature 252: 499.

Borek C, Hall EJ, Rossi HH (1978). Malignant transforamtion in cultured hamster embryo cells produced by x rays, 430-keV monoenergetic neutrons, and heavy ions. Cancer Res. 38: 2997.

Borek C, Hall EJ, Zaider M. X-rays have twice the potential of γ-rays, at low doses for malignant transformation. Nature, in press.

Borek C, Mehlman MA. Evaluation of health effects toxicity and biochemical mechanism of ozone. In Mehlman MA (ed): "The biomedical effects of ozone and related photochemical oxidants". In press

Borek C, Miller RC, Pain C, Troll W (1979). Conditions for inhibiting and enhancing effects of the protease inhibitor antipain on x-ray induced neoplastic transformation in hamster and mouse cells. Proc. Natl. Acad. Sci USA 76: 1800.

Borek C, Ong A (1981). The interaction of ionizing radiation and food pyrolysis in producing oncogenic transformation in vitro Cancer Lett. 12: 61.

Borek C, Sachs L (1966). In Vitro cell transformation by x-irradiation. Nature 210: 276.

Borek C, Sachs L (1967). Cell susceptibility to transformation by x-irradiation and fixation of the transformed state. Proc. Natl. Acad. Sci.(USA)57: 1522.

Borek C, and Sachs L (1968). The number of cell generations required to fix the transformed state in x-ray induced transformation. Proc. Natl. Sci.(USA)59: 83.

Borek C, Troll W (1983 in press). Modifiers of the dose radicals inhibited in vitro the oncogenic action of x-rays, bleomycin and tumor promotor TPA. Proc. Natl. Acad. Sci. (USA).

Carcinogenesis 7. (1982). Hecker E et al., (eds): New York Raven Press, p 593.

Cleaver JE (1980). DNA damage, repair systems and human hypersensitive diseases. J. Env. Pathol. Toxicol. 3: 53.

Geard CR, Rutledge-Freeman M, Miller RC, Borek C (1981).
Antipain and radiation effects on oncogenic transformation
and sister chromatid exchanges in Syrian hamster embyro
and mouse C3H/10T½ cells. Carcinogenesis 2: 1229.

Guernsey DL, Ong A, Borek C (1980). Thyroid hormone modulation
of x-ray-induced in vitro neoplastic transformation.
Nature 288: 591.

Guernsey DL, Borek C, Edelman IS (1981). Crucial role of
thyroid hormone in x-ray-induced neoplastic transformation
in cell culture. Proc. Natl. Acad. Sci. (USA) 78: 5708.

Hecker E (1971). Isolation and characterization of the
cocarcinogenic principles from croton oil. Methods Cancer
Res. 6: 439.

Kakunaga T (1978a). Neoplastic transformation of human diploid
cells by chemical carcinogens. Proc. Natl. Acad.Sci. (USA)
75: 1334.

Maher VM, Rowan LA, Silinskas KC, Kateley SA, McCormick JJ
(1982). Frequency of UV-induced neoplastic transformation
of diploid human fibroblasts is higher in xeroderma
pigmentosum cells than in normal cells. Proc. Natl. Acad.
Sci. 78: 2613.

Mishkin S, Morris HP, Yalovsky MA, Murthy PVN (1979).
Increased survival of rats bearing Morris Hepatoma 7800
after induction of hypothyroidism. Cancer Res. 39: 2371/

Miller RC, Geard CR, Osmak RS, Rutledge-Freeman M, Ong A,
Mason H, Napholta A, Perez N, Harisiadis L, Borek C
(1981). Modification of sister chromatid exchanges and
radiation-induced transforamtion in rodent cells by the
tumor promoter 12-0-tetradecanoylphorbol-13-acetate and
two retinoids. Cancer Res. 41: 655.

Milo GE, DiPaolo JA (1978). Neoplastic transformation of human
diploid cells in vitro after chemical carcinogen treatment.
Nature 275: 130.

Reznikoff CA, Bertram JS, Brankow DW, Heidelberger C (1973).
Quantitative and qualitative studies of chemical transformation of cloned C3H mouse embryo cells sensitive to
postconfluence inhibition of cell division. Cancer Res.
33: 3239.

Samuels HH, Stanley F, Casanova J (1979). Depletion of
L-3,5,3-triiodothytonine and L-thyroxine in euthyroid calf
serum for use in cell culture studies of the action of
thyroid hormone. Endocrinology 105: 80.

Silinskas KC, Kately SA, Tower JE, Maher VM, McCormick JJ
(1981). Induction of anchorage-independent growth in human
fibroblasts by propane sultone. Cancer Res. 4: 1620.

Sugimura T, Fujiki H, Mori M, Nakayasu M, Terada M,
Umezawa K, Moore, RE (1981). Teleocidin, New naturally

Sugimura T, Nagao M, Kawachi T, Honda M, Yahagi T, Seino Y, Sato S, Matsukura N (1977). Mutagen-carcinogens in food, with special reference to highly mutagenic pyrolytic products in broiled foods. In Hiatt HH, Watson JD, Winstein J (eds): "Origins of Human Cancer," New York:Cold Spring Harbor Laboratory.

Sutherland BM, Cimino JS,Delihas N, Shih AG, Oliver RP (1980). Ultraviolet light-induced transformation of human cells to anchorage-independent growth. Cancer Res. 40: 1934.

Troll W, Witz G, Goldstein B, Stone D, Sugimura T (1982). The role of free oxygen radicals in tumor promotion and carcinogenesis. In Hecker E,et al., (eds): "Carcinogenesis 7," New York: Raven Press p 593.

This investigation was supported by Grant No. 12536-11 to the Radiological Research Laboratory/Department of Radiology, and by Grant No. CA 13696 to the Cancer Center/Institute of Cancer Research awarded by the National Institute, DHHS.

13th International Cancer Congress, Part B
Biology of Cancer (1), pages 127–140
© **1983 Alan R. Liss, Inc., 150 Fifth Avenue, New York, NY 10011**

CELLULAR AND MOLECULAR MECHANISMS OF NEOPLASTIC TRANSFORMATION
OF HUMAN CELLS

Takeo Kakunaga[1], Janet D. Crow[1], John Leavitt[2] and
Hiroshi Hamada[1]
[1]Cell Genetics Section, National Cancer Institute
[2]Linus Pauling Institute
[1]Bethesda, MD 20205, USA. [2]Palo Alto, CA 94306,USA

The use of human cells has many advantages for studying
the chemically-induced neoplastic transformation compared to
using other species' cells (Kakunaga, 1979). It eliminates
the species barrier which is a serious obstacle in extrapo-
lating the results obtained with the system using other
species into human carcinogenesis. In addition, human cells
show one of the most stable karyotypes in a culture and give
relatively low frequency of non-specific changes in biological
and biochemical properties of the cells during cultivation.
Functional chromosomal mapping is established better with
human chromosomes than with other mammalian cells. One of
the most important features in the use of human cells is the
availability of the cells derived from a cancer-prone genetic
disease patients. These cells obtained from a patient serve
as the mutant cells which provide precious materials for
studying the genetic factors and molecular process involved
in the induction of cell transformation. The use of human
cells also enable us to investigate the environmental and
genetic factors in vitro in conjunction with epidemiological
studies.

Thus, the development of the transformation system using
human cells has been anticipated to facilitate our understanding of the mechanisms of cell transformation as well as establishing the optimum method to assess human risk against environmental carcinogens. Extensive efforts have been made to
develop the transformation system using human cells (Igel et
al 1975; Rhim et al 1975; Shimada et al 1976; Kakunaga 1977,
1978; DeMar, Jackson 1977; Freeman et al 1977; Mile, DiPaolo
1978; Namba et al 1978; Borek 1979; Sutherland et al 1980;

Salinskas et al 1981; Zimmerman, Little, 1981; Parsa 1981).

TRANSFORMATION SYSTEMS

Major reports of transformation of human cells by chemical or physical carcinogens are divided into three classes (Table 1). First, full transformation that covers the entire process of the neoplastic conversion: from normal diploid cells to neoplastic cells has been demonstrated by several groups using the fibroblasts from an adult skin or foreskin and the pancreatic epithelial cells. As far as the fully transformed phenotype, i.e., tumorigenicity upon transplantation into immuno-incompetent animals, is used as the end point of assay, no quantitative system has been developed as I will discuss later. On the other hand, another type of the transformation system is a partial transformation which is considered to cover a part of neoplastic transformation process. The systems of partial transformation are divided further into two classes, depending on the types of the cells used as the target cells: One system is the conversion of normal diploid cells into partially transformed cells. The partially transformed cells usually show anchorage-independent growth or morphological alteration but not tumorigenicity. This is analogous to the morphological transformation of hamster embryonic cells by carcinogen and the quantitation of phenotypic change has been made possible. The other system is the conversion of partially transformed cells into tumorigenic cells. In this case, the partially transformed cells have already acquired immortality and aneuploidy but they are morphologically normal and their growth is anchorage-dependent. This system is similar to the transformation system using 10T1/2 or Balb/3T3 cell line. With the hamster and mouse cells, there is plenty of evidence indicating that neoplastic transformation of diploid cells by chemical carcinogens is a multistep process. The diploid rodent cells treated with chemical carcinogens acquire distinguishable transformed phenotypes one by one. For example, they usually show morphological alteration first, then aneuploidy, anchorage-independence of cell growth, escape from senescence, tumorigenicity and finally metastatic potentials.

Because of this multistep nature of neoplastic transformation, the frequency of transformation is extremely low and the time required is very long when the acquisition of tumorigenicity is used as an assay end point. Thus, it is feasible

Table 1. Classification and characteristics of the transtormation systems using human and rodent cells.

Transformation system	Species	Assay indicators	Quanti- tation	Assay period
I. Full transformation	Hamster	Tumorigenicity (Focus & A.I.)	-	2-5 mo.
Diploid cell to Tumorigenic cell	Human	Tumorigenicity (Focus & A.I.)	-	3-12 mo.
II. Partial transformation				
1. Diploid cell to partially transformed cell	Hamster	clonal morphology	+	7-10 days
	Human	A.I.	+	2-6 wks.
2. Partially transformed cell(non-permanent line) to tumorigenic cell	Hamster	Tumorigenicity & A.I.	(+)	1-6 mo.
	Human	Not yet developed		
3. Partially transformed cell(permanent line) to tumorigenic cell	Mouse & Hamster	Focus formation A.I.	+ +	3-6 wks. 3-5 wks
	Human	Tumorigenicity	-	1-3 mo.

that all the quantitative assay system for transformation using rodent cells that have been developed adopt one step conversion as an assay end point. For examples, morphological alteration due to loss of contact inhibition of cell growth and movement is used as an end point of the quantitative assay of the transformation of the primary culture of the hamster embryonic cells or 10T1/2 and Balb/3T3 cell lines. Transformation of human cells seems to be a multistep process similar to that of the rodent cells.

SEQUENTIAL ORDER OF MULTIPLE PROGRESS

Human diploid fibroblasts treated with chemical carcinogens such as 4nitroquinoline-1-oxide (4NQO) showed a significant increase in the anchorage-independent cell growth after two to three weeks of continuous subcultivation. It is possible to estimate the induced frequency of anchorage-independent conversion based on a number of the cells which survived or were treated. However, these anchorage-independent

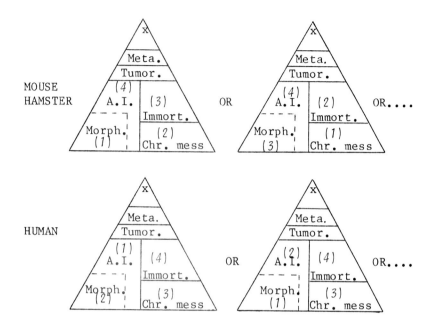

Fig. 1. Pyramid model for the multistep progress of neoplastic transformation of cultured mouse, hamster and human cells. Vertical height of pyramid represents the degree of malignancy of cells. Normal diploid cells become malignant by acquiring each phenotype one by one. Acquisition of phenotypes in the lower level is prerequisite to acquisition of the upper phenotypes. Numbers in parenthesis indicate the sequential order of the acquisition that is frequently observed. Meta., metastatic potential; Tumor., tumorigenicity; A.I., Anchorage-independent cell growth; Immort., Immortality; Chr. mess., chromosomal abnormality; Morph., morphological alteration.

cells showed senescence and failed to produce non-regressive tumors upon injection into nude mice. Thus, these anchorage-independent cells (partially transformed cells) seem to need one or more of the other phenotypic conversions to become fully tumorigenic cells (fully transformed cells). One of the most striking differences in the transformation between human cells and rodent cells is the sequential order of the acquisition of different phenotypes.

As summarized in Figure 1, rodent cells show morphological alteration in a short time after the carcinogen-treatment, and later they acquire both anchorage-independent cell growth and tumorigenicity almost simultaneously. On the other hand, human cells acquire anchorage-independent cell growth relatively quickly, but they acquire all of the other phenotypes later. Another peculiar feature of the human cell transformation is their extremely low frequency of acquisition of immortality compared to that of the rodent cells. If the acquisition of unlimited cell proliferation is a prerequisite for full transformation, the immortalization process is likely to be the rate-limiting step in the transformation of human diploid cells (Kakunaga, 1979). The cellular mechanisms as described above are still speculative in many aspects and would require further study to prove them. However, such a multistep model for transformation process should be reflected upon the study of the molecular mechanisms of transformation. It will be more practical to explore the molecular changes underlying each step of the conversion rather than to explore the almighty molecule which causes all phenotypic changes associated with neoplastic transformation.

APPROACHES
FOR ELUCIDATING MOLECULAR MECHANISMS OF TRANSFORMATION

Among the various advantages of the use of human cells for studying transformation as described in the beginning of the paper, the relatively low frequency of spontaneous changes in properties during cultivation and the availability of mutant cells from cancer-prone genetic disease patients are of extreme importance for studying molecular mechanisms of transformation. Drs. Maher and McCormic's group (1982) reported that the skin fibroblasts from xeroderma pigmentosum patients showed a much higher sensitivity to the induction of anchorage-independency by some carcinogens as compared to the normal skin fibroblasts in a manner similar to the induction of HGPRT⁻ mutation. This result suggests that the induction of anchorage-independent growth of human cells by carcinogens is a mutational process. There are many other indirect evidence suggesting the involvement of the mutational process in the carcinogen-induced cell transformation. However, these indirect evidence, usually an observation of the parallelism between mutational events and neoplastic transformation, does not provide the precise information on the type of mutation, much less on what kinds and portions of genes were mutated and how the mutation leads the cells to express the transformed state.

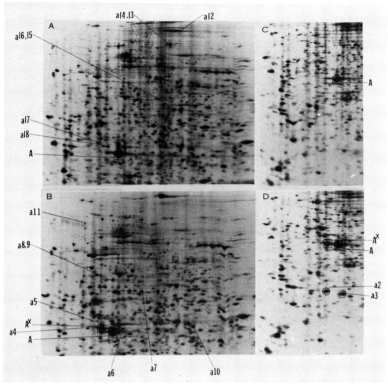

Fig. 2. Autoradiographs of two-dimensional gels containing [^{35}S]methionine polypeptides. A & C, KD polypeptides; B & D, HuT-14 polypeptides. A & B, 9% acrylamide slab gel; C & D, 12.5% acrylamide slab gels.

We have been taking direct approach in investigating the molecular mechanisms of neoplastic transformation utilizing the relative stability of human cells in culture. It is based on the widely accepted conception that the changes in the proteins synthesized in the transformed cells reflect the alteration of gene structure or expression, mutational or regulatory, that is associated with neoplastic transformation. Clonal transformed human fibroblast lines were obtained by a single treatment with 4NQO of human diploid fibroblasts (Kakunaga, 1978). They exhibited stable neoplastic properties and provided us a pair of normal and transformed cells of which biochemical alteration may be closely related to the expression of transformed phenotypes. [35S]-methionine-labeled proteins were extracted with Triton-X buffer from the human fibroblasts transformed by 4NQO and compared with those from their parental normal counterparts using two-dimensional gel electorphoresis developed by O'Farrell (1975) and Garrels (1979). About 2% of the proteins out of nearly 1000 polypeptides electrophoretic species were lost or newly gained in the transformed cells (Figure 2). One new polypeptide (designated A^X in Fig. 2) which was recognized in one of the transformed cell line (HuT-14) was identified as a varient form of actin by immunoprecipitation with anti-actin antibody and its tryptic peptide fingerprint pattern.

Actin is a major component of cytoskeleton. The most significant phenotypic characteristics of transformed malignant cells are alterations of cell shape, motility, movement, mobility of cell surface component including receptors, phagocytosis or endocytosis, responses of these functions to contact inhibition, etc. Cytoskeleton is a major body responsible for these cellular functions. Thus, it is a feasible hypothesis that alteration of actin molecule induced by carcinogens results in the changes of these cellular functions, i.e., the expression of transformation. In fact, organization of the actin cable network in association with the expression of transformed state has been reported with many transformed cells. (Pollack 1980). Thus, we have investigated the molecular mechanisms of alteration of the actin form and its role in the expression of transformed phenotypes.

MOLECULAR EVIDENCE FOR A POINT MUTATION

Several possibilities could explain why A^X-actin is expressed in HuT-14 cells and not in other human cells: (1) altered post-translational processing or modification, (2) altered processing of actin mRNA, (3) derepression of a silent actin gene, and (4) mutation in actin genes. The first possibility, i.e., alteration of post-translational processing or modification, was examined by analyzing in vitro translation products in the presence of poly(A)RNA extracted from HuT-14 cells (Hamada et al 1981). 2-D gel electrophoresis analysis showed that A^X-actin and its precursor unacetylated form as well as β- and γ- actin and their precursors were abundant in vitro translation products. A^X-actin was not found among the translation products in the presence of poly(A)$^+$RNA from any other human cells. These results indicated that A^X-actin is encoded from the

altered mRNA species in HuT-14 cells and excluded the possibility that A^X-actin is derived from the alteration of
post-translational processing or modification.

1   2

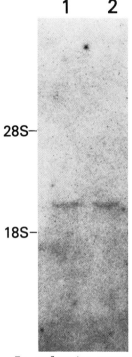

28S—

18S—

Fig. 3. Estimation of A^X-
and β-actin mRNA (20 ug)
from HuT-11 cells (lane 1)
or HuT-14 cells (lane 2) was
fractionated on a 1.4%
agarose gel containing 10 mM
methyl mercury hydroxide and
hybridized to nick-translated
pcDd actin [^{32}P]DNA.

In order to assess the complimentarity of the human
actin genes expressed in HuT-14 cells, to pcDd actin that
was used as a specific probe for actin mRNA or glues, poly-
(A)$^+$RNA was isolated from HuT-14 cells and hybridized to pcDd
insert DNA. The RNA that hybridized was isolated and then
assayed for its ability to direct the synthesis of actin in
the reticulocyte lysate translation system. 2-D gel electrophoresis of the translation products showed that HuT-14 mRNA
that hybridized to pcDd was capable of directing synthesis
of A^X- and β-actin but not r-actin (Hamada et al 1981). Thus,
pcDd actin sequence is similar to the human β-actin gene sequence in that it hybridizes to β-actin mRNA and dissimilar
to the human r-actin sequence to the degree that it fails to
hybridize to r-actin mRNA. These results indicate that
A^X-actin gene is similar to β-actin gene.

The size of A^X- and β-actin mRNA were compared by two different methods. First, HuT-14 poly(A)^2 RNA was fractionated on a sucrose gradient under undenaturing conditions and then each fraction was tested for its ability to direct the synthesis of actin polypeptides in the reticulocyte lysate translation system. 2-D gel electrophoresis of the _in vitro_

Table 2. Transformed phenotypes of subclones and variants of HuT-14 cells.

Cells	Cloning efficiency in soft agar (%)	Tumorigenicity (TD$_{50}$)
Normal diploid fibroblasts (KD)	<0.0001	>1 x 10^7
HuT-14	1.1	3 x 10^5
HuT-14-11	0.9	3 x 10^5
HuT-14-12	0.9	NT
HuT-14-13	1.0	NT
HuT-14-3-1	3.8	3 x 10^4
HuT-14-3-1T	8.5	1 x 10^4

translates showed that A^X-actin as well as β- and r-actin mRNAs are slightly larger than 18S ribosomal RNA (Hamada et al 1981). Second, total RNA from HuT-14 cells that synthesize A^X-actin and HuT-11 cells that do not synthesize A^X-actin were fractionated on an agarose gel, transferred to diazobenzyloxymethyl-paper, and hybridized to nick-translated pcDd insert DNA which hybridizes with A^X and B-actin mRNA. Only one band was observed in gels containing either HuT-14 or HuT-11 RNA (Fig. 3). Thus, the size of A^X and β-actin mRNA seems to be similar.

Complete amino acid sequence of A^X and β-actin that were isolated from HuT-14 cells was determined in collaboration with Drs. Vandekerckhove and Weber. A^X-actin differed from β-actin by only a single amino acid substitution, i.e., glycin at 244 position in β-actin was substituted to aspartic acid in A^X-actin (Vandekerckhove et al 1980). It is interesting to note that such a single amino acid substitution caused significant change in the mobility of actin molecule in SDS-gel electrophoresis which correspond to the increase in molecular weight by about 1,000 dalton.

These results indicate that a novel polypeptide recognized in HuT-14 cells, i.e., A^x-actin, is a product of a mutated β-actin gene. This provided the first molecular evidence for occurrence of a mutation in the chemically transformed cells.

ASSOCIATION OF β-ACTIN MUTATION WITH THE EXPRESSION OF TRANS-FORMED PHENOTYPES

Cytoplasmic actins, i.e., β- and γ-actin are the major molecules of which function is involved in cellular motility, contractility and shape. Since alteration of cellular morphology and motility is the most universal and remarkable characteristics of the neoplastic tissues or cells, it is conceivable that a mutation in β-actin is responsible for the expression of the transformed phenotypes in HuT-14 cells through the disturbance of cytoskeletal functions. In order to know further the cause-effect relationship, we have isolated the cell variants of HuT-14 cells with the increased tumorigenicity and examined how the expression of β-actin gene were altered in the cell variants. First, we attempted to obtain the cell variants without treatment of HuT-14 cells with mutagens and carcinogens. However, we found that HuT-14 cells are very stable in their tumorigenic potentials and did not produce spontaneously the progeny of higher malignancy at the frequency higher than 10^{-8} during cultivation. Even the cells recovered from the tumors which were produced in nude mice by injecting 2×10^6 HuT-14 cells showed no change in their tumorigenicity. Then, HuT-14 cells were exposed to ultraviolet light and many subclones were isolated. One of the subclones, HuT-14-3-1, showed an increased anchorage-independent growth and tumorigenicity in nude mice compared to the HuT-14 cells, while other subclones did not (Table 2). The cells were recovered from the tumors produced by the inoculation of HuT-14-3-1 cells and designated HuT-14-3-1 T cells. The HuT-14-3-1 T cells showed further increase in tumorigenicity and anchorage-independent cell growth (Table 2).

When the polypeptides synthesized in the cells were compared using 2-D gel electrophoresis, surprisingly, the mutant β-actin in HuT-14-3-1 T cells was slightly more acidic than that of β-tubulin subunit (Leavitt et al 1982). This new polypeptide was certainly identified as an actin polypeptide variant by the identical pattern of its tryptic peptide

finger print pattern to that of normal and mutant β-actin.
The new mutant β-actin was produced by in vitro translation
of poly(A)$^+$RNA extracted from either HuT-14-3-1 or HuT-14-3-1
T cells, indicating that new change in mutant β-actin is
ascribed to the alteration at the level of mRNA and/or DNA.
The density of each actin species on the autoradiographs of
2-D gel electrophoresis was quantitated by computerized
microdensitometry (Leavitt et al 1981). Table 3 summarizes
the changes in the relative density of mutant β-actin, normal
β-actin and γ-actin in Triton-soluble fraction, Triton-insol-
uble (cytoskeletal) fraction and in the in vitro translation
products between KD, HuT-14, HuT-14-3-1 and HuT-14-3-1 T
cells. The ratio of mutant β-actin to normal β-plus γ-actin
was increased in soluble fraction of HuT-14-3-1 T, and in
the in vitro translation products synthesized in the presence
of poly(A)$^+$RNA of HuT-14-3-1 and HuT-14-3-1 T compared to
those in HuT-14 cells. The ratio of mutant β-actin to normal
β-plus γ-actin of the cytoskeletal fraction was lower than
that of soluble fraction and of in vitro translation products,
and was markedly reduced in HuT-14-3-1 T cells. There was
no change in the ratio of normal β-actin to γ-actin between
soluble and cytoskeletal fractions in normal and variant
cells. These results indicate that mutant β-actin is defective in incorporation into cytoskeleton, and that the in-

Table 3. The stepwise changes in the cytoplasmic actins
in the variants of HuT-14 cells.

Relative ratio of actins	Cells			
	KD	HuT-14	HuT-14-3-1	HuT-14-3-1T
In cellular soluble fraction				
β' or β"	0	1.2	NT	1.7
β	1.0	1.0	NT	1.0
γ	1.2	1.2	NT	1.2
β' + β"/β + γ	0	0.53	–	0.7
In cytoskeleton				
β' or β"	0	0.6	NT	0.04
β	1.0	1.0	NT	1.0
γ	1.2	1.2	NT	1.2
β' + β"/β + γ	0	0.27	–	0.02
In in vitro translation				
β or γ	0	0.8	0.7	1.7
β	1.0	1.0	1.0	1.0
γ	1.0	2.0	1.1	2.0
β' + β"/β + γ	0	0.26	0.36	0.57

creased malignancy of HuT-14 variant cells was associated with the increased synthesis and deficiency of mutant β-actin.

Stable alteration of cell shape, motility and membrane fluidity have been considered one of the most striking and universal phenotypes characteristic of neoplastic cells. Changes in the organization of cytoskeleton which have been considered to be responsible for maintaining cell shape, motility and membrane mobility have been observed in the transformed fibroblasts. Indirect immunofluorescence with monoclonal anti-actin antibody showed that organized and long actin stressfibers observed in untransformed KD cells were replaced by unorganized and short microfilamentous fibers and by a diffuse cytoplasmic staining. This disorganization of actin structures aggravated from HuT-14 to HuT-14-3-1 to HuT-14-3-1 T cells. Although it is unknown which step of the multistep process of cell transformation as shown in Fig. 1 involves the actin mutation, all the results together suggest that a mutation in β-actin gene plays the role in the expression of transformed phenotypes of HuT-14 and it's variants.

We thank Ms. Linda Nischan for typing the manuscript.

REFERENCES

Borek C (1980). X-ray-induced in vitro neoplastic transformation of human diploid cells. Nature 283:776.

Demars R, Jackson JL (1977). Mutagenicity detection with human cells. j Environ Pathol Toxicol 1:55.

Freeman VH, Shin S (1977). Isolation of human diploid cell variants with enhanced colony-forming efficiency in semisolid medium after a single-step chemical mutagenesis. J Natl Cancer Inst 58:1873.

Freeman AE, Lake RS, Igel HJ, Gernard L, Pezzutti MR, Malone JM, Mark C, Benedict WF (1977). Heteroploid conversion of human skin cells by methylcholanthrene. Proc Natl Acad Sci USA 74:2451.

Garrels JI (1979). Two-dimensional gel electrophoresis and computer analysis of proteins synthesized by clonal cell lines. J Biol Chem 254:7961.

Hamada H, Leavitt J, Kakunaga T (1981). Mutated beta-actin gene: Coexpression with an unmutated allele in a chemically transformed human fibroblast cell line. Proc Natl Acad Sci USA 78:3634.

Kakunaga T (1977). Transformation of human diploid cells by chemical carcinogens. In Hiatt HH, Watson JD and Winsten JA (eds): "Origins of Human Cancer" Cold Spring Harbor Conference on Cell Proliferation 4:1537.

Kakunaga T (1978). Neoplastic transformation of human diploid fibroblast cells by chemical carcinogens. Proc Natl Acad Sci USA 75;3:1334.

Kakunaga T (1980). Approaches towards the development of human transformation assay system. In Mishra NK, Dunkel V and Mehlman MA (eds): "Advances in Environmental Toxicology: Mammalian Cell Transformation by Chemical Carcinogens," New York Pathotex Publishers p 355.

Leavitt J, Bushar G, Kakunaga T, Hamada H, Hirakawa T, Goldman D, Merril C (1982). Variations in expression of mutant β-actin accompanying incremental increases in human fibroblast tumorigenicity. Cell 28:259.

Leavitt J, Goldman D, Merril C, Kakunaga T (1982). Changes in gene expression accompanying chemically-induced malignant transformation of human fibroblasts. Carcinogenesis 3:61.

Leavitt J, Kakunaga T (1980). Expression of a variant form of actin and additional polypeptide changes following chemical induced in vitro neoplastic transformation and human fibroblasts. J Biol Chem 255:1650.

Maher VM, Rowan LA, Salinskas KC, Kateley SA, McCormick JJ (1982). Frequency of UV-induced neoplastic transformation of diploid human fibroblasts is higher in xeroderma pigmentosum cells than in normal cells. Proc Natl Acad Sci 79: 2613.

Milo G, DiPaolo JA (1978). Neoplastic transformation of human diploid cells in vitro after chemical carcinogen treatment. Nature 275:130.

Namba M, Nishitani K, Kimoto T (1978). Carcinogenesis in tissue culture 29: Neoplastic transformation of a normal human diploid cell strain WI-38, with ^{60}Co gamma rays. Jap J Exp Med 48:303.

O'Farrell PH (1975). High resolution two-dimensional electrophoresis of proteins J Biol Chem 250:4007.

Pollack R (1980). Hormones, anchorage and oncogenic cell growth. In Burchenal IJH and Oettgen HF (eds): Achievements, Challenges and Prospects for the 1980's. New York: Grune and Stratton: p 501.

Parsa I, Marsh WH, Sutton AL (1981). An in vitro model of human pancreas carcinogenesis: Effects of nitroso compounds. Cancer 47:1543.

Rhim JS, Park DK, Arnstein P, Huebner RJ, Weisburger EK, Nelson-Rees WA (1975). Transformation of human cells in culture by N—methyl—N'—nitro—N—nitrosoguanidine. Nature 256:751.

Shimada H, Shibata H, Yoshikawa M. (1976). Transformation of tissue cultured xeroderma pigmentosum fibroblasts by treatment with N—methyl—N'—nitro—N—nitrosoguanidine. Nature 264: 547.

Salinskas KC, Kateley SA, Tower JE, Maher VM and McCormick JJ (1981). Introduction of anchorage independent growth in human fibroblasts by propane sultone. Cancer Res 41:1620.

Sutherland BM, Ciminov JS, Delihas N, Shih AH, Oliver RP (1980). Ultraviolet light—induced transformation of human cells to anchorage independent growth. Cancer Res 40:1934.

Vandekerchkove J, Leavitt J, Kakunaga T, Weber K (1980). Coexpression of a mutant beta—actin and the two normal beta- and gamma—cytoplasmic actins in a stably transformed human cell line. Cell 22:893.

Zimmerman RJ, Little JB (1981). Starvation for arg and glu sensitizes human diploid cells to the transforming effects of N—Acetoxy—2—acetylaminofluorene. Carcinogenesis 2:1303.

13th International Cancer Congress, Part B
Biology of Cancer (1), pages 141–148
© **1983 Alan R. Liss, Inc., 150 Fifth Avenue, New York, NY 10011**

FACTORS THAT MODIFY IN VITRO TRANSFORMATION

Joseph A. DiPaolo

Laboratory of Biology, National Cancer Institute

Building 37, Room 2A-19, Bethesda, MD 20205

INTRODUCTION

Prevention of human cancer is the ultimate goal of
cancer research. Epidemiologists estimate that 70-90% of
all human cancer are attributable to carcinogens in the
environment (Higginson, 1979). Although most naturally occurring tumors, particularly in humans, do not appear to be
caused by viruses, cellular genes potentially capable of
inducing transformation have been identified by homology
to the transforming genes of retroviruses and by the biological activity of cellular DNA's in transfection assays
(Cooper, 1982; Shih and Weinburg, 1982), the role of cellular genes in the transformation process is not known. The
present remarks emphasize our in vitro transformation data
obtained using animal and human cells in conjunction with
chemical and physical carcinogens.

Mechanisms of carcinogenesis involve the carcinogenic agent,
the target cells, and the interaction of the transformed
cell with the host. Polycyclic hydrocarbons are found in
the environment and some are extremely potent tumor inducers. Probably the most widely studied is benzo(a)pyrene.
Analysis of the data indicates that the (+)-anti-benzo(a)-
pyrene diepoxide is the ultimate carcinogen; however, in
experiments designed to determine the reactivity of diol
epoxides, those of weak or noncarcinogenic polycyclic hydrocarbons also reacted with ϕX 174 DNA (Harvey, 1981).
Therefore, the important role of the carcinogen in the
transforming action is still unknown. At the target cell
level, the mechanism of "competence" that makes the cell

susceptible to transformation by a carcinogen must be understood; this will result in determining how transformability differs from nontransformability and how the transformation may be modified. The latter has been one of our main interests. Although host modification, conditions governing whether the transformed cells will form malignancies, does not directly involve in vitro transformation, factors that are affective in vitro may also be operative in vivo.

RESULTS AND DISCUSSION

A number of assays utilizing mammalian cell strains and cell lines have been used to demonstrate transformation by chemical and physical agents (Berwald and Sachs, 1965; Heidelberger, 1975; DiPaolo, 1979). Our laboratory has concentrated primarily on embryo cultures with an emphasis on Syrian hamster and more recently on human. Primary cell strains of Syrian hamster embryo cells share a very important property with normal human cells, namely, a diploid karyotype. Ordinarily these cells have a finite life span in culture and an extremely low rate of spontaneous transformation. A quantitative colony assay approach has made it possible to demonstrate dose–response relationships with a large variety of known chemical carcinogens, including organic and inorganics, and with ultraviolet irradiation (DiPaolo and Casto, 1978). It is important to demonstrate that in vitro observations have some counterpart in vivo. The relevance of the induced transformation is that a parallelism exists between the degree of in vivo response and in vitro transformation. Furthermore, transformed colonies give rise to cell lines with the ability to produce progressively growing tumors in either hamster or nude mice. After these studies, some fundamental questions concerning the cellular mechanisms of chemical carcinogenesis could be answered. Transformation was found to be inductive and not the result of selection pre–existing tumor cells (Gart, DiPaolo and Donovan, 1979); furthermore, the carcinogenic action was direct since there is no evidence of viral involvement (Reitz, Saxinger, Ting, Gallo and DiPaolo, 1977). The question concerning the mutation mechanism of chemical carcinogenesis is still unanswered. The transformation frequency is greater than the mutation frequency (DiPaolo and Donovan, 1976) and transformation can occur with nonmutagenic chemicals such as bisulfite

(DiPaolo, DeMarinis and Doniger, 1981; Barrett, Wong and McLachlan, 1981; DiPaolo, DeMarinis and Doniger, 1982).

With hamster cells in culture, cocarcinogenesis, promotion, and anticarcinogenesis have also been demonstrated. Studies involving chemical carcinogens and physical carcinogens such as X-irradiation or ultraviolet irradiation have demonstrated enhancement of the transformation frequency (DiPaolo, Donovan and Popescu, 1976; Doniger and DiPaolo, 1980). The enhancement of the transformation frequency was dependent on the time interval between the two insults; however, enhancement could not be attributed to either changes in chromosome aberrations or DNA repair. A noncarcinogen, caffeine, also enhanced the transformation frequency in a time and dose-dependent fashion (Donovan and DiPaolo, 1974). Caffeine affected the mode of DNA replication in hamster cells (Doniger and DiPaolo, 1980). It caused an increase in in nascent strands of DNA which may be pivotal to increasing the transformation frequency.

The in vitro Syrian hamster results parallelled the in vivo results demonstrating two-stage carcinogenesis, initiation and promotion. After a relatively low dose of either chemical or physical carcinogen, the addition of 12-0-tetradecanoylphorbol 13-acetate (TPA) caused an increase in the transformation frequency (Popescu, Amsbaugh and DiPaolo, 1980; DiPaolo, DeMarinis, Evans and Doniger, 1981). The TPA effect increased with doses to 150 mmol. Removal of the TPA resulted in the reduction of the transformation frequency, indicating that promotion is reversible and suggesting that there is more than one type of initiation. Phytohemaglutinin (PHA) or lymphotoxin, an immunologic hormone, caused a dose-dependent decrease in TPA promoted transformation (unpublished data). PHA in conjunction with lymphotoxin caused additional inhibition of TPA promoted transformation. As a result of kinetic studies, we concluded that PHA and lymphotoxin affect the biological activity of TPA by diverse mechanisms. Whereas lymphotoxin can alter the physiological state of the cell causing a change in the cellular response to TPA, PHA appears to affect the binding of TPA to a critical cellular receptor for promotion or a later step in promotion (unpublished data).

Unfortunately, transformation by carcinogenic agents has not been demonstrated as easily with human as with a few animal species, including hamster. As a consequence, a dilemma results in which the number of known potential human carcinogens that should be tested increases while the utilization of human diploid cells to dissect the process leading to cancer remains underdeveloped. Obviously, extrapolation of carcinogenesis data from human cells to human would be more logical. The adoption of the hamster cell procedure has been unsuccessful with human cells. Whether this reflects our lack of experience in culturing human cells and/or indicates evolutionary differences in control mechanisms is unknown. The first positive results of neoplastic transformation were reported in 1978 by Milo and DiPaolo who used foreskin fibroblast and by Kakunaga who used cells derived from a female lip biopsy.

The strong support for the hypothesis that genomic changes underly carcinogenesis as well as our inability to obtain reproducible transformation data with human cells, led to the use of a selective metabolic block to inhibit DNA synthesis (Milo and DiPaolo, 1980). In this way, it was possible to demonstrate neoplastic transformation in vitro by several direct-acting chemical carcinogens with early diploid fibroblast cells from human foreskin and human lung (MRC-5) (Greiner, Evans and DiPaolo, 1981; Milo and DiPaolo, 1978). A relatively high frequency of transformation appears to depend upon the synchronization of cells at the G1/S interphase. When these cells were returned to complete medium, insulin was added to facilitate their growth; carcinogen was added 8-12 hr later. The carcinogen was added at a time to coincide with the maximum number of cells in S phase of the cell cycle. After carcinogen treatment, the cells were subpassaged for 4-8 population doublings and 10^5 cells were seeded in low calcium Dulbecco's medium containing 0.35% soft agar. Colony frequency in soft agar was determined 17 days later. Untreated MRC-5 cells did not produce any colony growth in soft agar. The size of the colonies after carcinogen ranged between 50-500 cells.

UV irradiation resulted in the highest frequency of colony growth in soft agar (10^{-3}) while aflatoxin-B_1, and propane sultone treatment resulted in colony formation frequencies of 10^{-6}. Similarly, the addition of 4-nitroquinolone, β-propriolactine or N'methyl-N'-nitro-N-nitrosoguanidine to the MRC-5 culture medium produced colony formation frequencies in soft agar of $10^{-4.5}$, 10^{-5} and 10^{-4}, respectively. A quasi quantitative linear relationship exists between carcinogen dose and the acquisition of anchorage independent growth. The current need to subpassage rather than use the cell immediately after carcinogen insult precludes determination of exact transformation frequencies.

The colonies growing in soft agar were isolated, disaggregated and grown as mass cultures. Tumorigenicity was assessed by subcutaneous or intracranial injection of 5 X 10^5 cells suspended in minimal essential medium into 2-3 month old nude mice. Five to six weeks later, the nude mice which received the carcinogen-trated MRC-5 cells developed abnormal motor functions such as hyperkinesis, while the animals which received control MRC-5 remained normal. The carcinogen-treated nude mice were killed, brains removed and fixed in formalin for histology. Examination of the prepared brain sections from nude mice injected with 5 X 10^5 β-propriolactone-treated MRC-5 cells a highly invasive, disclosed undifferentiated fibrosarcoma. After three weeks, the subcutaneous injection resulted in fibrosarcoma; these tumors did not continue to grow as do the tumors obtained by transforming animal cells. Histological slides prepared from nude mice brains which received control MRC-5 cells and were killed at the same time interval revealed normal architecture. Therefore, colony growth in soft agar and the devlopment of undifferentiated fibrosarcomas in nude mice suggest the possibility of in vitro transformation of human embryonic lung cells.

Chromosome analysis of the various cell lines between passages 10-70 proved that all the transformation had stemlines of 44-47 chromosomes and were of human origin. G-band karyotype analysis did not show involvement of any specific chromosome in terms of either structure or number. In fact, some lines had no structurally abnormal chromosomes. The degree of chromosome deviation in these chemically transformed lines was much less than that observed in explanted primary spontaneous human sarcomas.

CONCLUSIONS

Mammalian cells in culture are unique for the study of cellular and molecular mechanisms of chemical carcinogenesis and for the screening of environmental chemicals that may be potential carcinogens. At this time, human cells are much more difficult to transform than are animal cells. At least three primary differences between using animal and human cells may account for the difficulties: a lack of experience in culturing human material; a difference in control mechanism which is probably responsible for the relatively stable human phenotype; and the heterogenicity of humans compared to the few animal species that are routinely used for transformation studies. Since transformation can occur in human cells with the same carcinogen concentrations used with animal cells, it should be possible eventually to obtain permanently transformed human cell lines and to relate cell transformation to cancer in humans.

REFERENCES

Barrett JC, Wong A, McLachlan JA (1981). Diethylstilbestrol induces neoplastic transformation without measureable gene mutation at two loci. Science 212:1402.

Berwald Y, Sachs L (1965). In vitro transformation of normal cells to tumor cells by carcinogenic hydrocarbons. J Natl Cancer Inst 35:641.

Cooper, GM (1982). Cellular transforming genes. Science 218:801.

DiPaolo JA (1979). Quantitative transformation by carcinogens of cells in early pasage. In Emmelot P, Kriek E (eds): "Environmental Carcinogenesis: Occurrence, Risk Evaluation and Mechanisms," Amsterdam: Elsevier/North-Holland, p 365.

DiPaolo JA, Casto BC (1978). In vitro carcinogenesis with cells in early passages. In Sanford K (ed): "Third Decennial Review Conference: Cell Tissue and Organ Culture. Gene Expression and Regulation in Cultured Cells," Natl Cancer Inst Monogr 48:245.

DiPaolo JA, DeMarinis AJ, Doniger J (1982). Asbestos and benzo(a)pyrene synergism in the transformation of Syrian hamster embryo cells. J Environ Pathol Toxicol 5:535.

DiPaolo JA, DeMarinis AJ, Doniger J (1981). Transformation of Syrian hamster embryo cells by sodium bisulfite. Cancer Lett 12:203.

DiPaolo JA, DeMarinis AJ, Evans CH, Doniger, J (1981). Expression of initiated and promoted stages of irradiation carcinogenesis in vitro. Cancer Lett 14:243.

DiPaolo JA, Donovan PJ (1976). In vitro morphologic transformation of Syrian hamster cells by UV-irradiation is enhanced by X-irradiation and unaffected by chemical carcinogens. Int J Radiat Biol 30:41.

DiPaolo JA, Donovan PJ, Popescu NC (1976). Kinetics of Syrian hamster cells during X-irradiation enhancement of transformation in vitro by chemical carcinogen. Radiat Res 66:310.

Doniger J, DiPaolo JA (1980). Excision and postreplication DNA repair capacities, enhanced transformation, and survival of Syrian hamster embryo cells irradiated by ultraviolet light. Cancer Res 40: 582.

Doniger J, DiPaolo JA (1981). Modulation of in vitro transformation and the early and late modes of DNA replication of uv-irradiated Syrian hamster cells by caffeine. Radiat Res 87:565.

Doniger J, DiPaolo JA (1980). The early and late modes of DNA replication in ultraviolet irradiated Syrian hamster embryo cell. Biophy J 31:247.

Donovan PJ, DiPaolo JA (1974). Caffeine enhancement of chemical carcinogen-induced transformation of cultured Syrian hamster cells. Cancer Res 34: 2720.

Gart JJ, DiPaolo JA, Donovan PJ (1979). Mathematical models and the statistical analyses of cell transformation experiments. Cancer Res 39:5069.

Greiner JW, Evans CH, DiPaolo JA (1981). Carcinogen-induced anchorage-independent growth and in vivo lethality of human MRC-5 cells. Carcinogenesis 2:359.

Harvey RG (1981). Activated metabolites of carcinogenic hydrocarbons. Acc Chem Res 14:218.

Heidelberger C (1975). Chemical carcinogenesis. Ann Rev Biochem 44:79.

Higginson J (1979). Environmental carcinogenesis: A global perspective. In Emmelot P, Kriek E (eds): "Environmental Carcinogenesis," North Holland: Elsevier, p 9.

Kakunaga T (1978). Neoplastic transformation of human diploid fibroblast cells by chemical carcinogens. Proc Natl Acad Sci USA 75:1334.

Milo GE, DiPaolo JA (1978). Neoplastic transformation of human diploid cells in vitro after chemical carcinogen treatment. Nature 275:130.

Milo GE, DiPaolo JA (1980). Presensitization of human cells with extrinsic signals to induced chemical carcinogenesis. Int J Cancer 26:805.

Popescu NC, Amsbaugh SC, DiPaolo JA (1980). Enhancement of N-methyl-N'-nitro-N-nitrosoguanidine transformation of Syrian hamster cells by a phorbol diester is independent of sister chromatid exchanges and chromosome aberrations. Proc Natl Acad Sci USA 77:7282.

Reitz MS, Saxinger WC, Ting RC, Gallo RC, DiPaolo JA (1977).
Lack of expression of type-C hamster virus after neoplastic
transformation of hamster embryo fibroblasts by benzo(a)-
pyrene. Cancer Res 37:3583.
Shih C, Weinberg RA (1982). Isolation of a transforming
sequence from a human bladder carcinoma cell line.

CONGRESS SYMPOSIA

FORMATION AND REACTION OF ULTIMATE CHEMICAL
CARCINOGENS Brookes, P., UK, Chairman;
Conney, A., USA, Co-Chairman; Flag Pavilion A

N-Nitroso Compounds and Other Alkylating
Agents. *Montesano, R., Lyon, France. (By
Title Only)

Structural Factors that Enhance or Attenuate
the Carcinogenicity of Polyclclic Aromatic
Hydrocarbons. *Yang, S. K., Bethesda, MD USA.

Reactive Forms of Aromatic Amines and Amides:
Chemical and Structural Features in Relation
to Carcinogenesis. *Kriek, E., Amsterdam,
The Netherlands.

Aflatoxin-DNA Interactions: Qualitative,
Quantitative and Kinetic Features in Relation to
Carcinogenesis. *Wogan, G. N., Cambridge, MA USA.
(By Title Only)

Mechanisms of Formation and Reactions of Electro-
philic Intermediates of Halogenated Olefins.
*Henschler, D., Bonse, G. and Dekant, W.,
Wurzburg, Germany.

Please note: Papers that are listed as "By Title
Only" were presented at the 13th International
Cancer Congress, but are not included in these
volumes.

13th International Cancer Congress, Part B
Biology of Cancer (1), pages 151–160
© 1983 Alan R. Liss, Inc., 150 Fifth Avenue, New York, NY 10011

STRUCTURAL FACTORS THAT ENHANCE OR ATTENUATE THE
CARCINOGENICITY OF POLYCYCLIC AROMATIC HYDROCARBONS

Shen K. Yang, Ph. D.

Department of Pharmacology, School of Medicine,
Uniformed Services University of the Health
Sciences, Bethesda, Maryland 20814 USA

Polycyclic aromatic hydrocarbons (PAHs) are the most
common particulate environmental pollutants and may be
responsible for some cancer induction in man. The biological properties of PAHs, such as mutagenicity, carcinogenicity, and covalent binding to cellular macromolecules,
require metabolic activation by the cytochrome P-450 containing drug-metabolizing enzyme systems. The metabolism of PAHs
has been studied intensively in the past thirty years and
the recent rapid progress in the understanding of their
activation pathways is largely due to the recognition of
benzo[a]pyrene (BaP) 7,8-dihydrodiol-9,10-epoxides as the
major carcinogenic and mutagenic metabolites (Fig. 1) (see
reviews Sims, Grover 1974 & 1981; Jerina, Daly 1974; Jerina
et al 1978; Yang et al 1978 & 1980; Harvey 1981). These findings and the performance of perturbational molecular orbital
calculations by the method of Dewar (1969) led to the development of the "bay-region" theory by Jerina and coworkers
(1977). Bay-region diol-epoxides of some unsubstituted
PAHs, such as chrysene, benz[a]anthracene (BA), dibenz[a,h]-
anthracene and benzo[c]phenanthrene have also been implicated
as major carcinogenic and mutagenic metabolites. Methyl-substituted PAHs, such as 5-methylchrysene, 7-methyl-BA (7-MBA),
8-MBA, 7,12-dimethyl-BA and 3-methylcholanthrene are also
believed to be metabolically activated at the bay-regions
(Sims,Grover 1981).

It has been widely accepted that metabolic conversion of
unsubstituted PAHs to highly mutagenic and carcinogenic bay-
region vicinal diol-epoxides involves three enzymatic reactions: PAH → epoxide → diol → bay-region diol-epoxide. Non-

bay-region vicinal diol-epoxides are also enzymatically formed but possess relatively weaker mutagenic and carcinogenic activities although they may be the metabolite that binds to cellular DNA. For PAHs with a methylene bridge (such as 3-MC) or with methyl substituents, initial hydroxylation reaction at the methylene carbons or methyl carbons (Sims, Grover 1981) and sulfate conjugation (Watabe et al 1982) may also play an important role in the activation pathways.

As illustrated in Fig. 1, studies of the factors that affect the metabolic conversion of the procarcinogenic diol to the ultimate carcinogenic bay-region vicinal diol-epoxides can provide more precise understanding of the relative carcinogenic potency of various PAHs. This review deals primarily with some structural factors that influence the diol → vicinal diol-epoxide pathway. Other aspects of PAH activation and detoxification have been discussed in detail in several recent review articles (Harvey 1981; Jerina et al 1978; Sims, Grover 1981; Yang et al 1980).

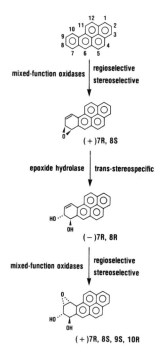

Fig. 1. Major metabolic activation pathway of benzo[a]pyrene. The absolute stereochemistries of intermediates are indicated.

CONFORMATION OF PAH DIHYDRODIOLS

In the absence of steric and electronic factors, non-bay-region trans-dihydrodiol (t-diol) of unsubstituted PAHs preferentially adopt quasi-diequatorial (EE) conformation (Fig. 2). Bay-region t-diols and other t-diols that have a peri methyl (alkyl, hydroxymethyl, fluoro, bromo, etc.) substituent are all preferentially in quasi-diaxial (AA) conformation (Fig. 2). (Chiu et al 1982; Yang et al 1980). All other t-diols, including dihydrodiols such as 9-MBA t-8,9-diol, are all in EE conformation (Fig. 2) (Yang et al 1980).

EFFECT OF DIHYDRODIOL CONFORMATION ON THE METABOLIC FORMATION OF VICINAL DIHYDRODIOL-EPOXIDES

Each of the non-K-region AA and EE diols can be divided into two classes: (i) EE-BR and AA-BR diols: non-K-region t-diols with a vicinal double bond situated in a bay or a "bay like" region and (ii) EE-NBR and AA-NBR diols: non-K-region t-diols with a vicinal double bond not situated in a bay or a "bay like" region.

Detailed metabolism studies of BaP t-9,10-diol (an AA-NBR diol) (Thakker et al 1978) and BeP t-9,10-diol (an AA-BR diol) (Wood et al 1979) have led Wood et al (1979) to suggest that all quasi-axial bay-region diol groups can shift metabolism away from vicinal diol-epoxide formation. However, recent metabolism studies of many non-K-region AA diols with rat liver microsomes indicate that the quasi-axial hydroxyl groups

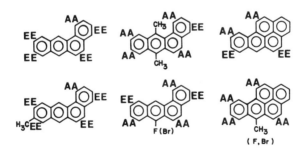

Fig. 2. Conformation of trans-dihydrodiol metabolites formed at various double bonds of the PAH molecules. EE = quasi-diequatorial and AA = quasi-diaxial.

do not necessarily shift the metabolism away from vicinal
diol-epoxide formation (Chou et al 1981). The extent of such
diol-epoxide formation is highly dependent on the geometric
location of the double bond adjacent to the diols and differs
among different PAH diols.

Metabolism of EE-NBR and EE-BR diols

The majority of EE-diols whose metabolism has been
studied are known to be epoxidized enzymatically at the
vicinal BR and NBR double bonds to form vicinal diol-epoxides
as the major metabolite (Fig. 3) (Yang et al 1980). However,
two exceptions are now known: (i) (-)-BA 3R,4R-diol is
metabolized to BA anti-3,4-diol-1,2-epoxide, whereas no
vicinal diol-epoxide was detected from the metabolism of
(+)-BA 3S,4S-diol (Thakker et al 1982) and (ii) 6-MBA t-10R,
11R-diol is predominantly metabolized at the 3,4-positions
(manuscript in preparation). EE-diols with a methyl group
sharing the saturated carbon (such as 8-MBA t-8,9-diol) or
at the adjacent double bond (such as 10-MBA t-8,9-diol) are
known not to be metabolized to vicinal diol-epoxide.

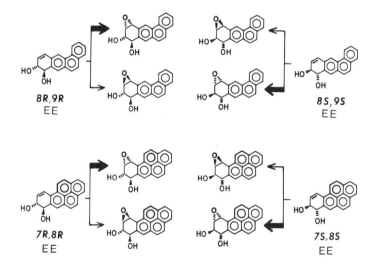

Fig. 3. Stereoselective metabolism of the enantiomeric BA
t-8,9-diols and BaP t-7,8-diols. The major pathways are
indicated by heavy arrows.

Metabolism of AA-NBR diols

Very minor amounts of vicinal diol-epoxides have been detected from the metabolism of the following AA-BR diols: BeP t-9,10-diol (Wood et al 1979), 6-MBaP t-7,8-diol (Yang et al 1980), and 7,12-DMBA t-8,9 diol (Yang et al 1980).

These results thus indicate that the metabolic formation of vicinal diol-epoxides is determined by the conformation of the hydroxyl groups as well as by the geometric location of the double bond of the diol precursors. The most prominent structural features unfavorable to the enzymatic formation of vicinal diol-epoxides are: (i) AA conformations of the diols with the adjacent double bond located in the bay or "bay-like" region and (ii) EE conformations of the diols with a methyl substituent at the hydroxylated carbon or at the adjacent double bond. In contrast to the previous suggestion (Wood et al 1979), it is now known that the axial hydroxyl groups alone do not determine the capability of the non-K-region diols to be further metabolized to vicinal diol-epoxides.

CHEMICAL REACTIVITY AND BIOLOGICAL ACTIVITY OF VICINAL DIHYDRODIOL EPOXIDES

Bay region diol-epoxides (e. g., BaP 7,8-diol-9,10-epoxide and BA 3,4-diol-1,2-epoxide) derived from EE diols are known to be chemically and biologically reactive (e. g., they are potent mutagens and carcinogens). Non-bay-region vicinal diol epoxides (e. g., BA 8,9-diol-10,11-epoxide and BA 10,11-diol-8,9-epoxide) derived from EE-diols are much less reactive chemically and in biological systems. Non-bay-region diol-epoxides derived from AA-diols (e. g., BaP 9,10-diol-7,8-epoxide and BA 1,2-diol-3,4-epoxide) are also less reactive molecules. The relative chemical reactivity of the above-mentioned diol-epoxides is in general agreement with the prediction by the bay-region theory (Jerina et al 1977). The reactivities not predicted by the bay-region theory are the "double bay-region" diol epoxides, such as BeP 9,10-diol-11,12-epoxide, triphenylene 1,2-diol-3,4-epoxide, 6-methyl(6-fluoro, 6-bromo)-BaP 7,8-diol-9,10-epoxide, 5,12-dimethylchry-sene 1,2-diol-3,4-epoxide. These double bay-region diol-epoxides are conformationally rigid molecules (Yagi et al 1979) and may therefore be less reactive chemically and in biological systems.

SUBSTITUENTS THAT ENHANCE CARCINOGENICITY

Methyl substitution at the 6-, 7-, 8-, and 12-positions of BA enhances carcinogenicity (Dipple 1975; Harvey 1981; Wislocki et al 1982). Di- and tri-methylated BA at the 6-, 7-, 8-, and 12-positions also greatly enhance the carcinogenicity (Dipple 1975, Harvey 1981). Although it has been demonstrated that 7-MBA, 8-MBA, and 7,12-DMBA are metabolically activated at the 1,2,3,4-benzo ring, the real reasons why the above-mentioned methylated BAs are more carcinogenic than the unsubstituted BA are not known. It is known that the methyl substituent(s) does not direct metabolism toward the angular benzo-ring, and in some cases, it does not inhibit the metabolism at the methyl-substituted double bonds (Yang et al 1980).

A methyl substitution at the 11-position of BaP and the 5-position of chrysene also enhances the carcinogenicity over the unsubstituted hydrocarbon (Iyer et al 1980 and Hecht et al 1974). Like the 12-methyl group of 12-MBA, the bay-region methyl groups of 11-MBaP and 5-methylchrysene force the molecules to buckle due to overcrowding (Glusker 1981). Other than for this structural feature, the reason that these methyl-substituted PAHs are considerably more carcinogenic than the unsubstituted hydrocarbons is not known. It is possible that the bay-region methyl group may enhance the chemical reactivity of the bay-region vicinal diol-epoxides.

METABOLIC AND STRUCTURAL CONSIDERATIONS FOR CARCINOGENIC POTENCIES

The first step in the metabolism of PAHs leading to the formation of vicinal diol-epoxides is the enzymatic epoxidation reaction catalyzed by the mammalian microsomal or nuclear aryl hydrocarbon epoxidase (AHE or MFO). The AHE (MFO) activity from different tissues or cells toward different regions of a PAH molecule varies greatly. This phenomenon is termed "regioselectivity" and there is no rule (contrary to the views of many theoreticians) to allow us to predict with any certainty the AHE's regioselectivity toward any particular PAH. The regioselectivity of AHE in the various tissues and cells is one of the major factors that determines the susceptibility of animals and humans to the carcinogenic effect(s) of a PAH. The epoxide intermediates formed may be reactive toward cellular macromolecules and may be responsible for the cytotoxic and carcinogenic effects of a PAH.

The enzymatically formed epoxide intermediates can be re-arranged nonenzymatically to phenols and/or can be hydrated trans-stereospecifically to trans-diols catalyzed by the mammalian microsomal or nuclear epoxide hydrolase (EH) (Fig. 4). The extent of rearrangement/hydration is dependent on

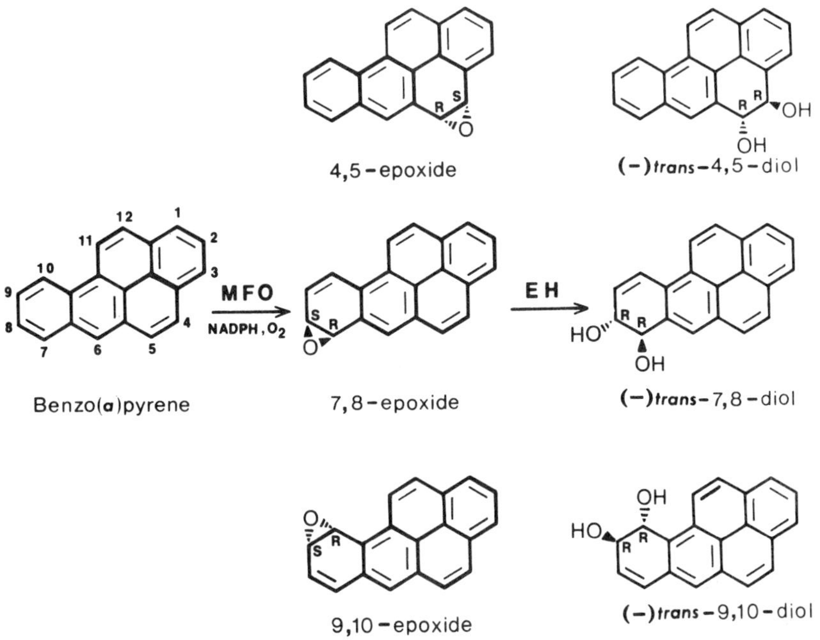

4,5-epoxide

(−)trans-4,5-diol

Benzo(a)pyrene

7,8-epoxide

(−)trans-7,8-diol

9,10-epoxide

(−)trans-9,10-diol

Fig. 4. Stereoselective metabolism at the 4,5-, 7,8-, and 9,10- positions of BaP. Absolute stereochemistries of the predominant enantiomeric intermediates are shown.

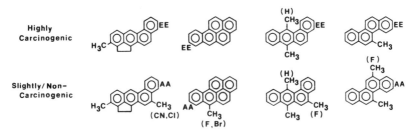

Fig. 5. Attenuation of carcinogenic activity by a substituent.

the stability of the epoxide intermediates and the endogenous
EH activity. Some epoxide intermediates are very unstable
(e. g., BaP 2,3-epoxide) and are rearranged nonenzymatically
to phenolic products. Some epoxide intermediates are more
stable (e. g., some K-region epoxides) and only diols are
formed from the metabolism of the parent hydrocarbons. The
level of EH in the drug-metabolizing enzyme complex plays an
important role in determining the relative amount of proximate
carcinogenic diol metabolite(s).

The stereospecificities of AHE and EH (Fig. 4) are important factors that ultimately determine the mutagenic and
carcinogenic activities of a PAH. Thus the regioselectivity
of AHE specifies the relative amounts of epoxide intermediates
that are formed from the metabolism of a PAH. The stability,
reactivity, and the extent of conjugation of the epoxide
intermediates ultimately determine the amount of diols formed.
The stereospecificity of the AHE and EH also determines the
trans configuration and the ratio of the (+) and (-) enantiomers of a diol metabolite.

Non-K-region diols may be further metabolized by the AHE
to form vicinal diol-epoxides. However, in addition to the
regioselectivity of the AHE, the extent and the occurrence of
this epoxidation reaction are also dependent on the conformation of the hydroxyl groups and the geometric location of the
adjacent double bond of the diol. The relative amount of syn-
and anti-diol-epoxides formed is dependent on the ratio of (+)
and (-) enantiomeric diol precursors and the stereoselectivity
of the AHE at the adjacent double bond. If the diol precursor
adopts a preferentially or exclusively quasi-diaxial conformation and the adjacent olefinic double bond is at the bay or
"bay-like" region, the extent of the epoxidation reaction by
the AHE is substantially reduced or completely abolished.
Based on the assumption that bay-region vicinal diol-epoxides
are the major ultimate carcinogenic metabolites, the weaker
carcinogenicity of compounds in Fig. 5 relative to the
corresponding hydrocarbons without a peri methyl (or F,Br)
group can thus be attributed to the conformations of the
critical diol metabolites whose adjacent double bonds are
all in the bay-regions.

REFERENCES

Chiu PL, Fu PP, Yang SK (1982) Effect of a peri fluoro substituent on the conformation of dihydrodiol derivatives of

polycyclic aromatic hydrocarbons. Biochem Biophys Res Commun 106:1405

Chou MW, Fu PP, Yang SK (1981) Metabolic conversion of dibenz-[a,h]anthracene (±)trans-1,2-dihydrodiol and chrysene (±)trans-3,4-dihydrodiol to vicinal dihydrodiol epoxides. Proc Natl Acad Sci USA 78:4270

Dewar MJS (1969) The Molecular Orbital Theory of Organic Chemistry. New York, McGraw Hill, pp. 214-217 & 304-306

Dipple A (1976) Polynuclear Aromatic Carcinogens. In Searle CE (ed) "Chemial Carcinogens", ACS Monograph Series, No. 173, ACS, p. 245

Glusker JP (1981) X-ray crystallographic studies on carcinogenic polycyclic aromatic hydrocarbons and their derivatives. In Gelbon HV, Ts'o POP (eds) "Polycyclic Hydrocarbons and Cancer" Vol 3, New York, Academic Press, p. 61

Harvey R (1981) Activated metabolites of carcinogenic hydrocarbons. Acc Chem Res 14:218

Hecht SS, Bondinell WE, Hoffmann D (1974) Chrysene and methyl-chrysenes: Presence in tobacco smoke and carcinogenicity. J Natl Cancer Inst 53:1121

Iyer RP, Lyga JW, Secrist JA III, Daub GH, Slaga TJ (1980) Comparative tumor-initiating activity of methylated benzo[a]-pyrene derivatives in mouse skin. Cancer Res 40:1073

Jerina DM, Daly JW (1974) Arene oxides: a new aspect of drug metabolism. Science 185:573

Jerina DM, Yagi H, Thakker DR, Karle JK, Mah HD, Boyd DR, Gadaginamath G, Wood AW, Buening M, Chang, RL, Levin W, Conney AH (1978) Stereoselective metabolic activation of polycyclic aromatic hydrocarbons. In Cohen Y (ed): "Advances in Pharmacology & Therapeutics", Vol 3, Pergamon Press, p. 53

Sims P, Grover PL (1974) Epxodes in polycyclic aromatic hydrocarbon metabolism and carcinogenesis. Adv Cancer Res 20:165

Sims P, Grover PL (1981) Involvement of dihydrodiols and diol epoxides in the metabolic activation of polycyclic hydrocarbons

other than benzo[a]pyrene. In Gelbon HV, Ts'o POP (eds):
"Polycyclic Hydrocarbons and Cancer", Vol 3, New York, Academic
Press, p. 117

Thakker DR, Yagi H, Lehr RE, Levin W, Buening M, Lu AYH, Chang
RL, Wood AW, Conney AH, Jerina DM (1978) Metabolism of trans-
9,10-dihydroxy-9,10-dihydrobenzo[a]pyrene occurs primarily by
arylhydroxylation rather than formation of a diol epoxide.
Mol Pharmacol 14:502

Thakker DR, Levin W, Yagi H, Tada M, Ryan DE, Thomas PE,
Conney AH, Jerina DM (1982) Stereoselective metabolism of the
(+)- and (-)-enantiomers of trans-3,4-dihydroxy-3,4-dihydro-
benz[a]anthracene by rat liver microsomes and by a purified
and reconstituted cytochrome P-450 system. J Biol Chem 257:
5103

Watabe T, Ishizuka T, Isobe M, Ozawa N (1982) A 7-hydroxy-
methyl sulfate ester as an active metabolite of 7,12-di-
methylbenz[a]anthracene. Science 215:403

Wislocki PG, Fiorentini KM, Fu PP, Yang SK, Lu AYH (1982)
Tumor-initiating ability of the twelve monomethylbenz[a]-
anthracenes. Carcinogenesis 3:215

Wood AW, Levin W, Thakker DR, Yagi H, Chang RL, Ryan DE, Thomas
PE, Dansette, PM, Whittaker N, Turujman S, Lehr RE, Kumar S,
Jerina DM, Conney AH (1979) Biological activity of benzo[e]-
pyrene. J Biol Chem 254:4408

Yagi H, Thakker DR, Lehr RE, Jerina DM (1979) Benzo-ring diol
epoxides of benzo[e]pyrene and triphenylene. J Org Chem
44:3439

Yang, SK, Chou MW, Fu, PP (1980) Metabolic and structural
requirements for the carcinogenic potencies of unsubstituted
and methyl-substituted polycyclic aromatic hydrocarbons.
In Pullman B, Ts'o POP, Gelboin H (eds) "Carcinogenesis:
Fundamental Mchanisms and Environmental Effects" D. Reidel
Publishing Co. p. 143

Yang SK, Roller PP, Gelboin, HV (1978) Benzo[a]pyrene metabolism: Mechanism in the formation of epoxides, phenols, dihydrodiols, and the 7,8-diol-9,10-epoxides. In Jones PW, Freu-
denthal RI (ed) "Carcenogensis, Vol 3: Polynuclear Aromatic
Hydrocarbons" New York, Raven Press, p. 285

13th International Cancer Congress, Part B
Biology of Cancer (1), pages 161–174
© 1983 Alan R. Liss, Inc., 150 Fifth Avenue, New York, NY 10011

REACTIVE FORMS OF AROMATIC AMINES AND AMIDES: CHEMICAL AND STRUCTURAL FEATURES IN RELATION TO CARCINOGENESIS

Erik Kriek, Ph.D.

Chemical Carcinogenesis Division, The Netherlands Cancer Institute, 121 Plesmanlaan, 1066 CX Amsterdam, The Netherlands.

Aromatic amines represent a large group of chemicals which are extensively used in a variety of industrial, processes, such as dyeing textiles, as dye intermediates and in the manufacture of drugs, pesticides and plastics. The toxic and carcinogenic properties of aromatic amines are well-known, and the experience obtained with this class of compounds suggests that in humans absorption may occur via the respiratory and gastrointestinal tracts and through the skin. The most important compounds from the standpoint of industrial epidemiology are ABP(4-aminobiphenyl), BZ(benzidine) and 2-NA(2-naphthylamine), which have now definitely been established as being responsible for almost all of the known industrial bladder cancer. In recent years, however, there is increasing evidence for the occurrence of certain groups of aromatic amines as environmental pollutants, which might be related to human carcinogenesis (Egan et al, 1981). Some typical examples of these groups of aromatic amines will be described below; the molecular structures of these compounds are illustrated in Fig. 1.

Benzidine-derived azo dyes, like DBL 6 (direct blue 6) are used for textiles such as cotton, silk, wool, nylon and acetate fibers. In addition to use as textile dyes, DBL 6 and direct black 38 are used in aqueous printing inks, biological stains, plastics and wood. Both compounds have been used in hair dyes. Benzidine-derived azo dyes are reduced to benzidine in at least three species; rhesus monkeys (Rinde and Troll, 1975), rats and mice (NCI, 1978). Recent data suggest that anaerobic intestinal bacteria play an important role in the metabolism of benzidine-

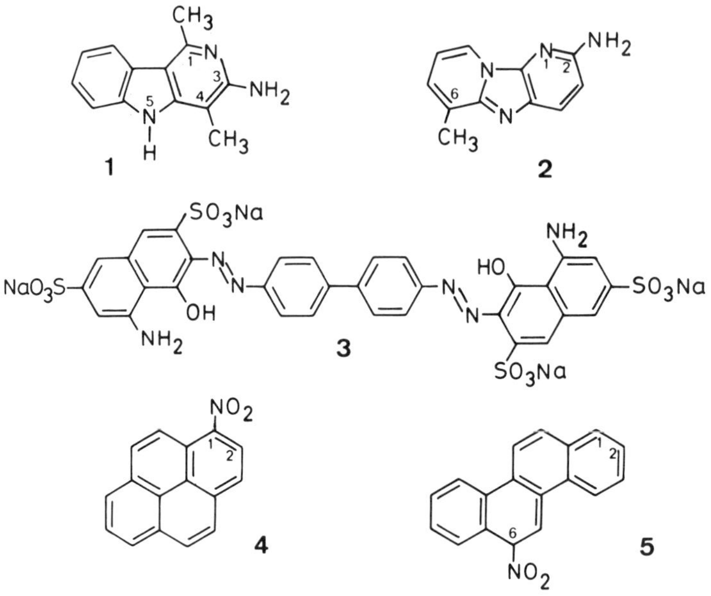

Fig. 1. Molecular structures of some typical environmental carcinogenic aromatic amino and nitro compounds. The compounds 1, 2, 4 and 5 are strong mutagens for S.typhimurium. All compounds have carcinogenic activity in experimental animals.
1. Trp-P-1 (3-Amino-1,4-dimethyl-5H-pyrido[4,3-b]indole);
2. Glu-P-1 (2-Amino-6-methyldipyrido[1,2-a:3',2'-d]imidazole);
3. DBL 6 (Direct blue 6); 4. 1-NP (1-Nitropyrene);
5. 6-NC (6-Nitrochrysene).

derived azo dyes (Cerniglia et al, 1982). Benzidine-derived azo dyes are at present being studied at NCTR (National Center for Toxicological Research, Jefferson, AR, USA) because of their potential for long-term exposure, both through industrial use and through contact with products containing these dyes. Benzidine is listed as a human carcinogen (IARC, 1979).

Recently, Matsushima and Sugimura (1982) isolated mutagenic heterocyclic aromatic amines from pyrolysis products of amino acids, proteins and proteinous foods, such as Trp-P-2 (3-Amino-1-methyl-5H-pyrido[4,3-b]indole), Trp-P-1 (4-methyl-Trp-P-2), Glu-P-2 (2-amino-dipyrido[1,2-a:3',2'-d]imidazole), Glu-P-1 (6-methyl-Glu-P-2) and others. A common feature of all compounds is that they have the 2-amino-pyridine group in their

structures. Three aminoimidazole derivatives were isolated
from cooked food and quinoline derivatives were isolated from
broiled sun dried sardines and from broiled beef. The heterocyclic amines behaved as typical frame-shift mutants in
S.typhimurium assays. The tryptophan and glutamic acid pyrolysis products induced hepatocellular carcinomas in CDF mice
which were fed a pellet diet containing 0.02% of Trp-P-1 or
Trp-P-2, and 0.05% of Glu-P-1 or Glu-P-2. The possible role
of heterocyclic aromatic amines in cancer of the gastrointestinal tract in humans remains to be established.

The nitropolycyclic aromatic hydrocarbons, 1-NP (1-Nitro-
pyrene) and 6-NC (6-nitrochrysene), are environmental contaminants and are present in the exhaust of diesel engines.
They belong to the most potent mutagens in the S.typhimurium
assay. As yet little is known about the carcinogenicity of
nitroaromatics and their metabolism in mammalian systems.
Recent evidence suggests that 1-NP and 6-NC have tumor-initiating activity on mouse skin (El-Bayoumy et al, 1982).
Howard et al (1982a) demonstrated that 1-NP is easily reduced
in the presence of a nitroreductase, xanthine oxidase, resulting in the formation of an electrophilic DNA binding
intermediate. One major DNA adduct was identified as N-(deoxy-
guanosin-8-yl)-1-aminopyrene, which is of similar nature as
the adducts formed by a number of arylhydroxylamines (Table
1). Rat intestinal anaerobic bacteria have the capacity to
reduce 1-NP to 1-aminopyrene (Howard et al, 1982b), suggesting
that the intestinal microflora may play a role in the in vivo
reduction and probably in the carcinogenicity in mammals of
nitroaromatics.

METABOLISM

The metabolism of aromatic amines is complex because of
the variety of reactions these compounds can undergo. Several
reviews on this subject are available (Kriek and Westra, 1979;
NCI, 1981) so that only the most important pathways will be
mentioned here. In most species the main detoxification pathway occurs through N-acetylation and oxidation at ring-carbons
by cytochrome P450 dependent reactions with the formation of
phenolic compounds that are excreted in the bile and urine
as stable O-glucuronides and O-sulfates. Although quantitatively a minor reaction, N-oxidation is a necessary first
step in the covalent binding, carcinogenicity and mutagenicity
of aromatic amines and amides. In this reaction N-arylacet-

amides are converted to N-hydroxy-arylacetamides, which are further activated by a variety of enzymatic reactions. Activation by the sulfotransferase-catalyzed formation of N,O-sulfates (Mulder, 1982) is restricted only to rat liver and does not occur in other tissues where aromatic amines have carcinogenic activity (Irving et al, 1971). Enzymatic activation by N,O-acetyl transfer of N-hydroxy-arylacetamides has been studied intensively by King and his group (King and Weber, 1981). Enzymatic transacetylation is an important general pathway of activation of N-hydroxy-arylacetamides. The enzyme N,O-acetyltransferase has been found in many tissues, such as colon, earduct sebaceous gland, kidney, liver, mammary gland and small intestine, but exhibits extreme species-dependent differences. The unstable O-acetyl esters formed are too reactive to be isolated, but their formation can be detected by trapping them with nucleophiles such as methionine, guanosine or tRNA. This reaction proceeds with the formation of nitrenium ions that exist as ground-state singlets as the result of electron transfer from the aromatic groups to the formally electron-deficient nitrogen atom. Thus, the singlet state is stabilized, rather than the triplet state which is the ground state of NH_2^+ and aliphatic nitrenium ions (Ford and Scribner, 1981). Consequently, the resulting aryl-nitrenium-carbonium ions carry only a part of the positive charge on their nitrogen, while the remainder can be delocalized throughout the aromatic ring system. Arylhydroxylamines can be formed by deacetylation of N-hydroxy-arylacetamides and from their N-glucuronides (Kadlubar et al, 1977). Aryl-hydroxylamines are less stable than their corresponding N-acetyl derivatives. The formation of arylnitrenium-carbonium ions from arylhydroxylamines under slightly acidic conditions was suggested by Kriek (1965). The importance of this reaction for bladder carcinogenesis by aromatic amines was emphasized later by Kadlubar et al (1981). The conversion of urinary aryl-hydroxylamines to carcinogenic electrophiles under mildly acidic conditions in the bladder lumen and the subsequent binding of these elctrophiles to urothelial DNA has been proposed by Kadlubar et al (1981) to be a critical event in the initiation of arylamine-induced bladder cancer. This concept is supported by recent experiments from Oldham et al (1981), who demonstrated that acidic pH substantially increased the frequency of neoplastic transformation of normal human skin fibroblasts exposed to N-hydroxy-1- and N-hydroxy-2-naphthylamine.

INTERACTION WITH DNA

The arylnitrenium-carbonium ions generated from N-arylhydroxylamines or their N- and O-acetyl derivatives react
with nucleophilic groups in nucleic acids and proteins with
the formation of covalent bonds. The reactive sites in nucleic
acids have been summarized in Tables 1 and 2. There is a
striking difference between the reaction products of aromatic
amines and those formed by simple alkylating agents, which
react with almost every nitrogen and oxygen of the bases and
also with the phosphate groups of DNA. This is not simply
because the substituent is large and aromatic. Favored sites
of reaction of aromatic amines are the C-8 of guanine and the
exocyclic amino groups of the purines. Neither pyrimidines
nor phosphate groups appear to react with aromatic amines and
their derivatives in vivo or in vitro. The carcinogen trans-
N-acetyl-4-aminostilbene (AAS) is an exception, but this
amine behaves like a typical alkylating agent (Scribner et
al, 1979). Reactive esters of AF (N-2-aminofluorene), BZ and
4-NQO (4-nitroquinoline-1-oxide) react predominantly with
C-8 of guanine. Biphenyl derivatives also have specificity
for guanine, but react about equally well with C-8 and N^2.
The sulfate and acetate esters of N-hydroxy-N-acetyl-2-amino-
phenanthrene react to the same extent with adenine and guanine
(Scribner and Naimy, 1975). N-arylhydroxylamines also react
preferentially with C-8 of guanine. As yet only one aromatic
amine derivative, N-hydroxy-1-NA, has been shown to react with
O^6 of guanine under in vitro conditions at acidic pH values
(Kadlubar et al, 1978).

The specificity for guanine in DNA is even greater for
the binding in vivo, as summarized in Table 3. In all cases
which have now been adequately studied, the major product
identified was an N-(deoxyguanosin-8-yl)-arylamine. Acetylated derivatives were found only in rat liver and kidney after
administration of AAF (N-acetyl-2-aminofluorene), AABP (N-
acetyl-4-aminobiphenyl) and AABP4'F (N-acetyl-4-amino-4'-
fluorobiphenyl), or their N-hydroxy derivatives, and were
always minor products. Interestingly, benzidine derivatives
in vivo were always present as N-(deoxyguanosin-8-yl)-N'-
acetylbenzidine. In addition to this adduct, other unidenti-
fied products were present in DNA from dog bladder (Beland
et al, 1982). It should be noted that the O^6-guanine derivatives of 1-NA were not detected in dog bladder DNA in vivo.
The ring-open form of N-(deoxyguanosin-8-yl)-AF, originally
characterized by Kriek and Westra (1981), was detected in

Table 1. Summary of reaction sites of nucleic acids and polynucleotides with N-arylhydroxylamines in vitro

Proximate carcinogen[a]	Sites of modification						References
	Guanine				Adenine		
	C-8	N-7	N^2	O^6	C-8	N^6	
ABP	+				+		Beland et al (1982)
AF	+[b]		+				Westra and Visser (1979)
APh	+[c]						Scribner and Woodworth (1982)
Glu-P-1	+			+[d]			Hashimoto et al (1980)
1-NA							Kadlubar et al (1978)
2-NA	+[e]		+			+	Kadlubar et al (1980)
1-NP	+						Howard et al (1982)
4-NQO						+	Kawazoe et al (1975)
Trp-P-2	+[f]						Hashimoto et al (1979)

Symbols: +, site found to be reactive without judgement as to the extent of reaction.

[a] Abbreviations are given in the text

[b] N-Trifluoroacetyl-O-acetyl derivative

[c] O-Acetyl derivative

[d] N-(deoxyguanosin-O^6-yl)- (60%) + 2-(deoxyguanosin-O^6-yl)-1-naphthylamine (30%)

[e] 1-Nitropyrene in the presence of xanthine oxidase/hypoxanthine

[f] Arylamine in the presence of rat liver microsomes

Table 2. Summary of reaction sites of nucleic acids and polynucleotides with N-arylacethydroxamic acid esters in vitro

Proximate carcinogen [a]	Sites of modification						References
	Guanine				Adenine		
	C-8	N-7	N^2	O^6	C-8	N^6	
ABP	+		+				Kriek (1971)
ABP4'F	+		+		−		Kriek and Hengeveld (1978)
AF	+		+		−		Kriek and Westra (1979)
AF		+					Tarpley et al (1982)
APh	+					+	Scribner and Naimy (1975)
BZ	+						Martin et al (1982)
MAB	+		+			+	Beland et al (1980)
4-NQO	+[b]						Bailleul et al (1981)

Symbols: +, site found to be reactive without judgement as to the extent of reaction.
−, reactivity looked for but not detected.

[a] Abbreviations are given in the text

[b] O,O'-diacetyl-4-hydroxylaminoquinoline-1-oxide

Table 3. Identified reaction sites of DNA with carcinogenic aromatic amines and amides in vivo

Proximate carcinogen[a]	Species	Organ	Arylamine Guanine C-8	Arylamine Guanine N²	N-acetylarylamine Guanine C-8	N-acetylarylamine Guanine N²	References
AABP	rat	liver	+		+	+	Kriek (1971)
ABP	dog	bladder	+		−	−	Beland et al (1982)
AABP4'F	rat	liver	+		+	+	Kriek and Hengeveld (1978)
AABP4'F	rat	kidney	+		+	+	Kriek and Westra (1979)
AAF	rat	liver	+		+	+	Poirier et al (1982)
AAF	rat	kidney	+		+		Allaben and Weis (1982)
AAF	rat	m.gl.	+		−	−	Beland et al (1982)
AAF	dog	bladder	+		−	−	Scribner and Koponen (1979)
AAPh	rat	liver	+		−	−	Martin et al (1982)
ABZ	rat	liver	+				Martin et al (1982)
BZ	rat	liver	+				Beland et al (1982)
BZ	dog	bladder	+				Martin et al (1982)
DBL 6	rat	liver	+	+[b]			Tullis et al (1981)
MAB	rat	liver	+				Beland et al (1982)
1-NA	dog	bladder	−				Beland et al (1982)
2-NA	dog	bladder	+				Beland et al (1982)

Symbols: +, site identified with the aid of synthetic marker nucleosides.
−, reactivity looked for but not detected.

[a] Abbreviations are given in the text.

[b] 3-(Deoxyadenosin-N⁶-yl)-MAB was also identified.

DNA from the mammary gland of female SD rats after administration of N-hydroxy-N-formyl- or N-hydroxy-N-acetyl-2-amino-
fluorene (Allaben and Weis, 1982). It is not absolutely certain, however, if the ring-open form is present in vivo or
formed during the isolation of DNA.

Of fundamental importance to our understanding of the
functional consequences of nucleic acid modification by bulky
carcinogens such as aromatic amines is information on two
points: (1) the orientation relative to the double-stranded
nucleic acid structure, and (2) alteration in the native
nucleic acid conformation resulting from the modification.
Various aspects of nucleic acid modification by AAF have been
reviewed recently by Grunberger and Santella (1981). Modification of DNA at the C-8 position of guanine by AAF results
in a large distortion of the DNA helix referred to as the
"base displacement model" with the aromatic ring system of
AAF inserted into the helix and deoxyguanosine displaced outside the helix. Specific features of this model are: (1) the
binding of AAF to C-8 of guanine is associated with a change
in glycosidic N-9/C-1' conformation from the anti form of
nucleosides in nucleic acids with Watson-Crick geometry to
the syn conformation, and (2) the strong stacking interaction
between fluorene and the bases adjacent to the substituted G.
A different situation exists for arylamines bound to C-8 of
guanine, when the N-acetyl group is missing. Recent results
from several laboratories (see Grunberger and Santella for
pertinent references) suggest that the local regions of de-
naturation induced by AF substitution are much smaller than
those associated with AAF modification. In contrast to the
C-8 adducts, substitution at the N^2 does not produce a significant change in conformation of the DNA helix, and the
fluorene can occupy the minor groove without major distortion.
Relevant to the in vivo significance of these specific conformational differences between the three types of adducts
are previous observations that N-acetylated C-8 products are
rapidly removed from rat liver DNA in vivo (Kriek and Westra,
1979). In a similar fashion Howard et al (1981) have shown
that guanine-8-AAF is rapidly removed in primary cultures of
rat hepatocytes, whereas the guanine-8-AF and N^2-AAF products
remained constant for 14 hr and then were removed at a slow
rate. Recent studies in our laboratory (Westra et al, 1982)
indicate that similar differences in rate of repair of the
guanine-AAF products exist in distinct liver cell populations.

No attempts have been made to account for the relative proportions of the various adducts, because these are largely dependent on the conditions of the experiment; e.g. species, strain, sex, route of administration and dose of the carcinogen. The action of repair enzymes also affects the amount of adducts present in DNA, as explained above. The major product found in vivo usually is a guanine-8-arylamine, which is removed at a different rate as compared to the corresponding N-acetyl derivative. Because N^2 derivatives are persistent, this type of adduct accumulates during chronic feeding of a carcinogenic aromatic amine. In this way, accumulation of the N^2-dG and N^6-dA adducts of MAB (N-methyl-4-aminoazobenzene) in rat liver DNA was demonstrated by Tullis et al(1981). When substitution occurs on a site required for base-pairing, like N^2-dG or N^6-dA, or on a site causing steric hindrance or electronic shielding of base-pairing atoms, the result is ambiguity in transcription leading to a base mutation (Kadlubar et al, 1980; Singer and Kuśmierek, 1982). On the other hand, C-8 products usually lead to frameshift mutations or deletions. In principle any unrepaired lesion can be expressed as an error after replication. Thus, promutagenic modifications persisting for prolonged periods of time may lead to cumulative effects of biological significance and may be important events in the initiation of carcinogenesis.

REFERENCES

Allaben WT, Weis CC(1982): Identification of the major DNA adduct in rat mammary gland after in vivo administration of the carcinogen N-hydroxy-N-formyl-2-aminofluorene. In Beland FA, Kadlubar FF, Thorgeirsson SS, Irving CC (eds): Proceedings Second International Conference on Carcinogenic and Mutagenic N-Substituted Aryl Compounds, in press.
Bailleul B, Galiegue S, Loucheux-Lefebvre M-H (1981): Adducts from the reaction of O,O'-diacetyl or O-acetyl derivatives of the carcinogen 4-hydroxyaminoquinoline-1-oxide with purine nucleosides. Cancer Res 41:4559.
Beland FA, Tullis DL, Kadlubar FF, Straub KM, Evans FE (1980): Characterization of DNA adducts of the carcinogen N-methyl-4-aminoazobenzene in vitro and in vivo. Chem-Biol Interact 31:1.
Beland FA, Beranek DT, Dooley KL, Heflich RH, Kadlubar FF (1982). Relationship of arylamine-DNA adducts to mutagenesis and bladder carcinogenesis. In Beland FA, Kadlubar FF, Thorgeirsson SS, Irving CC (eds): Proceedings Second Inter-

national Conference on Carcinogenic and Mutagenic N-substituted Aryl Compounds, in press.

Cerniglia CE, Freeman JP, Franklin W, Pack LD (1982): Metabolism of benzidine-, 3,3'-dimethylbenzidine- and 3,3'-dimethoxybenzidine-based azo dyes by rat intestinal bacteria. In Beland FA, Kadlubar FF, Thorgeirsson SS, Irving CC (eds) Proceedings Second International Conference on Carcinogenic and Mutagenic N-substituted Aryl Compounds, in press.

Egan H, Fishbein L, Castegnaro M, O'Neill IK, Bartsch H (eds) (1981): Environmental Carcinogens-Selected Methods of Analysis, Vol 4, Some Aromatic Amines and Azodyes in the General and Industrial Environment. IARC Scientific Publication No.40, Lyon, International Agency for Research on Cancer.

El-Bayoumy K, Hecht SS, Wynder EL (1982): Tumor-initiating activity and in vitro metabolism of 6-nitrochrysene and 1-nitropyrene.Proc Amer Assoc Cancer Res 23:331.

Ford GP, Scribner JD (1981): MNDO Molecular orbital study of nitrenium ions derived from carcinogenic aromatic amines and amides. J Am Chem Soc 103:4281.

Grunberger D, Santella RM (1981): Alternative conformations of DNA modified by N-2-acetylaminofluorene. J. Supramol Struct Cell Biochem 17:231.

Hashimoto Y, Shudo K, Okamoto T (1979): Structural identification of a modified base in DNA covalently bound with mutagenic 3-amino-1-methyl-5H-pyrido[4,3-b]indole. Chem Pharm Bull (Tokyo) 27:2532.

Hashimoto Y, Shudo K, Okamoto T (1980): Metabolic activation of a mutagen, 2-amino-6-methyl-dipyrido[1,2-a:3',2'-d]-imidazole. Identification of 2-hydroxyamino-6-methyldipyrido[1,2-a:3',2'-d]imidazole and its reaction with DNA. Biochem Biophys Res Commun 92:971.

Howard PC, Casciano DA, Beland FA, Shaddock Jr JG (1981): The binding of N-hydroxy-2-acetylaminofluorene to DNA and repair of the adducts in primary rat hepatocyte cultures. Carcinogenesis 2:97.

Howard PC, Beland FA, Evans FE, Heflich RH (1982a): Xanthine oxidase-catalyzed reduction of 1-nitropyrene to a potentially mutagenic DNA-binding species. Proc Amer Assoc Cancer Res 23:242.

Howard PC, Cerniglia C, Beland FA (1982b): Metabolism of 1-nitropyrene by rat intestinal bacteria. In Beland FA, Kadlubar FF, Thorgeirsson SS, Irving CC (eds): Proceedings Second International Conference on Carcinogenic and Mutagenic N-substituted Aryl Compounds, in press.

IARC (1979): IARC Monographs on the Evaluation of the Carcinogenic Risk of Chemicals to Humans. Supplement 1. Chemicals and industrial processes associated with cancer in humans, Lyon, International Agency for Research on Cancer.

Irving CC, Janss DH, Russell LT (1971): Lack of N-hydroxy-2-acetylaminofluorene sulfotransferase activity in the mammary gland and Zymbal's gland of the rat. Cancer Res 31:387.

Kadlubar FF, Miller JA, Miller EC (1977): Hepatic microsomal N-glucuronidation and nucleic acid binding of N-hydroxy-arylamines in relation to urinary bladder carcinogenesis. Cancer Res 37:805.

Kadlubar FF, Miller JA, Miller EC (1978): Guanyl O^6-arylamination and O^6-arylation of DNA by the carcinogen N-hydroxy-1-naphthylamine. Cancer Res 38:3628.

Kadlubar FF, Unruh LE, Beland FA, Straub KM, Evans FE (1980): In vitro reaction of the carcinogen N-hydroxy-2-naphthylamine with DNA at the C-8 and N^2 atoms of guanine and the N^6 atom of adenine. Carcinogenesis 1:139.

Kadlubar FF, Unruh LE, Flammang TJ, Sparks D, Mitchum RK, Mulder GJ (1981): Alteration of urinary levels of the carcinogen N-hydroxy-2-naphthylamine and its N-glucuronide in the rat by control of urinary pH, inhibition of metabolic sulfation and changes in biliary excretion. Chem-Biol Interact 33:129.

Kawazoe Y, Araki M, Huang GF, Okamoto T, Tada M, Tada M (1975): Chemical structure of QAII, one of the covalently bound adducts of carcinogenic 4-nitroquinoline-1-oxide with nucleic acid bases of cellular nucleic acids. Chem Pharm Bull (Tokyo) 23:3041.

King CM, Weber WW (1981): Formation, metabolic activation by N,O-acyltransfer, and hydrolysis of N-acyl-N-arylamine derivatives. In National Cancer Institute Monograph 58. "Carcinogenic and Mutagenic N-substituted Aryl Compounds" (NIH publication No.81-2379). Washington DC, US Government Printing Office, p 117.

Kriek E (1965): On the interaction of N-2-fluorenylhydroxylamine with nucleic acids in vitro. Biochem Biophys Res Commun 20:793.

Kriek E (1971): On the mechanism of action of carcinogenic aromatic amines. II. Binding of N-hydroxy-N-acetyl-4-aminobiphenyl to rat liver nucleic acids in vivo. Chem-Biol Interact 3:19.

Kriek E, Hengeveld GM (1978): Reaction products of the carcinogen N-hydroxy-4-acetylamino-4'-fluorobiphenyl with DNA in liver and kidney of the rat. Chem-Biol Interact 21:179.

Kriek E, Westra JG (1979): Metabolic activation of aromatic amines and amides and interaction with nucleic acids. In "Chemical Carcinogens and DNA", Vol II, Grover PL (ed), Boca Raton, Florida, CRC Press Inc., p 1.

Kriek E, Westra JG (1981): Structural identification of the pyrimidine derivatives formed from N-(deoxyguanosin-8-yl)-2-aminofluorene in aqueous solution at alkaline pH. Carcinogenesis 1:459.

Martin CN, Beland FA, Kadlubar FF (1982): DNA adducts of benzidine and benzidine-derived azodyes. In Beland FA, Kadlubar FF, Thorgeirsson SS, Irving CC (eds): Proceedings Second International Conference on Carcinogenic and Mutagenic N-substituted Aryl Compounds, in press.

Matsushima T, Sugimura T (1982): Mutagenicity and carcinogenicity of new heterocyclic amines produced by pyrolysis of amino acids, proteins and proteinous food. In Beland FA, Kadlubar FF, Thorgeirsson SS, Irving CC (eds): Proceedings Second International Conference on Carcinogenic and Mutagenic N-substituted Aryl Compounds, in press.

Mulder GJ (1981): Generation of reactive intermediates from xenobiotics by sulfate conjugation; their potential role in chemical carcinogenesis. In Mulder GJ (ed): "Sulfation of Drugs and Related Compounds", Boca Raton, Florida, CRC Press Inc., p 213.

NCI (1978): National Cancer Institute "13-Week subchronic toxicity studies of direct blue 6, direct black 38, and direct brown 95 dyes". (Tech Rep Ser No.108; DHEW Publ No. (NIH) 78-1358) Washington DC, US Government Printing Office.

NCI (1981): National Cancer Institute Monograph 58. "Carcinogenic and Mutagenic N-substituted Aryl Compounds" (NIH publication No. 81-2379). Washington DC, US Government Printing Office.

Oldham JW, Kadlubar FF, Milo GE (1981): Effect of pH on the neoplastic transformation of normal human skin fibroblasts by N-hydroxy-1-naphthylamine and N-hydroxy-2-naphthylamine. Carcinogenesis 2:937.

Poirier MC, True BA, Laishes BA (1982): Formation and removal of (guan-8-yl)-DNA-2-acetylaminofluorene adducts in liver and kidney of male rats given dietary 2-acetylaminofluorene. Cancer Res 42:1317.

Rinde E, Troll W (1975): Metabolic reduction of benzidine azodyes to benzidine in rhesus monkey. J Natl Cancer Inst 55:181.

Scribner JD, Naimy NK (1975): Adducts between the carcinogen 2-acetamidophenanthrene and adenine and guanine of DNA. Cancer Res 35:1416.

Scribner JD, Koponen G (1979): Binding of the carcinogen
2-acetamidophenanthrene to rat liver nucleic acids: lack
of correlation with carcinogenic activity, and failure of
the hydroxamic acid ester model for in vivo activation.
Chem-Biol Interact 26:201.

Scribner NK, Scribner JD, Smith DL, Schram KH, McCloskey JA
(1979): Reactions of the carcinogen N-acetoxy-4-acetamido-
stilbene with nucleosides. Chem-Biol Interact 26:27.

Scribner JD, Woodworth B (1982): Adducts of 2-aminophenan-
threne with nucleosides and rat liver nucleic acids.
In Beland FA, Kadlubar FF, Thorgeirsson SS, Irving CC (eds):
Proceedings Second International Conference on Carcinogenic
and Mutagenic N-substituted Aryl Compounds, in press.

Singer B, Kuśmierek JT (1982): Chemical Mutagenesis, Ann Rev
Biochem 51 in press.

Tarpley WG, Miller JA, Miller EC (1982): Rapid release of
carcinogen-guanine adducts from DNA after reaction with
N-acetoxy-2-acetylaminofluorene or N-benzoyloxy-N-methyl-
4-aminoazobenzene. Carcinogenesis 3:81.

Tullis DL, Straub KM, Kadlubar FF (1981): A comparison of the
carcinogen-DNA adducts formed in rat liver in vitro after
administration of single or multiple doses of N-methyl-4-
aminoazobenzene. Chem-Biol Interact 38:15.

Westra JG, Visser A (1979): Quantitative analysis of N-
(guanin-8-yl)N-acetyl-2-aminofluorene and N-(guanin-8-yl)-
2-aminofluorene in modified DNA by hydrolysis in trifluoro-
acetic acid and high pressure liquid chromatography.
Cancer Lett 8:155.

Westra JG, Visser A, Tulp A (1982): Binding and repair of
2-AAF adducts in distinct liver cell populations. In
Beland FA, Kadlubar FF, Thorgeirsson SS, Irving CC (eds):
Proceedings Second International Conference on Carcinogenic and Mutagenic N-substituted Aryl Compounds, in press.

13th International Cancer Congress, Part B
Biology of Cancer (1), pages 175–183
© 1983 Alan R. Liss, Inc., 150 Fifth Avenue, New York, NY 10011

MECHANISMS OF FORMATION AND REACTIONS OF ELECTROPHILIC
INTERMEDIATES OF HALOGENATED OLEFINS

Dietrich Henschler, M.D., Gerhard Bonse,
Ph.D., Wolfgang Dekant
Institute of Toxicology, University of
Würzburg, Germany

Since vinyl chloride has definitely been shown to be
carcinogenic in man (I.A.R.C. 1975) and experimental animals (Maltoni, Lefemine 1974), efforts have been made to
apply the well established principles of bioactivation mechanisms with vinyl chloride, namely epoxide formation and
alkylation of RNA and DNA, to the similarly structured but
higher chlorinated ethylenes to prove their genotoxic potential (van Duuren 1977). This paper tries to sum up presently available information on the mechanisms involved in
metabolism and reactivity of two important members in that
series of compounds, tri- and tetrachloroethylene, indicating their ineffectiveness as mutagens and carcinogens. Another part of the paper will deal with mechanisms active in
the genotoxic activity of halogenated allylic compounds.

1) Bioactivation of Vinyl Chloride (VC)

VC is converted, by the agency of P-450-catalyzed mono-
oxygenases, to the respective epoxide I which rearranges to
chloroacetaldehyde II (Bolt et al. 1976). I and II may react
with DNA and/or RNA to form cyclisized etheno derivatives,

alkylation of DNA and RNA
bases

e.g. $1,N^6$-etheno adenine III, $3,N^4$-etheno cytosine IV, N^2-3-etheno guanine V in vitro; in vivo, however 7-(2-oxo-ethyl)-guanine VI seems to be the major alkylation product (Laib et al. 1981).

III   IV   V   VI

VI seems to be in equilibrium with O^6-7-(1-hydroxyethano)-deoxyguanine VII (Scherer et al. 1981). It is generally accepted that these chemical modifications of DNA and/or RNA bases are responsible for miscoding in translation and transcription mechanisms (Hathway 1981).

Similar activation mechanisms may be operative in vinylidene chloride VIII activity but so far no alkylation products have been identified.

2) Trichloroethylene and Tetrachloroethylene

It has been postulated (Powell 1945) that trichloroethylene IX may be metabolically oxidized to 2,2,3-trichloro-oxirane XI which rearranges to chloral XII. The rationale behind this is the finding of trichloroethanol XIII and trichloroacetic acid XIV as urinary excretion products in vivo (Bonse, Henschler 1976):

IX   XI   XII   XIV

Spectral evidence has been provided for the formation of an epoxide by a specific P-450 binding spectrum (Uehleke et al. 1977). Studies with the synthesized oxirane XI revealed, however, that its thermal rearrangement entirely goes to dichloroacetyl chloride XV (Bonse, Henschler 1976). An explanation has been provided for the discrepancy between the behavior of XI in vitro and in vivo:

$$\text{CHCl}_2\text{-COCl} \xleftarrow{\text{in vitro}} \quad \underset{\text{XI}}{\text{XI}} \quad \xrightarrow{\text{in vivo}} \text{CCl}_3\text{-CHO}$$

XV	XI	XII

the rearrangement of XI to XII can be forced by Lewis acids
like $FeCl_3$, and the trivalent iron in the catalytic premise
of P-450 which converts IX to XI may act as a Lewis acid.
Support for this hypothesis is given by findings of a rearrangement of pure XI, in nonpolar solvents, to XII in the
presence of $FeCl_3$ as well as model protoporphyrins with certain thioether moieties as fifth ligands to Fe (Henschler,
Hoos 1982).

Furthermore, XI behaves completely differently in aqueous systems. Model experiments have shown that it decomposes
extremely rapidly to a variety of compounds:

Under in vivo conditions, no C_1-units like HCOOH or CO are
found (Henschler et al. 1979) which indicates that XI does
not escape the hydrophobic premise of P-450 before being re-
arranged to XII or having reacted with proteins or other
nucleophiles in the vicinity of the catalytic center of the
converting enzyme. In accordance with these assumptions, XI
has been found inactive in Salmonella typhimurium mutagenicity testing (Kline et al. 1982).

Only if extremely high oral doses of IX are administered to rodents is some dichloroacetic acid XVI formed (Hathway 1980), indicating an "overspill" of the normally operative rearrangement to chloral XII. Such an overpowering of this protective mechanism may be responsible for a questionably positive carcinogenicity experiment in an oversensitive strain of mice (NCI 1976). Other experiments with an exposure of another strain of mice to IX by gavage, or of three species of laboratory animals to IX by inhalation, have been negative (Henschler et al. 1980, 1982).

A comparative protective mechanism may work with tetrachloroethylene X which also undergoes oxidative metabolism:

$$\text{X} \longrightarrow \text{XVII} \longrightarrow CCl_3\text{-COCl} \longrightarrow CCl_3\text{-COOH}$$

X   XVII   XVIII   XIV

Trichloroacetyl chloride XVIII may react covalently with macromolecules but not by alkylation (Bonse et al. 1975); the formed acylation products are expected to undergo rapid esterolytic cleavage.

Again, the 2,2,3,3-tetrachlorooxirane XVII is rapidly decomposed in aqueous systems to products which are not detectable in vivo (Henschler, Hoos 1982):

$$\text{XVII} \longrightarrow Cl\text{-}\underset{Cl}{\overset{OH}{C}}\text{—}\underset{Cl}{\overset{OH}{C}}\text{-Cl} \longrightarrow Cl\text{-}\underset{Cl}{\overset{OH}{C}}\text{-H} + \overset{O}{\underset{Cl}{\overset{\|}{C}}}_{Cl} \longrightarrow CO_2 + HCl$$

$$\downarrow -HCl \qquad\qquad \downarrow$$

$$HCOOH + HCl + CO$$

$$\underset{Cl}{\overset{O}{\|}}C\text{—}C\overset{O}{\|}\underset{Cl}{}$$

$$\downarrow$$

$$HOOC\text{–}COOH$$

Another consideration is in favor of IX and X not being genotoxic: the conceivable adducts of their electrophilic intermediates should be expected to contain chlorine substitutions
at carbon atoms adjacent to heteroatoms in nucleic bases
which would render them rather unstable. Accordingly, no DNA
or RNA binding has been found after metabolic activation in
vivo from IX (Stott et al. 1982) or X (Schumann et al. 1980).
Carcinogenicity studies with X by inhalation in rats have
been found negative (Rampy et al. 1977). It seems, therefore,
that chlorine substitutions >2 in ethylene provide protective capacity against genotoxic activity.

3) Halogenated Allyl Compounds

Allyl chloride XIX is a well established carcinogen
(Public Health Service 1978; van Duuren et al. 1979) and
mutagen (Eder et al. 1980). Its genotoxic activity has been
attributed to a metabolic oxidation of the olefinic double
bond to an electrophilic epoxide, in analogy to vinyl chloride (van Duuren 1977). This assumption overlooks the strong
direct alkylating potential of allyl halides which may go
through a variety of mechanisms (Eder et al. 1982):

a) formation of cations stabilized by resonance:

$$\overset{3}{C}H_2=\overset{2}{C}H-\overset{1}{C}H_2-Cl \longrightarrow [CH_2 \cdots CH \cdots CH_2]^{\oplus}Cl^{\ominus}$$

b) S_N2'-reactivity with a nucleophile Nu:

$$Nu| + CH_2=CH-CH_2-Cl \longrightarrow [Nu-CH_2-CH-CH_2]^{\oplus}Cl^{\ominus}$$

c) radical formation, again with a resonance stabili-
zation:

$$CH_2=CH-CH_2-Cl \xrightarrow{-Cl^{\cdot}} [CH_2=CH-\overset{\cdot}{C}H_2 \longleftrightarrow \overset{\cdot}{C}H_2-CH=CH_2]$$

In fact, allyl chloride XIX, allyl bromide XX and allyl
iodide XXI are positive in the NBP alkylation-test, and also
are direct mutagens in the Ames S. typhimurium test system
(Eder et al. 1980). The strength of the −I-effect of the
respective halogen atoms determines the reactivity of allyl
halides, which increases in the order Cl< Br< I. Further chlorine substitution such as in 1,3-dichloropropenes, −cis and
−trans, increases, due to the −I-effect which supports cation

formation, the alkylating and mutagenic potential, the influence of substitutions at the different carbon atoms being in the order $\overset{3}{C}$>$\overset{1}{C}$>$\overset{2}{C}$ (Neudecker et al. 1980). Alkyl substitution also increases reactivity by virtue of +I- and +M-effects, as in the chlorobutenes. Cyclic allylic compounds are also active, like 3-chloro-1-cyclohexene, and benzyl chloride which contains an allylic moiety and is one of the most reactive compounds of the whole series. A good quantitative correlation between the direct alkylating (NBP-test) and the mutagenic (S. typhimurium TA 100) potencies has been found in a series of 11 halogenated allylic compounds (see Table 1). Exceptions to the correlation are found with just

Tab. 1. Correlation between direct alkylating (NBP-test, extinction at 560 nm) and direct mutagenic (S. typhimurium TA 100) activity in halogenated allyl and allylic compounds (Eder et al. 1982).

Compound	Mutagenicity, revertants/mmole	Alkylat. potency NBP, E 560 nm
Allyl chloride	9	0.285
Allyl bromide	700	54
Allyl iodide	2000	164
1,3-Dichloropropene-cis	500	2.24
1,3-Dichloropropene-trans	260	1.93
2,3-Dichloro-1-propene	26	0.248
1-Chloro-2-butene	130	1.04
3-Chloro-1-butene	68	n.d.
3-Chloro-2-methyl-1-propene	44	0.57
3-Chloro-2-methyl-1-butene	30	n.d.
1-Chloro-2-methyl-2-butene	64	2.06
Benzyl chloride	560	2.92
3-Chloro-1-cyclohexene	10	0.31

a few compounds (e.g. 2,3-dichloro-1-propene XXII), in which extremely electrophilic metabolites or subsequent derivatives thereof may be found (e.g. the epoxide of XXII which rearranges to 1,3-dichloroacetone).

Hence, the direct alkylating potential seems to compete with, or even exclude the metabolic biotransformation of allyl halides. With allyl bromide XX, the following adducts to DNA bases have been identified after single oral administration to mice: O^6-allyl guanine, 7-allyl guanine, N^2-allyl guanine,

3-allyl guanine and N[6]-allyl guanine (Eder, Sebeikat 1982); reaction products from the epoxide would, however, produce non-allylic adducts. This is indicative of direct alkylation being the predominant activation mechanism in this type of compound.

References

Bolt HM, Kappus H, Buchter A, Bolt W (1976). Disposition of [1,2-^{14}C]vinyl chloride in the rat. Arch Toxicol 35:153.

Bonse G, Henschler D (1976). Chemical reactivity, biotransformation, and toxicity of polychlorinated aliphatic compounds. CRC Crit Rev Toxicol 5:395.

Bonse G, Urban T, Reichert D, Henschler D (1975). Chemical reactivity, metabolic oxirane formation and biological reactivity of chlorinated ethylenes in the isolated perfused liver preparation. Biochem Pharmacol 24:1829.

Eder E, Neudecker T, Lutz D, Henschler D (1980). Mutagenic potential of allyl and allylic compounds. Structure-activity relationship as determined by alkylating and direct in vitro mutagenic properties. Biochem Pharmacol 29:993.

Eder E, Neudecker T, Lutz D, Henschler D (1982). Correlation of alkylating and mutagenic activities of allyl and allylic compounds: standard alkylation test vs. kinetic investigation. Chem-Biol Interact 38:303.

Eder E, Sebeikat D (1982). In vivo alkylation of DNA by allyl bromide. Naunyn-Schmiedebergs Arch Pharmacol Suppl 319:80.

Hathway DE (1980). Consideration of the evidence for mechanisms of 1,1,2-trichloroethylene metabolism, including new identification of its dichloroacetic acid and trichloroacetic acid metabolites in mice. Cancer Lett 8:203.

Hathway DE (1981). Mechanisms of vinyl chloride carcinogenicity/mutagenicity. Brit J Cancer 44:597

Henschler D, Elsässer HM, Romen W, Eder E (1983). Carcinogenicity study of trichloroethylene, with or without epoxide stabilizers, in mice. Arch Toxicol to be published.

Henschler D, Hoos WR (1982). Metabolic activation of di-, tri- and tetrachloroethylenes. In Snyder R et al (eds): "Biological reactive intermediates - II Part A," New York & London: Plenum Press.

Henschler D, Hoos WR, Fetz H, Dallmeier E, Metzler M (1979). Reactions of trichloroethylene epoxide in aqueous systems. Biochem Pharmacol 28:543.

Henschler D, Romen W, Elsässer HM, Reichert D, Radwan Z
(1980). Carcinogenicity study of trichloroethylene by
longterm inhalation in three animal species. Arch Toxicol
43: 237.

I.A.R.C. (1975). Report of a working group on epidemiological studies on vinyl chloride exposed people. Int Tech
Rep 75/001, Lyon/France.

Kline SA, McCoy EC, Rosenkranz HS, van Duuren BL (1982).
Mutagenicity of chloroalkene epoxides in bacterial systems. Mutat Res 101:115.

Laib RJ, Gwinner LM, Bolt HM (1981). DNA alkylation by
vinyl chloride metabolites: etheno-derivatives or 7-
alkylation of guanine? Chem-Biol Interact 37:219

Maltoni C, Lefemine G (1974). Carcinogenicity bioassays of
vinyl chloride. I. Research plans and early results.
Environ Res 7:387.

NCI Carcinogenesis bioassay of trichloroethylene (1976).
NCI Tech Rep Ser No 2, US DHEW Publ No 76-802. Washington,
DC.

Neudecker T, Lutz D, Eder E, Henschler D (1980). Structure-
activity relationship in halogen and alkyl substituted
allyl and allylic compounds: correlation of alkylating
and mutagenic properties. Biochem Pharmacol 29:2611.

Powell JF (1945). Trichloroethylene: absorption, elimination
and metabolism. Brit J Industr Med 2:142.

Public Health Service (1978). NCI-CG-TR-73, DHEW Publ No
(NIH) 78-1323. Washington, DC: US Gov Print Off.

Rampy LW, Quast JF, Leong BKJ, Gehring PJ (1977). Results
of longterm inhalation toxicity studies on rats of 1,1,1-
trichloroethylene and perchloroethylene formulations.
Paper presented at the 1st Int Congr Toxicol, Abstr p 27,
Toronto/Canada

Scherer E, van der Laken CJ, Gwinner LM, Laib RJ, Emmelot P
(1981). Modification of deoxyguanosine by chloroethylene
oxide. Carcinogenesis 2, 671

Schumann AM, Quast JF, Watanabe PG (1980). The pharmacokinetics and macromolecular interactions of perchloroethylene in mice and rats as related to oncogenicity.
Toxicol Appl Pharmacol 55:207.

Stott WT, Quast JF, Watanabe PG (1982). The pharmacokinetics
and molecular interactions of trichloroethylene in mice
and rats. Toxicol Appl Pharmacol 62:137

Uehleke H, Tabarelli-Poplawski S, Bonse G, Henschler D (1977).
Spectral evidence for 2,2,3-trichloro-oxirane formation
during microsomal trichloroethylene oxidation. Arch Toxicol
37:95.

van Duuren BL (1977). Chemical structure, reactivity, and carcinogenicity of halocarbons. Environ Hlth Perspect 21:17.

van Duuren BL, Goldschmidt BM, Loewengart G, Smith AC, Melchionne S, Seidman I, Roth D (1979). Carcinogenicity of halogenated olefinic and aliphatic hydrocarbons in mice. J Natl Cancer Inst 63:1433.

CONGRESS SYMPOSIA

MULTISTAGE CARCINOGENESIS BY CHEMICALS Hecker, E.,
FRG, Chairman; Diamond, L., USA, Co-Chairwoman;
Arena

Initiation and Promotion in Mouse Mammary
Tumorigenesis. *Medina, D., Houston, TX USA.

Specific Changes in Epidermal Function and
Biological Potential Induced by Initiators and
Promoters of Carcinogenesis. *Yuspa, S. H.,
Bethesda, MD USA. (By Title Only)

The Sequential Analysis of Cancer Development
in Liver. *Farber, E., Toronto, Ontario,
Canada. (By Title Only)

Multi-Stage Tumor Development in the Urinary
Bladder. *Hicks, R. M., London, England.

Multistage Tumor Development in the Human
Esophagus. *Hecker, E., Lutz, D., Weber, J.,
Goerttler, K., Morton, J. F. and Collectanea, M.,
Heidelberg, W. Germany and Coral Gables, FL USA.

Please note: Papers that are listed as "By Title
Only" were presented at the 13th International
Cancer Congress, but are not included in these
volumes.

13th International Cancer Congress, Part B
Biology of Cancer (1), pages 187–203

INITIATION AND PROMOTION IN MOUSE MAMMARY TUMORIGENESIS

Daniel Medina, Ph.D.

Baylor College of Medicine

Houston, Texas 77030

Introduction

It is almost axiomatic that neoplasms arising from epithelial cells of most organs develop as a consequence of multiple changes occurring in a cell population. This has been referred to as multiple stage carcinogenesis. The most popular hypothesis to explain this tumorigenic process is the "initiation-promotion" scheme developed from several pioneer experiments (Rous and Kidd, 1941; MacKenzie and Rous, 1941; Mottram, 1944a,b; Berenblum and Shubik, 1947,1949). Although the experiments which formulated the basis for this hypothesis were performed in the 1940's, it has been only in the past decade that the idea has been extended to organs other than skin. It has been difficult to translate this hypothesis to the mammary gland, although the mouse mammary gland still represents the most thoroughly documented example of multiple stage carcinogenesis. Today, I would like to develop an analogy between mouse mammary tumorigenesis and the initiation-promotion hypothesis and suggest that the information gained from each approach could be usefully applied to understanding some of the underlying mechanisms of the cancer process.

Morphological Types of Mammary Preneoplasias

Mouse mammary tumors develop from discrete foci of altered cells termed hyperplastic alveolar nodules or ductal hyperplasias. The original experiments in mice (DeOme et al., 1959; Blair and DeOme, 1961; Faulkin, 1966; Medina, 1976), along with those in rat (Beuving, 1968; Sinha and

Dao, 1977; Haslam and Bern, 1977; Russo et al., 1977),
human (Wellings et al., 1975; Jensen et al., 1976) and dog
(Cameron and Faulkin, 1971; Cardiff et al., 1977) mammary
glands support the hypothesis that breast pathologies in
the different species share much in common and that the
principle site of initial change occurs within the ductule
or terminal portion of the mammary tree. The extensive information available on MMTV-induced preneoplastic alveolar
hyperplasias has overshadowed the fact that chemical carcinogen-induced ductal dysplasias in the mouse and rat,
and human ductal dysplasias have very similar pathologies.
The unique alveolar hyperplasia in the mouse represents
the best model to examine the underlying cellular and
molecular events associated with neoplasia, although the
cell type which is transformed may be different from that
occurring in ductal dysplasias. Regardless, indirect and
direct data support the concept that these hyperplasias
are high risk lesions for tumor formation; i.e. they are
preneoplastic.

Expression of Preneoplasias

The occurrence of preneoplasias can be viewed in terms
of factors influencing induction and subsequent expression
of preneoplastic cell populations. The following scheme
illustrates this concept.

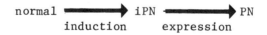

$$\text{normal} \xrightarrow{\text{induction}} \text{iPN} \xrightarrow{\text{expression}} \text{PN}$$

Preneoplasias (PN) are foci of alveolar or ductal hyperplasias. They are easily quantifiable, either in situ (Nandi,
1963; Medina, 1973) or in in vitro organ cultures (Banerjee
et al., 1974); thus they can serve as end-points in assays
to evaluate "potential" carcinogens or modulating factors.
This endpoint evaluates the preneoplastic process, but
does not dissect out the two independent events: induction
from expression. In order to critically dissociate the
two events, one has to make some assumptions: i) that a
population of normal mammary cells contains within it
numerous "altered" cells which remain undetectable for
prolonged periods of time; and ii) that the expression of
these cells can be modulated by exogenous or endogenous
factors. If these assumptions can be proven correct,
then the mammary system starts to develop an analogy

with skin and liver systems. Table 1 summarizes the data obtained by several investigators (DeOme et al., 1978a; Guzman et al., 1981; Ethier and Ullrich, 1982), who have demonstrated that the initiation and expression of mammary preneoplastic cells are dissociable events.

Table 1. Recovery of Dysplastic Cell Populations from Normal Appearing Mammary Gland

Strain	Donor Age (Mo.)	Treatment[a]	% of Dysplastic Outgrowths
BALB/cf C3HCrl	3-4	MMTVs, CD	15 (57/415)[a]
BALB/cf C3HCrl	2-4	MMTVs, Intact	0 (0/48)
C57BL/Crl	4.5	CD	0 (0/46)[b]
C57BL/Crl	4.5	Pit., CD	0 (0/42)
C57BL/Crl	4.5	DMBA, CD	19 (6/32)
C57BL/Crl	4.5	DMBA, Pit., CD	51 (21/41)
BALB/cAnNBd	3	CD	5 (6/132)[c]
BALB/cAnNBd	3	γ-Irradiation, CD	16 (12/77)
BALB/cAnNBd	3	DMBA, CD	15 (25/171)

[a] DeOme et al., 1978
[b] Guzman et al., 1981
[c] Ethier and Ullrich, 1982

Of interest is the observation that this process is valid for alveolar hyperplasias induced by MMTV and ductal hyperplasias induced by DMBA or irradiation. The major conclusion from these experiments is that altered cells appear soon after the exposure to carcinogens, however a long latent period is required to form detectable foci. A corollary to this hypothesis is that significant numbers of initiated cells or cells with enhanced neoplastic potential exist in tissues that appear normal or may develop tumors only rarely. Support for this concept comes from the well-documented spontaneous tumor incidence seen in most laboratory animals which have not been exposed to any overt carcinogen, i.e. the tumor incidence often cited as the control or background value. Additional support comes from the experiments of Marchok et al. (1977) and Terzagki

et al. (1981) who have demonstrated the presence of cells
with neoplastic potential in trachea, esophagus, and lung
long before their overt presence as preneoplastic or neoplastic foci. Whereas the factors regulating expression
of preneoplastic cells in respiratory epithelium are unknown, the expression of altered mamary cells can be
faciliated or promoted by altering the microenvironment
(DeOme et al., 1978), by the hormones of pregnancy (DeOme
et al., 1978b), and by genetic factors (Wolff et al.,
1979). In order to conceptualize the preneoplastic state
in terms readily translatable to other systems, I will
refer to the altered but undetectable cells as "initiated"
cells and the cell populations as preneoplastic. In this
context, the mammary system is more analogous to the liver
than the skin model, since in the liver system, preneoplastic cell populations are present as foci of liver nodules,
but initiated cells are assumed to be present within this
general population. It should be clear that the "preneoplastic" cell has not been clearly defined in any of the
three model systems, although some essential characteristics of the cell(s) have been identified. Within this
same context, it should be continually kept in mind that
the alternative hypothesis of a linear transformation (1-
step) model remains a vaiable hypothesis and is not dis-
proven by any data. All data from multiple stage carcinogenesis models deal with cell populations rather than the
isolated "preneoplastic" or "initiated" cell.

Essential Characteristics of Preneoplasias

Tomes can be written about the characteristics of preneoplasias and neoplasias. The principle lesson gained from
similar experiments on mammary cells is that the morphological, cytological, and ultrastructural characteristics of
mammary preneoplasias are very similar to normal mammary
cells (Medina and Asch, 1980). Even early arising mammary
tumors are remarkably similar to the normal mammary cells.
The main phenotypic characteristics which differ in preneoplastic cell populations relate to growth control. Table
2 illustrates the growth characteristics of mammary preneoplasias which have been examined in situ or in vitro.

Briefly, it is quite clear that the growth of preneoplastic populations is still stringently regulated. Firstly, preneoplastic cell populations will grow only in the
mammary fat pads and generally will not overgrow normal

Table 2: Phenotypic Characteristics Related to Growth Control of Mammary Preneoplastic Cell Populations as Compared to Normal Mammary Cell Populations.

Similar	Dissimilar
1. In situ	
Mammary Fat Pad-Dependent Does Not Overgrow Normal Duct	Indefinite Division Potential Estrogen-Independent for Growth
2. In vitro	
Saturation Density Contact Inhibition of DNA Synthesis Cytochalasin B-Induced Multinucleation Intracellular $[Na^+]$ Na^+ Transport Synthesis of Growth Factors	$[Ca^{++}]$Requirement for Growth

mammary epithelium, in direct contrast to neoplastic cell populations. These results indicate that growth factors operating via stromal constituents or normal mammary cells still stringently regulate or influence cell division and the cell cycle of preneoplastic cell populations. The interactions of stromal constituents on the growth of epithelial cells is an area which has recently regained attention with new methodology (Smith et al., 1982; Wicha et al., 1982; Salomon et al., 1981). Secondly, preneoplastic cells retain an intrinsic normal degree of control of cell division. This can be shown by examining DNA synthesis in cell cultures of preneoplastic and neoplastic cells during log and stationary phase growth conditions (Hosick et al., 1980) or by using the drug cytochalasin B to disrupt cytokinesis from karyokinesis (Medina et al., 1980). In both types of experiments, preneoplastic cells exhibit a normal control of nuclear events similar to normal cells, whereas neoplastic cells exhibit an abnormal control of DNA synthesis and nuclear division.

There are several cellular events which have been suggested as important factors in the uncontrolled regulation of DNA synthesis seen in neoplastic cells. Two events frequently mentioned are an altered ion flux [Na influx

(Rozengurt, 1982), Mg^{++} influx (Rubin et al., 1981), Ca^{++} requirement (Swierenga et al., 1978; Hennings et al., 1980)] and the constituitive production of growth factors (Roberts et al., 1982). These two events may be linked or independent. A review of the current data (Table 2) shows that most of these parameters are similar in normal and preneoplastic mammary populations with the possible exception of Ca^{++} requirement (Medina et al., 1982). The latter point is similar to the results of Kulesz-Martin et al. (1980) who have suggested that an altered Ca^{++} requirement for proliferation is a property of preneoplastic epidermal cells.

What factors can distinguish preneoplastic from normal cell populations? So far, there are two phenotypic characteristics by which preneoplastic cells have been identified: i) altered differentiated state; and ii) indefinitely prolonged life span which I am equating with the abrogation of senescence. Given these two phenotypic alterations, the important questions become: Are these characteristics unique to mammary preneoplasias? Are they essential properties of preneoplasias and significant to the carcinogenic process? With reference to the first phenotype, there is no doubt that mammary cell preneoplasias exhibit an altered differentiation phenotype. For instance, casein, a hormone-inducible protein in the terminally differentiated mammary gland is constituitively expressed in C3H mammary preneoplasias, regardless whether these preneoplasias are chemically or virally induced (Smith et al., 1982). Additionally, the alveolar phenotype and the growth of mammary preneoplasias in BALB/c mice are no longer dependent upon ovarian hormones (estrogen and progesterone), although in this strain casein does not appear to be constituitively expressed (Banerjee, 1976; Supowit et al., McGrath and Soule, 1982). It is worthwhile to note that one of the characteristics of TPA, the most documented tumor promoter, is the inhibition of terminal differentiation (Berenblum 1954; Raick, 1974; Marks, 1976; Rovera et al., 1977). Additionally, Yuspa and Morgan (1981) suggested that an alteration in the proliferative block associated with terminal differentiation may be significant in the initiating event.

With regard to the abrogation of senescence, meaning the rescinding of events associated with cellular aging, it is clear that established non-tumorigenic cell lines in vitro, i.e. 3T3, 10T1/2, by definition, are characterized by this property. Furthermore, the data of several investi-

gators support the concept that these cell lines are preneoplastic cell populations, neither normal nor neoplastic
(Boone, 1975; Boone and Jacobs, 1976; Sanford et al.,
1980; Tu and Sivak, 1982). To extend the analogy being
developed here, these are "initiated" cell populations,
at high risk for tumor formation and analogous to mammary
preneoplastic cell populations. This concept is further
supported by the results of Mordan et al. (1982) who described the isolation of a 10T1/2 "initiated" cell subline
and the observations of Colburn et al. (1978) who have
demonstrated that TPA is a promoter for epithelial cell
lines. It remains to be demonstrated if mammary preneoplastic cell populations are promotable by TPA or other
specific promoters.

Given the fact that mammary preneoplasias are akin to
initiated cells and are characterized by abrogated senescence, of what significance is this to the cell and the
process of carcinogenesis? Sonneborn (1978), in a thought-
ful discussion on the evolution of senescence, makes the
comment that senescence arose evolutionarily as a mechanism
to escape death. Additionally, it coincided, but was not
necessarily causally related to the evolution of diploidy.
Senescence arose with diploidy basically because genetic
redundancy was the most primitive way to extend life. It
required two hits to kill the cell, not one. Neoplasms,
and perhaps preneoplasms, are an example of this evolutionary principle taken one step further; namely the development
of genetic redundancy (gene amplification) at specific
loci which resulted in an indefinitely prolonged life span.
The phenomena of gene amplification is well-documented
with reference to the end-stages of the neoplastic process;
namely, tumor progression, especially in the development
of drug-resistance (Schimke et al., 1978) and metastases
(Cifone and Fidler, 1981). Recently, gene amplification
has been discussed as one of the underlying processes in
the development of neoplasia (Maskens, 1981; Morris et al.,
1980, Pall, 1981). It is an interesting possibility that
specific gene amplification might be the proximate cause
of abrogation of senescence and the development of preneo-
plasia. Whereas aneuploidy is a common feature of established cell lines, it has not been thoroughly evaluated
with modern techniques in epithelial preneoplasias. The
molecular consequences associated with this genetic event
also remain elusive, although several suggested possibilities have been ruled out (Table 2). The significance of

several other events, such as the generation and processing of free radicals and cell-generated oxidative damage, the capability of DNA repair, and the avoidance of terminal differentiation need investigation.

Given this type of mechanism and the consequence, of what advantage is it to escape senescence? Several investigators, namely Armitage and Doll (1957), Moolgavkar and Knudson (1981) and Potter (1981) have proposed that "cancer results from two or more relevant mutations" (Potter, 1981). Potter (1981) states that promoters enhance the proliferation of cells with one relevant mutation, thereby increasing the probability of obtaining a cell with two relevant mutations. The consequence of the abrogation of senescence is simply to maintain the population of cells at risk to a relevant second mutation. Armitage and Doll (1957) made the observation that "the incidence of human cancer is proportional to the number of initiated cells at risk due to the primary exposure and the strength of the second initiating event." Promotion, as Potter maintains, primarily serves to expand the initiated population, but a second event is necessary for the set of critical changes (inducible by TPA) to become constituitive. The sustained hyperplasia, maintained by the abrogation of senescence and the lack of terminal differentiation, provides a large population for a prolonged time period which increases the risk for the second critical event. Thus, it is not surprising that both $MMTV_S$, a highly oncogenic virus, and $MMTV_L$, a low oncogenic virus can neoplastically transform, at a very high rate, mammary preneoplastic lines. Similarly, chemical carcinogens such as DMBA and urethan, and irradiation are much more effective carcinogens for mammary preneoplasias than they are for normal virgin or pregnant mammary tissues.

What are the molecular consequences of the second event? Potter (1980) proposes an irreversible block in cellular communication. This event would be one type of mechanism which would allow a cell to grow progressively, assuming DNA synthesis and mitosis is regulated primarily by a negative feedback loop with the signal generated outside the recipient cell. Others have suggested the constituitive expression of cellular homologues of known viral oncogens is a critical event in neoplasia (Roberts et al., 1980; Chang et al., 1982; Parada et al., 1982). The integration of the viral genome into a host genomic site leading to constituitive expression of cellular genes is a variant of this theme and provides one specific mechanism. Such a scheme has been shown for avian leukosis virus, but not yet for mammary tumor viruses (Varmus, 1982). The second event can be induced by viral integration, chemical-carcinogen alteration of DNA, irradiation-mediated mutation, or spontaneous mutation due to inherent genetic instability as a consequence of the initial event. This latter mechanism is suggested by the data of Cifone and Fidler (1981) in the generation of metastases and the mathematical model for the two-stage induction of colon carcinogenesis (Masken, 1981). A consideration of the data on mammary tumorigenesis from preneoplasias would be consistent with a model where the second event occurs spontaneously at a constant rate (Medina and DeOme, 1970; Medina, 1973).

What then are mammary preneoplasias? The hypothesis proposed here is that the preneoplastic process can be divided into an induction event leading to an initiated cell (cells) which can be promoted by hormones and intercellular changes into a discrete preneoplastic population. Mammary hyperplasias are cell populations which have the essential characteristics of initiated preneoplastic cells, namely the abrogation of senescence and alteration of terminal differentiation. Furthermore, these preneoplastic cell populations are analogous in their growth and differentiation properties to initiated epidermal cells, carcinogen-induced hepatic nodules, initiated trachea cells and established cell lines like 3T3 and 10T1/2. The resultant mammary hyperplasia represents a population at high risk for the second critical event which is an event akin to that proposed by Potter (1980), although the molecular alteration results in the constituitive expression of one or a set of cellular proteins which directly or indirectly regulate growth (e.g., growth factor). The events inducible by known promoters (increased ornithine decarboxylase, increased cell proliferation, decreased terminal differentiation, decreased cell communication, are permissive events in the neoplastic process which increase the population at risk.

In summary, the first event, i.e., initiation, is an alteration in the cell cycle characteristics of the cell which results in a cell population with an indefinitely prolonged life span. The second event [(conversion in Boutwell's terminology (Boutwell, 1964) or second initiation in Potter's terminology (1981)] is an alteration in the regulation of cell growth (i.e., DNA synthesis, mitosis). This event can be due to molecular changes affecting any one of a number of cellular components. Promotion, in its classical concept, is an important event which influences both the first and second initiating events in Potter's hypothesis; however, its underlying nature is permissive. Promoting agents, like hormones, provide the necessary conditions for the occurrence of the second critical event.

Acknowledgements

I am deeply thankful to Drs. Gilbert Smith, Raymond Gantt, and Janet Butel whose comments and advice helped clarify the ideas presented in this manuscript.

References

Armitage P, Doll R (1957). A two-stage theory of carcinogenesis in relation to the age distribution of human cancer. Brit J Cancer 11:161.

Banerjee MR (1976). Responses of mammary cells to hormones. Int Rev Cytol 47:1.

Banerjee MR, Wood BG, Washburn LL (1974). Chemical carcinogen-induced alveolar nodules in organ culture of mouse mammary gland. J Natl Cancer Inst 53:1387.

Berenblum I (1954). Carcinogenesis and tumor pathogenesis. Adv Cancer Res 2:129.

Berenblum I, Shubik P (1947). The role of croton oil applications, associated with a single painting of a carcinogen, in tumor induction of the mouse's skin. Br J Cancer 1:379.

Berenblum I, Shubik P (1949). The persistence of latent tumor cells induced in the mouse's skin by a single application of 9:10-dimethylbenzanthracene. Br J Cancer 3:384.

Beuving LJ (1968). Mammary tumor formation within outgrowths of transplanted hyperplatic nodules from carcinogen-treated rats. J Natl Cancer Inst 40:1287.

Blair PB, DeOme KB (1961). Mammary tumor development in transplanted hyperplastic alveolar nodules of the mouse. Proc Soc Exp Biol Med 108:289.

Boone CW (1975). Malignant henangioendotheliomas produced by subcutaneous inoculation of BALB/3T3 cells attached to glass beads. Science 188:68.

Boone CW, Jacobs JB (1976). Sarcomas routinely produced from putatively nontumorigenic BALB/3T3 and C3H/10T-1/2 cells by subcutaneous inoculation attached to plastic platelets. J Supramol Struct 5:131.

Boutwell RK (1964). Some biological aspects of skin carcinogenesis. Prog. Exp. Tumor Res. 4:207.

Cameron AM, Faulkin LJ Jr (1971). Hyperplastic and inflammatory nodules in the canine mammary gland. J Natl Cancer Inst 47:1277.

Cardiff RD, Wellings SR, Faulkin LJ Jr (1977). Biology of breast neoplasia. Cancer 39:2734.

Chang EH, Furth ME, Scolnick EM, Lowy DR (1982). Tumorigenic transformation of mammalian cells induced by a normal human gene homologous to the oncogene of Harvey murine sarcoma virus. Nature 297:479.

Cifone MA, Fidler IJ (1981). Increasing metastatic potential is associated with increasing genetic instability of clones isolated from murine neoplasms. Proc Natl Acad Sci USA 78:6949.

Colburn NH, Vorder Bruegge WF, Bates J, Yuspa SH (1978). Epidermal cell transformation in vitro. In Slaga TJ, Sivak A, Boutwell RK (eds): "Mechanisms of Tumor Promotion and Cocarcinogenesis," New York, Raven Press, p. 257.

DeOme KB, Faulkin LJ Jr, Bern HA, Blair PB (1959). Development of mammary tumors from hyperplastic alveolar nodules transplanted into gland-free mammary fat pads of female C3H mice. Cancer Res 19:515.

DeOme KB, Miyamoto MJ, Osborn RC, Guzman RC, Lum K (1978a). Detection of inapparent nodule-transformed cells in the mammary gland tissues of virgin female BALB/C3H mice. Cancer Res 38:2102.

DeOme KB, Miyamoto MJ, Osborn RC, Guzman RC, Lum K (1978b). Effects of parity on recovery of inapparent nodule-transformed mammary gland cells in vivo. Cancer Res 38:4050.

Ethier SP, Ulbrich RL (1982). Detection of ductal dysplasia in mammary outgrowths derived from carcinogen-treated virgin female BALB/c mice. Cancer Res 42:1753.

Faulkin LJ Jr (1966). Hyperplastic lesions of mouse mammary glands after treatment with 3-methylcholanthrene. J Natl Cancer Inst 36:289.

Guzman RC, Osborn RC, DeOme KB (1981). Recovery of transformed nodule and ductal mammary cells from carcinogen-treated C57BL mice. Cancer Res 41:1808.

Haslam SZ, Bern HA (1977). Histopathogenesis of DMBA-induced rat mammary tumors. Proc Natl Acad Sci USA 74:4020.

Hennings H, Michael D, Cheng C, Steinert P, Holbrook K, Yuspa SH (1980). Calcium regulation of growth and differentiation of mouse epidermal cells in culture. Cell 19:245.

Hosick HL, Anderson LW, Angello JC, Danielson KG (1980). Properties that distinguish tumorigenic mammary cells: A cell line approach. In McGrath CM, Brennan MJ, Rich MA (eds): " Cell Biology of Breast Cancer," New York: Academic Press, p 393.

Jensen HM, Rice JR, Wellings SR (1976). Preneoplastic lesions in the human breast. Science 191:295.

Kulesz-Martin MF, Koehler B, Hennings H, Yuspa SH (1980). Quantitative assay for carcinogen altered differentiation in mouse epidermal cells. Carcinogenesis 1:995.

MacKenzie I, Rous P (1941). The experimental disclosure of latent neoplastic changes in tarred skin. J Exp Med 73:391.

Marchok AC, Rhoton JC, Griesemer RA, Nettesheim P (1977). Increased in vitro growth capacity of tracheal epithelium exposed in vivo to 7,12-dimethylbenzanthracene. Cancer Res 37:1811.

Marks F (1976). Epidermal growth control mechanisms, hyperplasia, and tumor promotion in the skin. Cancer Res 36:2636.

Maskens AP (1981). Confirmation of the two-step nature of chemical carcinogenesis in the rat colon adenocarcinoma model. Cancer 41:1240.

McGrath CM, Soule HD (1982). Resistance to terminal differentiation in precancerous mammary hyperplasia. Proc Am Assoc Cancer Res 23:229.

Medina D (1973). Preneoplastic lesions in mouse mammary tumorigenesis. Meth Cancer Res 7:3.

Medina D (1976). Mammary tumorigenesis in chemical carcinogen-treated mice. VI. Tumor-producing capabilities of mammary dysplasias in BALB/cCrgl mice. J Natl Cancer Inst 57:1185.

Medina D, Asch BB (1980). Cell markers for mouse mammary preneoplasias. In McGrath CM, Brennan MJ, Rich MA (eds): "Cell Biology of Breast Cancer," New York: Academic Press, p 363.

Medina D, DeOme KB (1970). Effects of various oncogenic agents on tumor-producing capabilities of series D BALB/c mammary nodule outgrowth lines. J Natl Cancer Inst 45:353.

Medina D, Oborn CJ, Asch BB (1980). Distinction between preneoplastic and neoplastic mammary cell populations by cytochalasin B-induced multinucleation. Cancer Res 40:329.

Medina D, Miller F, Oborn CJ, Asch BB (submitted for publication). Effects of selenium on cytoplasmic filaments and ultrastructural characteristics of mouse mammary epithelial cell lines.

Moolgavkar SH, Knudson AG Jr (1981). Mutation and cancer: A model for human carcinogenesis. J Natl Cancer Inst 66:1037.

Mordan LH, Bergin LM, Budnick JEL, Meegan RR, Bertram JS (1982). Isolation of methylcholanthrene "initiated" C3H/10T 1/2 cells by inhibiting neoplastic progression with retinyl acetate. Carcinogenesis 3:279.

Morris VL, Vlaschaert JE, Beard CL, Milazzo M, Bradaburg WC (1980). Mammary tumors from BALBc mice with a reported high mammary tumor incidence have acquired new mammary tumor virus DNA sequences. Virology 100:101.

Mottram JC (1944a). A developing factor in experimental blastogenesis. J Path Bact 56:181.

Mottram JC (1944b). A sensitizing factor in experimental blastogenesis. J Path Bact 5:391.

Nandi S (1963). New method for detection of mouse mamary tumor virus. I. Influence of foster nursing on incidence of hyperplastic mammary nodules in BALB/cCrgl mice. J Natl Cancer Inst 31:57.

Pall ML (1981). Gene-amplification model of carcinogenesis. Proc Natl Acad Sci USA 78:2465.

Parada LF, Tabin CJ, Shih C, Weinberg RA (1982). Human EJ bladder carcinoma oncogene is homologue of Harvey sarcoma virus ras gene. Nature 297:474.

Potter VR (1980). Initiation and promotion in cancer formation. The importance of studies on intercellular communication. Yale J Biol Med 53:367.

Potter VR (1981). A new protocol and its rationale for the study of initiation and promotion of carcinogenesis in rat liver. Carcinogenesis 2:1375.

Raick AN (1974). Cell differentiation and tumor promoting activity in skin carcinogenesis. Cancer Res 34:2915.

Roberts AB, Lamb LC, Newton DL, Sporn MB, DeLarco JE, Todaro GJ (1980). Transforming growth factors: Isolation of polypeptides from virally and chemically transformed cells by acid/ethanol extraction. Proc Natl Acad Sci USA 77:3494.

Rous P, Kidd JG (1941). Conditional neoplasms and sub-threshold neoplastic states: A study of the tar tumors of rabbits. J Exp Med 73:365.

Rovera G, O'Brien TG, Diamond L (1977). Tumor promoters inhibit spontaneous differentiation of Friend erythro-leukemia cells in culture. Proc Natl Acad Sci USA 74:2894.

Rozengurt E (1981). Stimulation of Na influx, Na-K pump activity and DNa synthesis in quiescent cultured cells. Adv Enz Reg 19:61.

Rubin H, Vidair C, Saniu H (1981). Restoration of normal appearance, growth behavior, and calcium content to transformed 3T3 cells by magnesium deprivation. Proc Natl Acad Sci USA 78:2350.

Russo J, Saby J, Isenberg WM, Russo I (1977). Pathogenesis of mammary carcinomas induced in rats by DMBA. J Natl Cancer Inst 59:435.

Salomon DS, Liotta LA, Kidwell WR (1981). Differential response to growth factor by rat mammary epithelium plated on different collagen substrata in serum-free medium. Proc Natl Acad Sci USA 78:382.

Sanford KK, Boone CW, Merwin RM, Jones GM, Garrison CU (1980). The plate-implant as a bioassay for the neo-plastic potential of cultured cells. Int J Cancer 25:509.

Schimke RT, Kaufman, RJ, Alt FW, Kellems RE (1978). Gene amplification and drug resistance in cultured murine cells. Science 202:1051.

Sinha D, Dao TL (1977). Hyperplastic alveolar nodules of the rat mammary gland: Tumor-producing capability in vivo and in vitro. Cancer Lett 2:153.

Smith GH, Vonderhar BK, Medina D (1982). Premalignant alveolar transformation of virgin mouse mamary gland results in differentiation-specific gene activity that is independent of hormonal induction or DNA synthesis in vitro. J Cell Biol (in press).

Smith JC, Singh JP, Lilliquist JS, Goon DS, Stiles CD (1982). Growth factors adherent to cell substrate are mitogenically active in situ. Nature 296:154.

Sonnenborn TM (1978). The origin, evolution, nature, and causes of aging. In Behnke JA, Finch CE, Moment GB (eds): "Biology of Aging," New York: Plenum Press, p. 361.

Supowit SC, Asch BB, Rosen JM (1980). Casein gene expression in normal and neoplastic mammary tissue. In McGrath CM, Brennan MJ, Rich MA (eds): "Cell Biology of Breast Cancer," New York: Academic Press, p. 247.

Swierenga SHH, Whitfield JF, Karasaki S (1978). Loss of proliferative calcium dependence: Simple in vitro indicator of tumorigencity. Proc Natl Acad Sci USA 75:6069.

Terzaghi M., Nettesheim P, Yarita T, Williams ML (1981). Epithelial focus assay for early detection of carcinogen-altered cells in various organs of rats exposed in situ to N-nitrosoheptamethyleneimine. JNCI 67:1057.

Tu A, Sivak A (1982). Comparison of oncogenic potential of carcinogen-induced transformed populations of BALB/c3T3 and C3H/10T 1/2 cells. Proc Am Assoc Cancer Res 23:295.

Varmus H (1982). Form and function of retroviral proviruses. Science 216:812.

Wellings SR, Jensen HM, Marcum RG (1975). An atlas of subgross pathology of the human breast with special reference to possible precancerous lesions. J Natl Cancer Inst 55:231.

Wicha MS, Lowrie G, Kohn E, Bagavandoss P, Mahn T (1982). Extracellular matrix promotes mammary epithelial growth and differentiation in vitro. Proc Natl Acad Sci USA 79:3213.

Wolff GL, Medina D, Umholtz RL (1979). Manifestation of hyperplastic alveolar nodules and mammary tumors in "viable yellow" and non-yellow mice. J Natl Cancer Inst 63:781.

Yuspa SH, Morgan DL (1981). Mouse skin cells resistant to terminal differentiation associated with initiation of carcinogenesis. Nature 293:72.

13th International Cancer Congress, Part B
Biology of Cancer (1), pages 205–218
© **1983 Alan R. Liss, Inc., 150 Fifth Avenue, New York, NY 10011**

MULTI-STAGE TUMOUR DEVELOPMENT IN THE URINARY BLADDER

R. Marian Hicks, Ph.D. D.Sc. FRCPath.

Professor, Experimental Pathology
School of Pathology
Middlesex Hospital Medical School
London W1P 7LD England

Bladder cancer is a prescribed industrial disease in
Great Britain (Somerville et al 1980) and it is accepted
that occupations involving exposure to certain aromatic
amines and carcinogenic dye-stuff intermediates can incur
high risk for bladder cancer (Hueper 1969, Davies et al 1976).
Prolonged exposure to 2-naphthylamine, benzidine or 4-amino-
diphenyl can cause bladder cancer but the majority of bladder
cancer patients have never been exposed to such industrial
chemicals and the aetiology of their disease is unknown
(UICC Report 1981). Other chemicals, including some chemotherapeutic agents (chlornaphazine and cyclophosphamide),
the analgesic phenacetin, artificial sweeteners (cyclamate
and saccharin), tryptophan metabolites, certain N-nitroso
compounds and a nitrofuran, are capable of elevating age-
related bladder cancer incidences in man and/or rodents.
Other less easily definable factors associated with excess
coffee drinking and hormonal status may also increase the
risk and there is a positive   dose-related association
between cigarette smoking and an increased risk of bladder
cancer (Cole et al 1971, Wynder and Goldsmith 1977, Stevens
and Moolgavkar 1979, Howe et al 1980). It is said that an
"average" consumption of cigarettes about doubles the
incidence of bladder cancer (Doll and Peto 1981) and, in
view of the size of the exposed population, cigarette
smoking may well be the major single "cause" of bladder
cancer in man.

It is experimentally demonstrable that bladder cancer
can develop either following exposure to a single genotoxic
carcinogen, or by a multi-stage process in response to the

cumulative effect of numerous factors, not all of which need
be carcinogenic per se (Hicks 1980, 1981, 1982a). This is
comparable to the response of mouse skin either to high doses
of a complete carcinogen or to a low "initiating" dose of
carcinogen followed by non-genotoxic "promoting" factors. In
skin, the nature of the tumour and the process of carcinogenesis elicited by high doses of solitary carcinogens are not
necessarily identical to those elicited by multiple factors
(Berenblum 1974). This appears to be true for the bladder
also (Hicks 1982b). The concept of multi-stage carcinogenesis involving discrete stages of initiation, promotion and
non-specific propagation was developed from studies on skin
models, using polycyclic hydrocarbon carcinogens and the
diterpene series of promoters present in croton oil
(Berenblum 1941, Friedenwald and Rous 1944, Boutwell 1964,
Hecker 1968). It is not yet clear whether every observation
made with the mouse skin model can be applied rigidly to
carcinogenesis in the bladder.

THE FIRST STAGE IN BLADDER CARCINOGENESIS; "INITIATION".

In the rat bladder, neoplastic change can be initiated
either by a single intravesicular instillation of a low dose
of N-methyl-N-nitrosourea (MNU) (Hicks et al 1975,1978a), or
by a few weeks treatment with low doses of N-butyl-N-(hydroxy-
butyl)nitrosamine (BBN) (Nakanishi et al 1980), or by feeding
N-(4-(5-nitro-2-furyl)-2-thiazolyl)formamide (FANFT) (Jacobs
et al 1977). Few animals treated with a low threshold dose
of carcinogen will develop bladder cancer unless also exposed
to a subsequent regime which will promote further change in
the initiated cells. In skin, the initiating event is
believed to involve a rapid interaction of the carcinogen
with the target cell DNA to produce a mutagenic change which
will persist more or less indefinitely (Berenblum 1974,
Scribner and Suss 1978). This may well prove to be substantially true for the bladder; thus after MNU treatment,
O^6-methylguanine accumulates and persists in rat urothelial
cell DNA (Cox and Irving 1977). However the rigid concept of
"permanence" may have to be modified for much carcinogen-
induced DNA damage is eliminated by enzymatic repair mechanisms (Roberts 1980). The degree of permanence of the initiating damage may vary depending on the exact nature of the
interaction between a specific carcinogen and the genome. In
the bladder there is some decay of initiation in the first
six weeks following treatment with initiating doses of FANFT

(Cohen et al 1979) whereas the initiating effect of MNU persists undiminished for up to at least 25 weeks (Hicks et al 1978a,Severs et al 1982).

THE SECOND STAGE IN BLADDER CARCINOGENESIS; "PROMOTION".

The second stage in multi-stage skin carcinogenesis is refered to as "promotion" and in that system the most extensively studied promoter has been 12-O-tetradecanoyl phorbol-13-acetate (TPA). Recently, however, incomplete first and second stage promoters have been identified in the mouse skin model, e.g. the calcium ionophore A23817 is an incomplete first stage promoter and mezerein a second stage promoter.

In experimental bladder cancer models several compounds have been identified which significantly increase the tumour incidence in bladders previously treated with a low threshold dose of carcinogen. Thus in the rat, sodium cyclamate after MNU (Hicks et al 1975) sodium saccharin after either MNU (Hicks et al 1975,1978a), or FANFT (Cohen et al 1979) or BBN (Nakanishi et al al 1980), phenacetin after BBN (Nakanishi et al 1978) tryptophan either after FANFT (Cohen et al 1979, Matsushima 1977) or in the dog after 4-amino-biphenyl and 2-naphthylamine (Radomski et al 1977) all act as late stage carcinogens and accelerate the development of transitional cell carcinoma in carcinogen-treated urothelia. Because these chemicals have the ability to increase the tumour yield above that produced by an "initiating" dose of carcinogen alone they have been regarded as promoters, i.e. second stage carcinogens in the bladder. The data to support this is far from unequivocal, for with one exception (Hicks et al 1975) the carcinogen was used not at a sub-threshold or initiating dose, but at a level sufficient to produce a few bladder cancers on its own. On the published evidence, therefore, these compounds could well be acting at a later stage than promotion.

The use of the term promoter for any tissue other than mouse skin is somewhat ambiguous. Unfortunately at present, even in the mouse skin there is no single specific marker which will unequivocally identify a second stage carcinogen (promoter) other than its ability or inability to function at a particular point in a strictly defined temporal sequence in a multi-stage process of carcinogenesis. Thus, one commonly used "marker" for promotion, increased ornithine decarboxylase (ODC) activity, may be induced in the mouse skin either by applications of complete carcinogens or by promoters such as TPA. Similarly in the rat bladder, ODC activity is induced in vivo by the carcinogen FANFT (Matsushima and Bryan 1980) and in vitro by MNU or metabolites of FANFT and BBN (Izumi et al 1981). ODC can also be induced in vitro by the "promoters" saccharin and 3-hydroxyanthranilic acid, a metabolite of tryptophan, and also by TPA; it is also induced by insulin and epidermal growth factor (Izumi et al 1981). Furthermore, ODC activity is inducible in vitro by unidenti-fied, heat-stable, filterable factors in rat urine which also have promoting and/or late-stage carcinogenic activity in the rat bladder (Oyasu et al 1980, Crissey et al 1980, Rowland et al 1980, Babaya et al 1982). Increased ODC activity and polyamine synthesis are probably markers for cell prolifer-ation rather than for second stage carcinogenesis and thus it is not surprising that they are also induced by other growth-promoting stimuli. In the liver, partial hepatectomy (Russell and McVicar 1971), in the salivary gland isoproter-enol (Inoue et al 1974), and in other organs growth-promoting hormones (Janne et al 1968, Cohen et al 1970, Pegg et al 1970) and epidermal growth factor (Stastny and Cohen 1970) all induce ODC activity and polyamine synthesis and at the same time produce hyperplasia.

In order to understand the biogenesis of cancer it will be necessary to identify the discrete biochemical events which characterise each sequential stage of carcinogenesis. In terms of identifying risk factors, however, if exposure to any factor increases the risk of developing bladder cancer and conversely if removal of that factor decreases the risk, it is largely irrelevant whether the agent happens to act predominantly at the second stage, i.e. as a promoter, or at one of the later stages in the carcinogenic process.

THE IMPORTANCE OF LATE-STAGE EVENTS IN INCREASING THE AGE-RELATED RISK FOR BLADDER CANCER

Recent investigations with experimental bladder cancer models have emphasised the over-riding importance of late-stage events in controlling the age-related prevalence of bladder cancer (Hicks et al 1980, Cohen et al 1982, Babaya et al 1982). The normal urothelium has a remarkably low rate of cell turnover. Even after exposure to carcinogens latent tumour cells (i.e. cells which have been both initiated and promoted by the carcinogen) can remain dormant for many years before their neoplastic potential is expressed as an autonomously growing cancer; the long latent period between exposure to a carcinogen and development of symptomatic bladder cancer has been well documented (e.g. Case, 1966). However, any factor, either chemical or physical, which increases the mitotic rate in the urothelium will cause both normal and latent tumour cells to divide, and if the latter have any growth advantage over their normal neighbours, will accelerate the differential development of the cancer. Thus, hyperplastic agents can act as late-stage carcinogens or propagating factors and reduce the latent period before histologically detectable or symptomatic cancers develop. If it is accepted that human bladders may contain undetectable foci of latent cancer cells produced by exposure to as yet unidentified environmental or endogenous carcinogens, then nearly all conflicting experimental and epidemiological data on the ability of diverse factors to "promote" bladder cancer can be explained in terms of increased cell turnover and acceleration of tumour growth. For example, high concentrations of dietary saccharin cause focal hyperplasia of the urothelium with increased numbers of cells entering into mitosis (Chowaniec and Hicks 1979). Contrary to a previous report (Cohen et al 1979) this was later confirmed by Fukushima and Cohen (1980) who observed an increased uptake of tritiated thymidine into focal areas of bladder urothelium in saccharin-treated rats. The ability of saccharin to act as bladder carcinogen per se, without prior initiation of the urothelium with any other genotoxic carcinogen, is itself greatly enhanced by hyperplastic agents (Cohen et al 1982). Vitamin A deficiency also increases the mitotic activity of basal cells of the urothelium and accelerates the rate of development of experimentally-induced rat bladder cancer (Wolbach and Howe 1925, Hicks 1968, 1969).

Another compound which may be added to the list of late-stage carcinogens in the bladder is methylmethanesulphonate (MMS). MMS (sc) produces tumours at the site of injection or (ip) in the nervous system in rats (Druckery et al 1970, Swann and Magee 1969). We have tested it both as a complete carcinogen and as a late-stage carcinogen in the rat bladder. The F344 rat was used and animals were given six intravesicular doses of 2.5mg MMS, either alone or after a low carcinogenic dose of MNU. Appropriate vehicle-treated controls and MNU-only treated animals were set up in parallel and the incidence at two years of macroscopically visible tumours is shown in the Table.

TABLE I: Effect of MMS on MNU-induced
bladder cancer in female F344 rats

Treatment (Intravesicular instillation)	Number of animals	Number of tumours*	Percent. incidence
1 x 0.3mg MNU	30	7	23
6 x 2.5mg MMS	32	2	6
1 x 0.3mg MNU + 6 x 2.5mg MMS	37	18	49
7 x vehicle only	27	0	0

*Macroscopic observations. Preliminary data from R.J. Tudor, N. Severs, S. Barnes and R.M. Hicks.

Final numbers may be modified after completion of all the histology, but these preliminary results demonstrate for the first time that MMS behaves on its own as a very weak complete bladder carcinogen, but is also capable of "promoting" the effect of MNU. This suggests that MMS has a weak first-stage but powerful late-stage carcinogenic potential for the urothelium. A similar conclusion was reached about 2-acetylaminofluorene (2-AAF) in the mouse bladder (Littlefield et al 1979). Both MMS and 2-AAF produce urothelial hyperplasia, and it is their hyperplastic action which is probably associated with their late-stage carcinogenic activity.

Another compound which may well behave like MMS and 2-AAF is cyclophosphamide (CP). Life-time treatment of rats with a high total dose of CP can produce a low incidence of bladder cancer; 1,270mg/kg bw produced 19% in male rats (Schmahl and Habs 1979). On the other hand, a total dose of 800mg/kg bw given twice weekly for 40 weeks was not carcinogenic on its own, but did increase the incidence of bladder cancer after pretreatment of the animals with FANFT (Arai et al 1977). This is consistent with CP, like 2-AAF and MMS, being a weak first-stage but more effective late-stage carcinogen. CP is cytotoxic for the urothelium and also causes severe atypical hyperplasia (Koss 1967, Chaves 1968, Locher and Cooper 1970). It is noteworthy that in most reports of CP-induced human bladder cancer, the patient already had neoplastic disease elsewhere in the body and

that CP was used frequently in conjunction with other cytotoxic and mutagenic therapeutic agents.

The role of calculi in the aetiology of bladder cancer
has been much debated and a direct causal role was claimed
(Clayson 1974). Mechanical irritation was implicated in
many of the earliest theories (e.g. Virchow 1863) but was
subsequently shown to be insufficient on its own to produce
cancer (Berenblum 1974). The effect of urinary calculi on
latent tumour cells in the urothelium is more comparable to
that of wounding on previously tarred rabbit ears (Mackenzie
and Rous 1941) or of irritant chemicals such as turpentine on
initiated and promoted skin (Boutwell 1964). Thus, in experimentally constructed rat bladder pouches exposed to urine,
tumour incidence was increased from 27% to 66% by inserting a
stone into the pouch (Chapman et al 1973). Since 27% of the
animals developed bladder cancer without the stone they had
probably been exposed already to an unidentified urine-borne
carcinogen. In this system, surgical trauma alone was enough
to produce reparative hyperplasia and accelerate carcinogenesis; the additional diffuse irritation caused by the stone
then accelerated still further neoplastic growth in the transformed urothelium.

Another illustration of the effect of irritation on the
prevalence of bladder cancer is seen in populations endemic-
ally exposed to Schistosoma haematobium infection. In most
parts of the World the peak incidence of bladder cancer is in
the sixth decade of life and only 12% of cases occur in people
under the age of 50. By contrast, in Egyptians infected with
S.haematobium the mean age of incidence of bilharzial bladder
cancer is 46 years old and 73% of cases occur below the age
of 50 (El-Bolkainy et al 1972, Aboul Nasr et al 1962). This
massive shift in the prevalence curve for bladder cancer towards a younger age group in Egypt can be attributed to the
late-stage carcinogenic effect of the S.haematobium ova on
the urothelium (Hicks et al 1978b, Hicks, 1982c). Using
another primate species, the baboon, we have been able to
demonstrate that S.haematobium infection will indeed act as a
late-stage carcinogen in animals also treated with low doses
of the bladder carcinogen, BBN.In the duration of the experiment, neither the S.haematobium infection alone nor the dose
of BBN used on its own produced bladder cancer, but in animals
exposed to both factors about half developed urothelial cancer
of the bladder and/or ureters (Hicks et al 1980). It has to

be assumed that the S.haematobium infected Egyptian population
at high risk for bladder cancer must also be exposed to low
doses of some first-stage, initiating carcinogen. Undoubtedly, many of them are exposed to low doses of N-nitroso
compounds formed in the urine by bacteria capable of reducing
urinary nitrate to nitrite and then nitrosating secondary
amine precursors also present in the urine (Hicks et al 1978b,
1982, Hicks 1982c). In this population the widespread urothelial damage and consequent increase in cell turnover
caused by the schistosomiasis is apparently sufficient to
accelerate carcinogenesis. The accelerating effect of the
schistosomiasis then results in the development of symptomatic
bladder cancer at an age when, in the absence of the infection, the individuals concerned should be in their prime. The
high mortality from bladder cancer in S.haematobium infected
people demonstrates very clearly the effect that late-stage
as opposed to early-stage carcinogens can have on prevalence
rates for human cancers.

CONCLUSIONS

     Multi-stage carcinogenesis in the urinary bladder
provides a unifying theory which satisfactorily accommodates
most experimental and epidemiological evidence for a multifactorial aetiology for bladder cancer. As Doll and Peto
(1981) emphasise, if cells have to experience both early and
late events before cancer can develop, then elimination of
exposure to either early or late carcinogens will reduce the
eventual risk of cancer, and the only determinant of which is
more "important" is which is more easily avoided. With the
mouse skin model it has been possible to separate late-stage
carcinogens into second-stage promoters and propagators which
act at later stages. In the bladder, no such rigid distinction can be made as yet, although available evidence suggests
that saccharin and perhaps some other compounds may act at an
earlier stage than those factors which simply cause reparative hyperplasia. All late-stage factors have the potential
to accelerate tumour development and thus lower the age at
which cancer becomes symptomatic. It is therefore just as
important to reduce exposure to late-stage carcinogens as to
avoid exposure to first stage genotoxic carcinogens. Indeed,
in terms of human cancer prevalence, the removal of exposure
to late-stage factors has a more immediate effect on the
subsequent relative risk of developing cancer than does
removal of exposure to initiating carcinogens (Day and Brown

1980, Doll and Peto 1981).

Recognition that carcinogenesis is a multi-stage process has a bearing on all aspects of bladder cancer including its aetiology, biology, clinical progress and treatment. Because even brief exposure to a low dose of a first-stage carcinogen can theoretically initiate the process, there is no such thing as a "safe" dose for a genotoxic carcinogen below which there is no effect. Because local irritation can accelerate the development of symptomatic cancer in a bladder previously exposed to such a carcinogen, indwelling catheters, repeat biopsies of the tissue, the presence of urinary calculi or use of drugs such as CP which are cytotoxic for the urothelium may lead to unexpected complications. On the other hand, the fact that various stages may be involved in the development of this frequently fatal cancer, opens the way for new treatment modalities designed to prevent or delay specific stages in neoplastic progression. Chemoprevention of bladder cancer by the use of retinoids and non-steroidal anti-inflammatory agents which can theoretically antagonise the effect of some late-stage factors is now being investigated.

Most of this work was made possible by generous support over many years from the British Cancer Research Campaign.

REFERENCES

Aboul Nasr AL, Gazayerli RM, Fawzi RM, and El-Sebai I (1962). Epidemiology and pathology of cancer of the bladder in Egypt. Acta Un Int Cancer 18:528.
Arai M, Cohen SM and Friedell GH (1977). Promoting effect of cyclophosphamide (CP) following initiation by N-(4-(5-nitro-2-furyl)-2-thiazolyl)formamide (FANFT). Proc Jp Cancer Ass 36th Ann Meeting Tokyo p 39. Pub as supplement to Gann. Tokyo:Jp Cancer Ass.
Babaya K, Miyata Y, Chmiel JS, and Oyasu R (1982). Effects of rat urine fractionated by molecular weight on urinary bladder carcinogenesis. Cancer Res 42:15.
Berenblum I (1941). The mechanism of carcinogenesis: A study of the significance of co-carcinogenic action and related phenomena. Cancer Res 1:807.
Berenblum I (1974). Carcinogenesis as a biological problem. Amsterdam: North Holland.

Boutwell RK (1964). Some biological aspects of skin carcinogenesis. Prog Exp Tumor Res 4:207.

Case RAM (1966). Tumours of the urinary tract as an occupational disease in several industries. Ann Roy Coll Surg Engl 39:213.

Chapman WH, Kirschheim D, McRoberts JW (1973). Effect of the urine and calculus formation on the incidence of bladder tumours in rats implanted with paraffin wax pellets. Cancer Res 33:1225.

Chaves E (1968). Induction of bladder hyperplasia in rats after a single dose of cyclophosphamide. Rev Franc Etudes Clin Biol 13:56.

Chowaniec J, Hicks RM (1979). Response of the rat to saccharin with particular reference to the urinary bladder. Br J Cancer 39:355.

Clayson DB (1974). Bladder carcinogenesis in rats and mice: possibility of artefacts. J Natl Cancer Inst 52:1685.

Cohen S, O'Malley BW, Stastny M (1970). Estrogenic induction of ornithine decarboxylase activity in vivo and in vitro. Science 170:336.

Cohen SM, Arai M, Jacobs JB, Friedell GH (1979). Promoting effect of saccharin and DL-tryptophan in urinary bladder carcinogenesis. Cancer Res 39:1207.

Cohen SM, Murasaki G, Fukushima S, Greenfield RE (1982). Effect of regenerative hyperplasia on the urinary bladder: carcinogenicity of sodium saccharin and N-(4-(5-nitro-2-furyl)-2-thiazolyl)formamide. Cancer Res 42:65.

Cole P, Monson RR, Haning H et al (1971). Smoking and cancer of the lower urinary tract. N Engl J Med 284:129.

Cox R, Irving CC (1977). Selective accumulation of O^6-methyl-guanine in DNA of rat bladder epithelium after intravesical administration of N-methyl-N-nitrosourea. Cancer Lett 3:265.

Crissey MM, Steele GD, Gittes RF (1980). Rat model for carcinogenesis in ureterosigmoidostomy. Science 207:1079.

Davies JM, Somerville SM, Wallace DM (1976). Occupational bladder tumour cases identified during ten years' interviewing of patients. Br J Urol 48:561.

Day NE, Brown CC (1980). Multistage models and primary prevention of cancer. J Natl Cancer Inst 64:977.

Doll R, Peto R (1981). The causes of cancer. J Natl Cancer Inst 66:1191.

Druckrey H, Kruse H, Preussmann R, Ivankovic S, Landschutz C (1970). Cancerogene alkylierende Substanzen. III. Alkyl-halogenide, -sulfate, -sulfonate und ringgenspannte Heterocyclen. Z Krebsforsch 74:241.

El-Bolkainy MN, Ghoneim MA, Mansour MA (1972). Carcinoma of the bilharzial bladder in Egypt; clinical and pathological features. Br J Urol 44:561.

Friedenwald WF, Rous P (1944). The initiating and promoting elements in tumor production. An analysis of the effects of tar, benzpyrene and methyl cholanthrene on rabbit skin. J Exp Med 80:101.

Fukushima S, Cohen SM (1980). Saccharin-induced hyperplasia of the rat urinary bladder. Cancer Res 40:734.

Hecker E (1968). Cocarcinogenic principles from the seed oil of Croton tiglium and from other Euphorbiaceae. Cancer Res 28:2338.

Hicks RM (1968). Hyperplasia and cornification of the transitional epithelium in the vitamin A-deficient rat. J Ultrastruct Res 22:206.

Hicks RM (1969). Nature of the keratohyalin granules in hyperplastic and cornified areas of transitional epithelium in the vitamin A-deficient rat. J Anat 104:327.

Hicks RM (1980). Multistage carcinogenesis in the urinary bladder. Br Med Bull 36:39.

Hicks RM (1981). Carcinogenesis in the urinary bladder: a multistage process. In Connolly JG (ed): "Carcinoma of the Bladder" New York: Raven Press, p 75.

Hicks RM (1982a). Promotion in bladder cancer. In Hecker E et al (eds): "Carcinogenesis, Vol. 7" New York: Raven Press, p 139.

Hicks RM (1982b). The scientific basis for regarding vitamin A and its analogues as anti-carcinogenic agents. Proc Nutr Soc. In press.

Hicks RM (1982c). Nitrosamines as possible aetiological agents in Bilharzial bladder cancer. In Magee PN (ed). "The Possible Role of Nitrosamines in Human Cancer". Cold Spring Harbor Laboratory, Banbury Report 13. In press.

Hicks RM, Wakefield J.St.J., Chowaniec J (1975). Evaluation of a new model to detect carcinogens and co-carcinogens: results obtained with saccharin, cyclamate and cyclophosphamide. Chem-Biol Interact 11:225.

Hicks RM, Chowaniec J, Wakefield J.St.J. (1978a). Experimental induction of bladder tumours by a two-stage system. In Slaga TJ, Sivak A, Boutwell RK (eds), "Carcinogenesis, Vol. 2" New York: Raven Press p 475.

Hicks RM, Gough TA, Walters CL (1978b). Demonstration of the presence of nitrosamines in human urine: preliminary observations on a possible aetiology for bladder cancer in association with chronic urinary tract infection. In Walker EA et al (eds) "Environmental Aspects of N-nitroso-compounds"IARC Scientific Pubs No 19 Lyon: IARC p465.

Hicks RM, James C, Webbe G (1980). Effect of Schistosoma haematobium and N-butyl-N-(4-hydroxybutyl)nitrosamine on the development of urothelial neoplasia in the baboon. Br J Cancer 42:730.

Hicks RM, Ismail MM, Walters CL, Beecham PT, Rabie MF, El-Alamy MA (1982). Association of bacteriuria and urinary nitrosamine formation with Schistosoma haematobium infection in the Qalyub area of Egypt. Trans Roy Soc Trop Med Hyg 76:(4) in press.

Howe GR, Burch JD, Miller AB et al (1980). Tobacco use, occupation, coffee, various nutrients and bladder cancer. J Natl Cancer Inst 64:701.

Hueper WC (1969). Occupational and Environmental Cancers of the Urinary System. New Haven and London: Yale University Press.

Inoue H, Tanioka H, Shiba K, Asada A, Kato Y, Takeda Y (1974). Effect of isoproterenol on polyamine metabolism in mouse salivary glands. J. Biochem (Tokyo) 75:679.

Izumi K, Hirao Y, Hopp L, Oyasu R (1981). In vitro induction of ornithine decarboxylase in urinary bladder carcinoma cells. Cancer Res 41:405.

Jacobs JB, Arai M, Cohen SM, Friedell GH (1977). A long-term study of reversible and progressive urinary bladder cancer lesions in rats fed N-(4-(5-nitro-2-furyl)-2-thiazolyl) formamide. Cancer Res 37:2817.

Janne J, Raina A, Simes M (1968). Mechanism of stimulation of polyamine synthesis by growth hormone in rat liver. Biochim Biophys Acta 166:419.

Koss LG (1967). A light and electron microscopic study on the effects of a single dose of cyclophosphamide on various organs of the rat. 1. The urinary bladder. Lab Invest 16:44.

Littlefield NA, Greenman DL, Farmer JH, Sheldon WG (1979). Effects of continuous and discontinued exposure to 2-AAF on urinary bladder hyperplasia and neoplasia. J Environ Pathol Toxicol 3:35.

Locher GW, Cooper EH (1970). Repair of rat urinary bladder epithelium following injury by cyclophosphamide. Invest Urol 8:116.

MacKenzie I, Rous P (1941). Experimental disclosure of latent neoplastic changes in tarred skin. J Exp Med 73:391.

Matsushima M (1977). The role of the promoter L-tryptophan on tumorigenesis in the urinary bladder. 2. Urinary bladder carcinogenicity of FANFT (initiating factor) and L-tryptophan (promoting factor) in mice. Jpn J Urol 68:731.

Matsushima M, Bryan GT (1980). Early induction of mouse urinary bladder ornithine decarboxylase activity by rodent vesical carcinogens. Cancer Res 40:1897.

Nakanishi K, Fukushima S, Shibata M, Shirai T, Ogiso T, Ito, N (1978). Effects of phenacitine and caffeine on the urinary bladder of rats treated with N-butyl-N-(4-hydroxy-butyl)nitrosamine. Gann 69:395.

Nakanishi K, Hagiwara A, Shibata M, Imalda K, Tatematsu M, Ito N (1980). Dose response of saccharin in induction of urinary bladder hyperplasia in Fischer 344 rats pre-treated with N-butyl-N-(4-hydroxybutyl)nitrosamine. J Natl Cancer Inst 65:1005.

Oyasu R, Hirao Y, Izumi K (1980). Promotion by urine of urinary bladder carcinogenesis. Proc Am Ass Cancer Res 21:70.

Pegg AE, Lockwood DH, Williams-Ashman HG (1970). Concentrations of putrescine and polyamines and their enzymic synthesis during androgen-induced prostatic growth. Biochem J 117:17.

Radomski JL, Radomski T, MacDonald WE (1977). Carcinogenic interaction between DL-tryptophan and 4-aminobiphenyl or 2-naphthylamine in dogs. J Natl Cancer Inst 58:1831.

Roberts JJ (1980). Carcinogen-induced DNA damage and its repair. Br Med Bull 36:25.

Rowland RG, Henneberry MO, Oyasu R, Grayhack JT (1980). Effects of urine and continued exposure to carcinogen on progression of early neoplastic urinary bladder lesions. Cancer Res. 40: 4524.

Russell DH, McVicker TA (1971). Polyamine metabolism in mouse liver after partial hepatectomy. Biochim Biophys Acta 244:85.

Schmähl D, Habs M (1979). Carcinogenic action of low-dose cyclophosphamide given orally to Sprague-Dawley rats in a life-time experiment. Int J Cancer 23:706.

Scribner JD, Suss R (1978). Tumour initiation and promotion. Int Rev Exp Pathol 18:137.

Severs NJ, Barnes SH, Wright R, Hicks RM (1982). Induction of bladder cancer in rats by fractionated intravesicular doses of N-methyl-N-nitrosourea. Br J Cancer 45:337.

Somerville SM, Davies JM, Hendry WF, Williams G (1980). Bladder cancer as a prescribed industrial disease: A guide for clinicians. Br Med J 280:540.

Stastny M, Cohen S (1970). Epidermal growth factor. IV. The induction of ornithine decarboxylase. Biochim Biophys Acta 204:578.

Stevens RG, Moolgavkar SH (1979). Estimation of relative risk from vital data: smoking and cancers of the lung and bladder. J Natl Cancer Inst 63:1351.

Swann PF, Magee PN (1969). Induction of rat kidney tumours by ethylmethanesulphonate and nervous tissue tumours by methylmethanesulphonate and ethylmethanesulphonate. Nature 223:947.

UICC Technical Report Series (1981). Vol. 60. Bladder Cancer. Skrabanek P, Walsh A (eds) Geneva: International Union Against Cancer.

Virchow R (1863). Die Krankhaften Geschwülste. Berlin: Hirschwald.

Wolbach SB, Howe PR (1925). Tissue changes following deprivation of fat-soluble A vitamin. J Exp Med 42:753.

Wynder EL, Goldsmith R (1977). The epidemiology of bladder cancer: a second look. Cancer 40:1246.

13th International Cancer Congress, Part B
Biology of Cancer (1), pages 219-238
© 1983 Alan R. Liss, Inc., 150 Fifth Avenue, New York, NY 10011

MULTISTAGE TUMOR DEVELOPMENT IN THE HUMAN ESOPHAGUS – the
first identification of cocarcinogens of the tumor promoter type as principal carcinogenic risk factors in a local
life style cancer

E. HECKER [*)]+), D. LUTZ +), J. WEBER +),
K. GOERTTLER ++), and J.F. MORTON +++)
+) Institute of Biochemistry and ++) Experimental
Pathology, German Cancer Research Center, D-6900
Heidelberg, FRG and +++) Morton Collectanea,
Univ. of Miami, Coral Gables, FL 33124, USA

SUMMARY. An experimental analysis is described which demonstrates that the epidemiologically established high rate of
esophageal cancer among blacks and creoles in Curacao most
likely is the result of a multistage process involving
initiators and promoters. As part of local lifestyle, the
group at risk utilizes for various purposes plant parts of
an indigenous bush Croton flavens L. ("Welensali"). Moreover they consume, as an everyday beverage, a "bush tea"
made from the leaves of the bush. The roots, leaves and tea
are shown to contain a multitude of irritant croton factors
which are characterized as diterpene esters of the tigliane
type. In mouse skin these exhibit strong promoting activity
comparable to that of TPA. As the latter, also the croton
factors isolated, show no solitary carcinogenic activity.
One cup of Welensali tea contains the equivalent of about
12-times the irritant dose of croton factor F_1; in addition, the equivalent of about 1.4-times the irritant dose
50 of the corresponding "cryptic" promoter F_1-20-decanoate
is present. These amounts are considered sufficient to maintain chronic irritation of the esophagus as an important
element of co-carcinogenesis, especially of tumor promotion.
Also, persons at risk in Curacao have been exposed at times
previously to certain initiators. Mice treated by an initia-
tion/promotion protocol with DMBA (or other initiators) and
TPA develop tumors of the forestomach. Therefore, esophageal cancer on Curacao may be considered the first case for
cocarcinogens of the tumor promoter type being principal
risk factors in a life style cancer.
*) Dedicated to Prof.Dr.rer.nat.Dr.med.h.c. Otto Westphal,
Vorsitzender des Stiftungsvorstands, Deutsches Krebsforschungszentrum, on the occasion of his 70th birthday.

INTRODUCTION

Numerous clinical, experimental and epidemiologic investigations indicate that, in the etiology of human cancer,
as CAUSATIVE AGENTS certain risk factors of the environment
play an important role. Moreover, the participation of endogenous factors, well established in the generation of certain cancers, demonstrates that in processes of carcinogenesis, in addition to the impact of the ENVIRONMENT, contributions of the INDIVIDUAL HOST, such as genetic susceptibility, hormonal influences etc. also have to be considered. Therefore, carcinogenesis of animals and human beings
is a highly interactive system with a considerable degree
of complexity (Hecker 1981a).

In animal experiments to date over 700 exogenous SOLI-
TARY CARCINOGENS have been detected (for terminology used
see Hecker 1981a,b). Of these, by the WHO International
Agency for Research on Cancer (IARC), about 30 have been
identified conclusively as CARCINOGENIC RISK FACTORS in the
generation of HUMAN CANCERS (Tomatis et al. 1978). For example, in established etiologic model situations such as
occupational and iatrogenic exposures, clearly solitary carcinogens are involved representing one principal class of
well defined carcinogenic risk factors. The existence in
carcinogenesis of a second and different principal class of
defined risk factors, of so-called "CO-CARCINOGENS", has
been established by animal experiments in the last 15 years:
The discovery in Euphorbiaceae (and Thymelaeaceae) of polyfunctional diterpene esters exhibiting strong irritant activities in many animal tissues and the concommittant development of assay-monitored isolation techniques as well
as of methods of determination of chemical structures of
complex molecules revealed the first highly active physico-
chemically and biologically well defined cocarcinogens especially of the initiation(or tumor) promoter type (Hecker
1968, 1972, 1978, 1981b; van Duuren 1969). This new class
of defined risk factors has given a new dimension to the
investigation of the biochemical mechanisms involved in
carcinogenesis at the tissue, the cell and the molecular
levels (e.g. Hecker et al. 1982) and to the assessment of
exogenous risk factors in carcinogenesis (Hecker 1981b). The
issue of co-carcinogenesis has been taken up also by epidemiologists, especially with respect to "life style cancers" (e.g. Wynder and Hoffmann 1979, Higginson 1979,
Hirayama 1981). Yet, complete experimental analyses of
etiologic model situations of human cancers in terms of cocarcinogenesis, especially of the initiation/promotion type,

employing well defined the risk factors suspicious to be involved, were lacking up until recently (Hecker 1981b, Cheng et al. 1982).

CANCER OF THE ESOPHAGUS - THE CURACAO CASE AND ETIOLOGIC HYPOTHESES

The incidence of esophageal cancer varies considerably all over the world as established by descriptive epidemiological investigations (Waterhouse et al. 1976). Regions with particular high incidence rates are located, for example, in Japan, northern China, Iran, southern Africa, northern France and in middle America (Caribbean region) especially on Curacao (table 1). The latter region provides an almost ideal etiologic model situation for epidemiologic investigations (Hartz 1940, 1958; Eibergen 1961; Morton 1968 a,b).

Table 1

AGE-STANDARDIZED INCIDENCE RATES OF ESOPHAGEAL CARCINOMA IN PLACES OF THE CARIBBEAN REGION related to 100,000 of the European-, U.S.A.- and World-population

Region	Europe		U.S.A.		World		References
	♂	♀	♂	♀	♂	♀	
CURACAO[a]	32.3	19.4	-	-	21.2	12.9	de BOER, 1979
Aruba	b)	b)	b)	b)	b)	b)	MORTON, 1968a
Bonaire	c)	c)	c)	c)	c)	c)	de BOER, 1979
VENEZUELA							
Caracas	-	-	6.7	5.2	-	-	DUNHAM and BAILAR, 1968
Falcon,	d)	d)	d)	d)	d)	d)	MORTON, 1974
Coro							
PUERTO RICO	21.5	8.1	-	-	14.8	5.4	WATERHOUSE et al. 1976
CUBA	8.7	3.7	-	-	5.7	2.4	" "
JAMAICA							
Kingston	13.4	6.6	-	-	9.1	4.7	" "

a) Data refer to Netherland Antilles (Aruba, Curacao, Bonaire, St.Maarten, Saba, St.Eustatius) without Aruba and cover the period of 1962-1973. 90% of these islands population live in Curacao.
b) In the period between 1963-1966, 5 male and 2 female patients out of a population of about 60,000 suffered from esophageal carcinoma.
c) For the island of Bonaire no secured statistical data are available.
d) Approximately 15 esophageal carcinoma in 28 months out of a population of about 45,000.

Thus, for the period of 1962-1973, carefully registered autopsies at St. Elizabeth, the only hospital on Curacao, revealed that the island, with its black/creole and mostly poor population, exhibits one of the highest rates of esophageal cancer in the Caribbean region of central America (see table 1) and in the world. The sex ratio appears to be controversial (about 2:1 - see table 1; about 1:1 - Eibergen 1961; O'Gara 1968). Recently, for the Nether-

lands Antilles follow-up data were presented (Freni and
Freni-Titulaer 1981) indicating for 1974-1979 a slight decrease in the incidence rates described previously for Curacao while the sex ratio remains essentially unchanged.

In trials to analyse this "Curacao case" by interviewing many individuals from the Netherlands Antilles and
neighbouring regions, it was brought to light that people
on the island use, in everyday life particularly for folk
medicine and for beverages, preferably plant preparations
made up from many local plants. The most frequently used
23 species were specified and the hypothesis was postulated
that unknown carcinogenic risk factors originating from
some of these plants would be responsible for the high rate
of esophageal cancer (Morton 1968a,b). Consequently, in experimental animals, extracts of 22 of the most frequently
used plants were tested: Solitary carcinogenic activity
was found associated with Heliotropum angiospermum, Annona
muricata, Krameria ixina, Acacia villosa and Melochia to-
mentosa. These findings were interpreted in support of a
SOLITARY CARCINOGEN HYPOTHESIS of esophageal cancer on Curacao (O'Gara 1968, O'Gara et al. 1971, 1974; Dunham et al.
1974). More specifically, in the case of the last three
botanically unrelated plant species, their contents of condensed tannins was associated with the high risk of esophageal cancer (Morton 1970, 1972, 1979).

A general correlation between chronic irritation (including inflammation) and cancer was pointed out by clinicians at the beginning of this century (R. Virchow). Nowa-
days it may be associated preferably with co-carcinogenic,
especially promoting activities (e.g. Hecker 1972, 1981b).
In the Curacao case, such a correlation is supported strongly by the autopsies recorded at St. Elizabeth: especially
in patients above the age of 50, and without manifested cancer, the esophagus frequently showed severe chronic inflammation (Hartz 1958). Therefore, seemingly, the local situation implicates an important element of a COCARCINOGEN HYPO-
THESIS of esophageal cancer. This would require exposure(s)
to submanifestational doses of certain solitary carcinogen-
(s) as "initiator(s)" simultaneously with or followed by
chronic irritation (for terminology used see Hecker 1981
a,b). For example, as in other high risk esophageal cancer
regions, in the Curacao case the custom of eating meals as
hot as possible was considered to contribute to chronic
irritation of the esophagus (Eps 1970). However, detailed
investigation of habits in the Curacao case and also the
localization of cancer in the esophagus appear to exclude

this possibility. Yet, amongst the 23 plants utilized most frequently by people on Curacao are Croton flavens L. and Jatropha gossypifolia L. (Morton 1968a,b, 1971; Morton 1981) belonging to the family of the Euphorbiaceae of which many species contain strong irritants. Many, but not all of them, are well known to be highly active cocarcinogens on mouse back skin, especially of the initiation-promoter type (e.g. Hecker 1981b).

If tumors are developing from human tissue as a consequence of chronic exposure to irritant promoters, hypothetical "potential tumor cells" must have been generated by previous (or simultaneous) exposure of the target tissue to initiator(s) (Hecker 1978, 1981b). To account, in the Curacao case, for exposure to putative initiators – thus completing a cocarcinogen hypothesis – the idea was put forward that heavy contaminations of the drinking water of the island with petrol may have been a source of initiators in the past (Morton 1968b). Further, use of the tannin containing plant Krameria ixina (Morton 1974; Merino et al. 1980) or of other plants containing solitary carcinogenic activity may be correlated with initiation of esophageal and gastric cancer.

Our investigational program to clarify the possibility of Croton flavens and Jatropha gossypifolia containing defined irritant and cocarcinogenic risk factors (Hecker and Weber 1977) has been concluded with regard to Croton flavens recently (Lutz 1982). In this paper experimental evidence will be presented to show for the first time, that in an epidemiologically established geographic and ethnic situation of human life style cancer, well defined cocarcinogens of the initiation promoter type – combined with previous and/or simultaneous exposure to certain initiators – most likely represent principal environmental risk factors of cancer.

DITERPENE ESTER IRRITANTS OF CROTON FLAVENS INVOLVED AS CO-CARCINOGENS OF THE PROMOTER TYPE

Croton flavens, locally called "Welensali" (Morton 1971), is a bush two to six feet high, and grows abundantly on the Caribbean islands as well as in southern Mexico and in northern South America (Morton 1971). On Curacao, several parts of this plant are utilized in everyday life to an extent which represents a means of chronic exposure: The roots of the bush are chewed for their stimulating effect and its aromatic green leaves and tips of young twigs are used to prepare, as a free or inexpensive everyday beverage, a "bush tea" ("Welensali tea", Brenneker 1961; Morton 1968 a). Occasionally the leaves of the bush are kept in the mouth as a counterirritant, used as a detergent to clean ovens and dishes, particularly after fish, and also as an insect repellent (Morton 1971).

1. Detection of irritant and promoting croton factors in roots and in fresh green leaves of "Welensali"; estimation of true minimum content

Chart 1

TYPICAL SCHEME OF FRACTIONATION OF ROOTS AND LEAVES OF CROTON FLAVENS L.

Extracts prepared from the plant parts, monitoring of fractionation by irritancy assay on the mouse ear for isolation of pure irritant Croton factors; estimation of their minimum total amount.

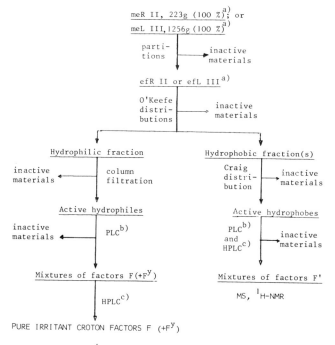

ROOTS: 17 Croton factors, F, F', minimum total amount: 1,4 % (of meR II);
LEAVES: 28 Croton factors, F, F', F^y, minimum total amount: 0,06 % (of meL III)

a) methanol extracts, ethyl acetate fractions, roots (R), leaves (L)
b) preparative layer chromatography
c) high performance liquid chromatography

Extracts of roots and of fresh green leaves of the plant, when tested in the standardized assay on the mouse ear (Hecker 1971; Hecker and Schmidt 1974) exhibit definite irritant activity, when compared to the already classical (Hecker 1968, van Duuren 1969) irritant cocarcinogen and initiation-promoter 12-O-tetradecanoylphorbol-13-acetate (TPA, croton oil factor A_1, see table 2). Moreover, in the standardized assay for promoters on the back skin of NMRI mice with 7,12-dimethylbenz(a)anthracene (DMBA) as initiator (Hecker 1971; Hecker and Schmidt 1974), the extracts of roots and leaves exhibit definite promoting activity, attributed to irritant "Croton flavens factors" (Hecker and Weber 1977; Lutz and Hecker 1979). - Remarkably, extracts of Croton flavens L. do not show solitary carcinogenic activity on the back skin of mice when assayed in the initiation/promotion protocol without initiator and at doses in which they otherwise are fully active as promoters (Lutz 1982). Also in other assays using mice, rats and hamsters (O'Gara 1968; O'Gara et al. 1971; Dunham et al. 1974) no solitary carcinogenic activity of Croton flavens extracts was observed.

Table 2

STRUCTURES AND IRRITANT ACTIVITIES OF FOUR CROTON FACTORS with R = OH/H TYPICAL FOR BOTH ROOTS AND LEAVES AS COMPARED TO CROTON OIL FACTOR A_1 (TPA) Irritant dose 50 (ID_{50}^{24}) in the standardized quantitative assay read 24 hs. after administration to the mouse ear, irritancy = $1/ID_{50}^{24}$ (I^{24}).

Parent alcohol	Factor (abbrev.)	R	R^1	R^2	R^3	ID_{50}^{24} [b] (nmoles)	I^{24} [b] $^{-1}$ (nmoles)	Activity type
Phorbol	A_1	HO-	$CH_3(CH_2)_{12}CO-$	H-	H-	0.016	63	F
16-hydroxy-phorbol	F_1 F_1-20-decanoate[a]	HO- HO-	$CH_3(CH_2)_{14}CO-$ $CH_3(CH_2)_{14}CO-$	HO- HO-	H- $CH_3(CH_2)_8CO-$	0.033 0.11	30 9	F F'
4-deoxy-16-hydroxy-phorbol	F_2 F_2-20-octanoate[a]	H- H-	$CH_3(CH_2)_{14}CO-$ $CH_3(CH_2)_{14}CO-$	HO- HO-	H- $CH_3(CH_2)_6CO-$	0.042 0.31	24 3	F F'

a) F_1-decanoate and F_2-20-octanoate are typical "CRYPTIC IRRITANTS" in contrast to the corresponding IRRITANTS F_1 and F_2 b) per mouse ear

To isolate and purify the irritant and promoting croton factors from the extracts as well as to estimate the
contents of roots and fresh green leaves, assay-monitored
fractionation schemes were developed using separation techniques such as counter current distribution and chromatographic methods, including high performance liquid chromatography (HPLC). All fractions generated were tested with
our standard assay for irritation. Derivatization and mostly high resolution spectroscopic methods (uv, ir, [1]H- nmr,
mass-spectroscopy) served in final chemical characterization of pure irritants. Thus, in both roots and leaves a
multitude of individual irritant croton factors was detected (chart 1). Chemically they were shown to be related to,
but not identical with, TPA (Hecker and Weber 1977; Lutz
and Hecker 1979; Lutz 1982).

Typical and more abundant irritants of roots and leaves are, for example, croton factors F_1 and F_2 (table 2).
They were identified as 12,13-diesters of the polyfunctional
diterpenes 16-hydroxy- and 4-deoxy-16-hydroxyphorbol, respectively. While somewhat different in chemical structure,
as irritants (table 2) and as promoters (fig.1) F_1 and F_2

Fig. 1

CO-CARCINOGENIC AS INITIATION PROMOTING ACTIVITY OF TYPICAL CROTON FACTORS
F_1, F_2 AND THEIR 20-DECANOATES IN THE STANDARDIZED ASSAY ON BACK SKIN OF
NMRI-MICE IN COMPARISON TO CROTON OIL FACTOR A_1 (TPA)

Initiator: DMBA, i = 100 nmol   28 females/group

Promoter: A_1, F_1 F_2 and 20-decanoates, solvent; doses p as indicated.
20-decanoates are "CRYPTIC PROMOTERS"

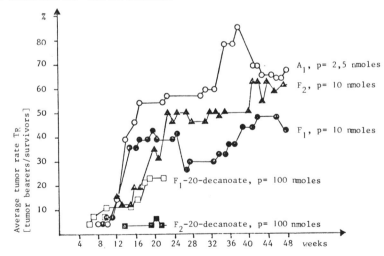

A_1, p= 2,5 nmoles

F_2, p= 10 nmoles

F_1, p= 10 nmoles

F_1-20-decanoate, p= 100 nmoles

F_2-20-decanoate, p= 100 nmoles

Average tumor rate Tr [tumor bearers/survivors]

are both almost as active as TPA. Yet, F_1 and F_2 represent
- together with the rest of the 12,13-diesters contained in
roots and leaves (see chart 1) - one activity type of the
croton factors of this plant, generally called ACTIVITY
TYPE F (table 2). A further ACTIVITY TYPE designated F' is
represented by 12,13,20-triesters e.g. by the F_1-20-decano-
ate or F_2-20-octanoate (table 2). They are considered biochemically as "cryptic" irritants and promoters (Hecker 1981
b): per se they are definitely less active than the corresponding croton factors F_1 and F_2 (table 2, fig.1). However,
during exposure of tissues to the low activity type F' factors, due to their particular 20-ester group, they may be
activated metabolically by esterases or lipases in releasing
the corresponding high activity 12,13-diesters, e.g. F_1 and
F_2. As a source of highly active promoters difficult to detect by biological assay, activity types F' deserve particular attention ("cryptic" co-carcinogenic risk factors, e.g.
Hecker 1981b). From extracts of leaves, but not from roots,
besides the two groups of activity type F and F' croton
factors, a third group F^y was isolated (chart 1) in very
low amount. Also, their irritancy is even lower than that
of the activity type F'. Group F^y comprises 12,13,16-tri-
esters of 16-hydroxyphorbol. Due to lack of material they
could not be identified much further. - As already shown for
the extracts from roots and leaves, also the croton factors
F_1 and F_2 isolated from them, as well as their corresponding cryptic types, proved inactive on mouse back skin when
assayed for solitary carcinogenic activity in the promotional protocol without initiator and at doses p identical
with those shown in fig.1 (data not shown).

In assay-monitored extractions of materials and subsequent fractionations such as described in chart 1, the yield
of pure factors determined by isolation of the biologically
active entities represents the minimum total amount of these
factors contained in the materials. In the methanol extract
of ROOTS, a total of 17 irritant croton factors of activity
types F and F' was detected (minimum total amount: 1.4 % of
meR II, see chart 1). Similarly, the methanol extract of
FRESH GREEN LEAVES contained a total of 28 croton factors
of activity types F, F'and F^y (minimum total amount: 0.06 %
of meL III, see chart 1). Of these, group F^y with eight
factors and a minimum total amount of 0.009 % of meL III is
neglegiable. The minimum total amount of factors thus determined may or may not be identical with the true minimum
content of factors in the materials extracted, depending
essentially on the chemical stability of the factors and the

efficiency of the procedures used as regards minimizing loss of irritant activity in extraction of the plant materials and in their fractionation (chart 1). In the present case, the minimum total amounts of activity types F and F' in roots and leaves as determined (chart 1) may be considered defacto a reliable estimation of the true minimum contents of these plant parts. They are: 0.32 ^{o}/oo croton factors F and F' in the roots and 0.04 ^{o}/oo croton factors F, F' and F^{y} in the fresh green leaves.

2. Detection of irritant and promoting croton factors in "Welensali tea"; estimation of true minimum content

The know-how developed in analysing the roots and the leaves of Welensali enabled us to also investigate that preparation from Croton flavens consumed most frequently on Curacao i.e. Welensali tea. About 400 l of a tea concentrate were prepared on the Caribbean island according to the local recipe, using 10 times the usual amount (4 g) of fresh

Chart 2

TYPICAL SCHEME OF FRACTIONATION OF WELENSALI TEA
168 l batch IIa of tea concentrate prepared from fresh leaves without flowers according to local recipe, preparation of ethyl acetate fraction and monitoring of fractionation by irritancy assay on mouse ear for isolation of pure Croton factors; estimation of their minimum total amount

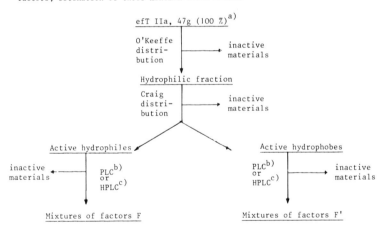

6 Croton factors F and F', minimum total amount: 0,001 % and 0,002 % of mixtures F and F', respectively. i.e. total of 0.003 % corresponding to 0,75 ppb in Welensali tea as used on Curacao.

---

a) ethyl acetate fraction tea concentrate IIa
b) preparative layer chromatography
c) high performance liquid chromatography

green leaves per cup (about 240 ml). Of a typical 168 l batch IIa of the tea concentrate, corresponding to 1930 l tea as consumed on Curacao, the ethyl acetate fraction efT was prepared. According to previous experience such fraction could be expected to contain all Welensali factors which possibly might be extracted from the leaves during brewing of the tea. In fraction efT IIa, by careful assay-monitored fractionation, two mixtures of three croton factors type F and F', respectively, were detected (chart 2). Together they represent a minimum total amount of 0.003 % in efT IIa, corresponding to 0.75 ppb in Welensali tea as consumed in Curacao (chart 2).

The mixture of ACTIVITY TYPES F isolated was found to contain the croton factors F_1, F_3 and F_5 (table 3, minimum total amount 0.001 %). The mixture of ACTIVITY TYPES F' contains F_1-20-octanoate and F_1- and F_3-20-decanoates (minimum total amount 0.002 %, table 3). F^y types, occuring

Table 3

ESTIMATION OF THE TRUE MINIMUM CONTENTS OF DITERPENE ESTER ACTIVITY TYPES F AND F' CONTAINED IN ONE CUP OF WELENSALI TEA FROM THEIR MINIMUM TOTAL AMOUNTS DETERMINED

Structural types identified	Activity types	Minimum total amounts determined a)			True minimum contents estimated b)		
		relative (%)	absolute (μg)	ratio F/F'	in 193 l (μg)	in 1 cup (μg)	ratio F/F'
F_1, F_3, F_5	F	0.001	500		2090	0,27	
				0.5/1			2.2/1
F_1-20-octanoate F_1-20-decanoate F_3-20-decanoate	F'	0.002	950		950	0.12	

a) from efT IIa of 168 l batch of Welensali tea
b) calculated for 1930 l tea as used on Curacao, local recipe: 4g of fresh leaves/ cup of about 240 ml

in the leaves, were not detected in the tea concentrate. Also, it is interesting to see that all of the six croton factors identified are esters of 16-hydroxyphorbol (no esters of 4-deoxy-16-hydroxyphorbol). The esters of 16-hydroxyphorbol represent the more hydrophilic and, referring to the tea brewing procedure, obviously also the more stable entities of all the 28 croton factors contained in the leaves (see chart 1).

In terms of quantities, the minimum total amounts of the croton factors found in the tea concentrate can hardly

be expected to correspond to the amounts found in the methanol extract of the leaves. However, it may be assumed
that the ratio of the minimum total amounts of activity
types F/F' as determined in leaves (i.e. F/F' = 2.2/1,
table 3) and that determined in tea (i.e. F/F' = 0.5/1)
should be about identical. Based on this assumption, the
ratio F/F' found for the tea concentrate (table 3) indicates that isolation of the F-types from it is less efficient than that of the corresponding cryptic types. This
may be attributed to the high content of hydrophilic contaminations in the tea concentrate (as an aqueous preparation, in contrast to the methanolic extract of leaves).
As experienced during fractionation they complicate the
isolation of F-types which are more hydrophilic than the
corresponding F'-types. Therefore, the true minimum content
of croton factors F in the tea in fact may be higher than
the minimum total amount determined in efT IIa (0.001 %,
table 3). For a realistic estimation of the true minimum
content of F-types in the tea, the minimum total amount in
the tea concentrate of the easier to isolate F'-factors
may be taken as an internal standard in correcting the
amount of F-factors isolated to meet the ratio F/F' found
in leaves. Hence, as compared to the 950 μg of activity
types F' isolated the estimated true minimum content of
ACTIVITY TYPE F amounts to 2090 μg in the tea concentrate
(see table 3). The estimated true minimum content of croton
factors in one cup of tea as used on Curacao may be calculated to be 0.27 μg of the mixture of F types and 0.12 μg
of the mixture of F' types, ratio 2.2 : 1 (table 3). This
corresponds to an estimated true minimum content of croton
factors of 1.6 ppb in the tea as compared to the minimum
total amount determined of 0.75 ppb (see above).

3. Biological relevance of the estimated true minimum content of croton factors present in "Welensali"

   Individual croton factors contained in the mixtures of
activity types F and of F', respectively, exhibit comparable
irritant and promoting activities in mouse skin. Therefore,
the biological activities of the mixtures of croton factors
F and F' isolated from the tea may be represented by one of
their prototypes, e.g. by the croton factors F_1 and F_1-20-
decanoate, respectively for which irritant (table 2) and
promoting (fig.1) doses have been determined. Such data
allow judgement of the biological relevance of the contents
of activity types F and F' present in one cup of the tea as
consumed on Curacao. As may be seen from table 4, in one

Table 4

COMPARISON OF TRUE MINIMUM CONTENT OF DITERPENE ESTER ACTIVITY
TYPES F AND F' IN ONE CUP OF WELENSALI TEA WITH IRRITANT DOSE 50
OF PROTOTYPE CROTON FACTORS, THE 16-HYDROXYPHORBOL-12,13-DI- AND
12,13,16-TRIESTERS F_1 AND F_1-DECANOATE, RESPECTIVELY

Activity types	True minimum contents estimated (μg) (nmoles)		Prototype factors	TD^{24}_{50} [a] (nmoles)	Ratio [b]
F	0.27	0.41	F_1	0.033	~ 12/1
F'	0.12	0.15	F_1-20-decanoate	0.11	~ 1.4/1

[a] per mouse ear

[b] true minimum contents of factors type F and F' respectively, over irritant dose 50 of corresponding prototype factor.

cup of the tea the estimated true minimum content of activity types F corresponds to 12-times the irritant dose 50 of croton factor F_1 as determined for the mouse ear. The estimated true minimum content of activity types F' in the same cup of tea corresponds to 1.4-times the irritant dose 50 of F_1-20-decanoate.

If the tissues used for animal testing (epidermis of the mouse ear) and the human tissue exposed to the tea (epidermis of human esophagus) were comparably responsive to the irritant diterpene esters present in the tea, the data presented would suggest: daily consumption of only one cup (about 240 ml) of Welensali tea provides already a substantial "basal dose" of cocarcinogens. As seen from table 4 it is in excess of that required to induce and maintain chronic irritation in mouse skin. On Curacao, in fact, persons at risk consume more than one cup of Welensali tea (Brennecker 1961; Morton 1968a; Morton 1971). Also, the other less regular utilization of parts of the plant reported, perhaps together with concomitant utilization of plant parts of the other Euphorbiacea, Jatropha gossypifolia, would add further to such "basal dose". Thus, if in persons at risk,

exposure times, -frequencies and -doses to Welensali alone
are taken into account, clearly, a situation of cocarcinogenesis i.e. of initiation-promotion, as well as, perhaps,
of initiation-stimulation (Hecker 1981a,b) may be in
operation.

With reference to the origin and nature of carcinogenic risk factors involved in the Curacao case, the experimental results presented support strongly an etiologic CO-
CARCINOGEN HYPOTHESIS with the specification of initiation-
(or tumor) promoters being principal etiologic risk factors.
Epidemiologic evidence appears to support the experimental
findings: in both males and females incidence rates of esophageal cancer are declining (see above). This may be attributed to a trend in the younger generations on the island to skip "old-fashioned" customs, such as preferential
use of plant preparations, especially drinking of Welensali
tea, and to replace them by habits considered more fashionable. Indeed, customary changes of this kind would reduce
the risk of carcinogenesis by exposure to the promoters
incriminated.

PUTATIVE INITIATORS: COMPLETION OF AN ETIOLOGIC CO-CARCINO-
GEN HYPOTHESIS INVOLVING PROMOTERS

To complete the analysis of the Curacao case in terms
of initiation/promotion, local possibilities of initiation
of the esophagus were evaluated experimentally. Assays for
"initiating activity" of an extract of Krameria ixina using
the initiation/promotion protocol in mouse skin with TPA as
promoter were negative (Adolf and Hecker, unpublished). In-
tubation of a single small dose of DMBA (stomach tube) followed by the promoter TPA produced tumors of the forestomach (Goerttler et al. 1979). In similar initiation/promo-
tion studies in rats, using N-methyl,N'-nitro,N-nitroso-
guanidine (MNNG) as initiator and croton oil as promoter,
adenocarcinomas of the glandular stomach have been obtained
(Matsukura et al.1979). Also, from in vitro experiments,
evidence is available for polycyclic aromatic hydrocarbons
(PAH) or nitrosamines acting as initiators of esophageal
tissue (e.g. Cheng et al. 1982). Further, responsiveness of
rat esophagus to promotion was demonstrated by a significant increase of ^{3}H-thymidine incorporation following administration of croton oil (Mirvish, et al. 1979). These
experimental results together demonstrate that the upper
digestive tract of mice and rats is prone to initiation/
promotion carcinogenesis.

In the Curacao case, similar initiators as used in
these animal experiments may be effective - for example
solitary carcinogenic PAH from petrol-contaminated drinking
water. Even if PAH or nitroso compounds, as solitary carcinogens, seem to show no correlation with esophageal cancer
in the studies pursued in Iran (Mahboubi and Aramesh 1980),
this does not exclude their capability to act as initiators
of that same target tissue.

Thus, from experimental and epidemiologic evidence, in
the high incidence life style esophageal cancer on Curacao,
previous exposure to initiators combined with habitual exposure to well-defined cocarcinogens of the tumor promoter
type appears to be the principal elements of environmental
risk. Apart from this, for high incidence areas of human
esophageal cancer in Japan (Hirayama 1981) and in North
China (Cheng et al. 1982) some epidemiologic and/or experimental evidence is available to support also the initiation/
promotion protocol.

In using experimental protocols, such as for example
CO- or SOLITARY CARCINOGENESIS, to mimic life-style cancers,
intentionally, the complex reality of every day human life
is oversimplified to allow clarification of the carcinogenic risk factors and of (combination) patterns of exposure
involved. In real life and concerning various human individuals it is highly unlikely that just one initiator and one
promoter or some "pure" pattern of combined exposure will
occur (e.g. Hecker 1981a). Therefore, the experimental evidence presented here does not mean to exclude the possibility that under the local conditions prevailing on Curacao,
besides the principal initiator(s) and promoter(s) suggested, also other carcinogenic risk factors may additionally
contribute to the high risk of esophageal cancer, such as
condensed tannins (see above), excessive consumption of
alcohol and/or cigarettes, hot meals or nutritional deficiencies. Also, of course, in other high risk areas of esophageal cancer (see table 1) other "local" risk factors
(e.g. "local promoters", Ito and Hirayama 1981) or other
combination pattern of exposure different from those specified here may be operative (e.g. Wynder et al. 1957;
Wynder and Hoffmann 1979; Tuyns 1979; Cheng et al. 1982).

IMMEDIATE CONSEQUENCES AND GENERAL CONCLUSIONS

As a concluding step in the scientific evaluation of
the Curacao case it might appear desirable to investigate
the etiologic cocarcinogen hypothesis by prospective epidemiologic research. The recent installation of a cancer re-

gistry on the island (Freni and Freni-Titulaer 1981) may be
of great help towards this goal. However, before final results of such time consuming (and expensive) investigations
become available, responsible local health authorities
might consider the evidence presented here to be sufficient
for immediate risk/benefit considerations followed by appropriate actions to prevent exposure.

Finally, and generally, it appears important to point
out to the public that in both principal classes of defined
carcinogenic risk factors - solitary and cocarcinogens -
the most active entities known, the aflatoxins produced by
moulds, as well as the diterpene ester type promoters produced by many, but not all, Euphorbiaceae (and Thymelaeaceae) species, are of PLANT ORIGIN. Therefore, the presence
in the human environment of "natural" carcinogenic risk factors certainly cannot be neglected. Nevertheless, in some
societies around the world, it appears fashionable to sole-
ly and collectively incriminate our technological civilization for pollution of the human environment with anthro-
pogenic carcinogenic risk factors. The essence is, however,
that carcinogenic risk factors, of whatever origin - "God-
made or Man-made" - NEED TO BE DETECTED AND IDENTIFIED to
prevent or at least control exposure of mankind by the best
possible techniques which our technological civilization is
capable to provide.

ACKNOWLEDGEMENT

Generous financial support of the Welensali project in
its many stages by the Wilhelm and Maria Meyenburg Stiftung,
Heidelberg-Leimen, is gratefully acknowledged. We are greatly indepted to Dr. med. R. Hess, Heidelberg-Nussloch and to
Mr. and Mrs. E. Dankmeijer, Curacao, Netherlands Antilles,
for valuable assistance in collecting Welensali materials.

REFERENCES

Brenneker P (1961). Jerba: Kruiden van Curacao en hun ge-
    bruik. Boekhandel St. Augustinus, Curacao. p 67.
de Boer SY (1979). Frequentie van Kanker van Mond-Tong-Pha-
    rynx-Slokdarm en de Nederlandse Antillen. Dissertation
    (Landslaboratorium voor de Volkszondheid, Afdeling Patho-
    logisch anatomisches Laboratorium Curacao, Niederländische
    Antillen).

Cheng JS, Sala M, Li MH, Chouroulinkov I (1982). Esophageal
   Cancer in Linxian County, China: A possible etiology and
   mechanism (initiation and promotion) in Carcinogenesis,
   vol.7, Cocarcinogenesis and the Biological Effects of
   Tumor Promoters, edit by E Hecker et al, Raven Press,
   New York p 167-174.
Dunham LJ, Bailar JC (1968). World maps of cancer mortality
   rates and frequency ratios. J Natl Cancer Inst 41:155-203.
Dunham LJ, Sheets RH, Morton JF (1974). Proliferative
   lesions in cheek pouch and esophagus of hamsters treated
   with plants from Curacao, Netherlands Antilles. J Natl
   Cancer Inst 53:1259-1269.
Eibergen R (1961). Kanker op Curacao. JB Wolters, Gronin-
   gen. p 134.
Eps LW (1970). Esophageal Cancer (post graduate course
   1970) paper from Medical Library of the St. Elisabeth
   hospital, Curacao.
Freni SC, Freni-Titulaer LWJ (1981). Cancer incidence in
   the Netherland Antilles. A survey covering the period
   1968-1979, Cancer 48:2535-2541.
Goerttler K, Loehrke H, Schweizer J, Hesse B (1979). Systemic two-stage carcinogenesis in the epithelium of the
   forestomach of mice using 7,12-dimethylbenz(a)anthracene
   as initiator and the phorbol ester 12-0-tetradecanoylphor-
   bol-13-acetate as promoter. Cancer Res 39:1292-1297.
Hartz PH (1940). The incidence of malignant tumors in un-
   selected autopsy material at Curacao, Netherlands West
   Indies. Am J Cancer 40:355-358.
Hartz PH (1958). The incidence of carcinoma of the esophagus in the Caribbean region and in Venezuela, compared
   with that of gastric cancer. Acta Unio Internat Cancrum,
   14:548-553.
Hecker E (1968). Cocarcinogenic principles from the seed
   oil of Croton tiglium L. and from other Euphorbiaceae.
   Cancer Res 28:2338-2349 (see also Planta Med suppl (1968)
   pp 24-45)
Hecker E (1971). Isolation and characterization of the co-
   carcinogenic principles from croton oil. In: Methods in
   Cancer Research, Vol 6, edit by H. Busch, pp 439-484.
   Academic Press, New York-London.
Hecker E (1972). Aktuelle Probleme der Krebsentstehung.
   Z Krebsforschung 78:99-122.
Hecker E (1978). Co-carcinogene oder bedingt krebsauslö-
   sende Faktoren - Aktuelle neue Aspekte der Ätiologie
   menschlicher Tumoren und des molekularen Mechanismus der
   Krebsentstehung. Naturwissenschaften 65:640-648.

Hecker E (1981a). Prototype processes as experimental models in multifactorial carcinogenesis. J Cancer Res Clin Oncol. 99: A29.

Hecker E (1981b). Cocarcinogenesis and Tumor Promoters of the Diterpene Ester Type as possible Carcinogenic Risk Factors. J Cancer Res Clin Oncol. 99:103-124.

Hecker E, Fusenig NE, Kunz W, Marks F, Thielmann HW (1982). Cocarcinogenesis and biological effects of tumor promoters Vol.7 in Carcinogenesis - a comprehensive Survey, Raven Press, New York.

Hecker E, Schmidt R (1974). Phorbolesters - the irritants and cocarcinogens of Croton tiglium L. Progr Chem Org Natur Prod. 31:377-467.

Hecker E, Weber J (1977). Cocarcinogens from Croton flavens L. and the high incidence of esophageal cancer in Curacao. 7th International Symposium on the Biological Characterization of Human Tumors. Budapest, April 13-15, 1977 Abstracts p 52; see also Experientia (Basel) 34:679-682 (1978).

Higginson J (1979). Environmental carcinogenesis: A global perspective of environmental carcinogensis. Emmelot P, Kriek E (eds) Elsevier/North Holland, Biochemical Press, Amsterdam, p 9-22.

Hirayama T (1981). Operational epidemiology of cancer. J Cancer Res Clin Oncol. 99:15-28.

Ito Y, Hirayama T (1981). First UICC conference on "Cancer Prevention in the Developing Countries", Nagoya, Japan, Aug 25.-29. 1981. Conference Proceedings, in press.

Lutz D (1982). Vorkommen von cocarcinogenen Diterpenestern in "Welensali" (Croton flavens L.) sowie in dem auf Curacao gebräuchlichen Welensali-Tee. Dr.rer.nat. thesis, University of Heidelberg.

Lutz D, Hecker E (1979). Esophageal Cancer on Curacao - Further new Tumor promoters from Croton flavens L. 8th Internat Symposium on the Biological Characterization of Human Turmors, May 8-11, Athens, Greece, Book of Abstracts.

Mahboubi EO, Aramesh B (1980). Epidemiology of esophageal cancer in Iran, with special reference to nutritional and cultural aspects. Prev Med. 9:613-621.

Matsukura N, Kawachi T, Sano R, Sasajima K, Sugimura T (1979). Promoting action of croton oil on gastrocarcinogenesis by N-methyl-N'-nitro-N-nitroso-guanidine. J Cancer Res Clin Oncol 93:323-327.

Merino F, Zaisman I, Grand R, Lopez V, Amesty C, Garnica H, Montserrat R, Palao R, Bonstein M, Lugo JA, Boada PP, Serrano MC (1980). Cancer gastrico en el Estado Falcon: epidemologia, immunologia y pesquisa. Acta Oncologica

Venezolana. 13:219–286.

Mirvish SS, Rose EF, Sutherland DM (1979). Studies on the Esophagus. II. Enhancement of 3H-thymidine incorporation in the rat esophagus by Bidens pilosa and Croton oil. Cancer Lett. 6:159–165.

Morton JF (1968a). A survey of medicinal plants of Curacao. Econ.Bot. 22:87–102.

Morton JF (1968b). Plants associated with esophageal cancer cases in Curacao. Cancer Res. 28:2268–2271.

Morton JF (1970). Tentative correlations of plant usage and esophageal cancer zones. Econ Bot. 24:217–226.

Morton JF (1971). Welensali (Croton flavens): folk uses and properties. Econ Bot. 25:457–463.

Morton JF (1972). Further associations of plant tannins and human cancer. Quart J Crude Drug Res. 12:1829–1841.

Morton JF (1974). Folk remedy plants and esophageal cancer in Coro, Venezuela. Morris Arboretum Bull. 25:24–34.

Morton JF (1979). Plant tannins and esophageal cancer. Proc. 10th Internat Conf on Toxicology and Occup Medic. Elsevier North Holland, Inc. 129–137.

Morton JF (1981). Atlas of Medicinal Plants of Middle America. Charles C Thomas Publisher, Springfield, Illinois, USA.

O'Gara RW (1968). Biologic screening of selected plant material for carcinogens. Cancer Res 28:2272–2275.

O'Gara RW, Lee C, Morton JF (1971). Carcinogenicity of extracts of selected plants from Curacao after oral and subcutaneous administration to rodents. J Natl Cancer Inst 46:1131–1137.

O'Gara RW, Lee CW, Morton JF, Kapadia GJ, Dunham LJ (1974). Sarcoma induced in rats by extracts of plants and by fractionated extracts of Krameria ixina. J Natl Cancer Inst 52:445–448.

Tomatis L, Agathe C, Bartsch H, Huff I, Montesano T, Saracci R, Walker E, Wilbourn I (1978). Evaluation of the carcinogenicity of chemicals. A review on the monograph program of the International Agency of Research on Cancer 1971 to 1977. Cancer Res 38:877–885.

Tuyns AJ, Pequignot G, Abbalucci JS (1979). Oesophageal cancer and alcohol consumption: importance of type of beverage. Intl J Cancer 23:443–447.

van Duuren BL (1969). Tumor promoting agents in two stage carcinogenesis. Progr Exp Tumor Res II:31–68.

Waterhouse J, Muir C, Correa P, Powell J (1976). Cancer incidence in five continents. Vol III, Lyon, IARC Scientific Publication No 15.

Wynder EL, Hoffmann DH (1979). Tobacco and health: A societal challenge, New Engl J Med 300:894-903.

Wynder EL, Hultberg S, Jacobson F, Bross IJ (1957). Environmental factors in cancer of the upper alimentary tract Cancer 10:470-487.

CONGRESS SYMPOSIA

DNA REPAIR IN RELATION TO CHEMICAL CARCINOGENESIS
Latarjet, R., France, Chairman; Strauss, B.,
USA, Co-Chairman; Flag Pavilion A

Enzymatic Removal of Mutagenic and Lethal Lesions
from Alkylated DNA. *Lindahl, T. and Karran, P.,
London, England.

Cellular Aspects of DNA Repair. *Sklar, R.,
Strauss, B., Ayeres, K., Larson, K., Lindgren, V.
and Sagher, D., Chicago, IL USA.

Chromatin and DNA Repair after Treatment with
Simple Alkylating Agents; Relation to Carcinogenesis. *Verly, W. G., Liege, Belgium.

Repairability and Biological Effects of Carcinogen-
Induced DNA-Damage. *Cerutti, P. A., Lausanne,
Switzerland. (By Title Only)

Cancer-Prone Hereditary Diseases in Relation to
DNA Repair. *Takebe, H., Takashi, Y. and
Yoshiaki, S., Kyoto, Japan.

Please note: Papers that are listed as "By Title
Only" were presented at the 13th International
Cancer Congress, but are not included in these
volumes.

13th International Cancer Congress, Part B
Biology of Cancer (1), pages 241–250
© **1983 Alan R. Liss, Inc., 150 Fifth Avenue, New York, NY 10011**

ENZYMATIC REMOVAL OF MUTAGENIC AND LETHAL LESIONS FROM
ALKYLATED DNA

Tomas Lindahl and Peter Karran

Imperial Cancer Research Fund,
Mill Hill Laboratories,
London NW7 1AD, U.K.

Alkylating agents comprise a large and important group
of environmental carcinogens. In spite of their mutagenic
properties, several alkylating agents are presently in
clinical use for tumor chemotherapy. We have been
investigating the cellular defense mechanisms against simple
alkylating agents, such as monofunctional nitrosoureas,
because the effectiveness of these drugs will to a large
extent show an inverse correlation with the cell's ability
to perform DNA repair. Since the DNA correction pathways in
question appear to be universally distributed (for a recent
review, see Lindahl 1982), we have carried out many of the
initial studies on various enzymatic mechanisms of DNA
repair in *Escherichia coli*. This approach allows detailed
genetic analysis to complement the biochemical data. However,
these investigations are now being extended to human cells
in tissue culture. Here, we give an outline review of
recent work from our laboratory. For more detailed accounts
of experimental details, strategies and bibliographies, the
original publications quoted should be consulted.

The main mutagenic and carcinogenic lesion introduced
by methylating agents such as N-methyl-N-nitrosourea (MNU),
streptozotocin, and N-methyl-N'-nitro-N-nitrosoguanidine
(MNNG) is O^6-methylguanine (see e.g., Newbold *et al.*, 1980).
For cell killing, 3-methylpurines are important lesions,
the relative contributions of 3-methyladenine and 3-methyl-
guanine probably varying between different cell types.

REPAIR OF O^6-METHYLGUANINE IN *E. COLI*
A repair function for O^6-methylguanine was first

characterized *in vivo* (for a review, see Cairns *et al.*, 1981).
An inducible process counteracting the mutagenic and lethal
effects of MNNG was discovered and termed the adaptive
response to alkylating agents. The response comprised, in
part, an activity which removed O^6-methylguanine from DNA in
a rapid reaction, displaying the unusual and unexpected
property of being consumed during the repair process.
Subsequent experiments with cell-free systems have defined
the activity that accounts for the adaptive response to
mutagenesis by alkylating agents as a small monomeric enzyme
of mol. wt. 18,000, termed O^6-methylguanine-DNA methyltransferase (Karran *et al.*, 1979; Olsson and Lindahl, 1980;
Demple *et al.*, 1982). This protein, which has been purified
to homogeneity, transfers a methyl group from the O^6
position of guanine to one of its own cysteine residues. No
cofactor is required in the reaction, and there is no
appreciable change in mol. wt. of the protein as a
consequence of the methylation. However, the methylated
enzyme cannot be reactivated, so the enzyme catalyzes its
own inactivation in the DNA repair process. A recent kinetic
study has verified that the homogeneous enzyme displays
rapid suicide inactivation by a stoichiometric reaction with
O^6-methylguanine in DNA (Lindahl *et al.*, 1982a). Thus the
O^6-methylguanine-DNA methyltransferase forms a covalent
methyl adduct on interaction with its substrate, but in
contrast to other enzymes that act by covalent catalysis,
the intermediate is not efficiently cleaved in a subsequent
reaction with water. Instead, methylated enzyme
accumulates as a dead-end product. This novel biochemical
reaction differs from transmethylation processes such as
those involved in chemotaxis in *E.coli*, in which a distinct
methyl acceptor protein is methylated (on glutamic acid
residues) by a separate methyltransferase.

The O^6-methylguanine-DNA methyltransferase cannot act on
other alkylation products in DNA, such as N-methylated
purines (Lindahl *et al.*, 1982a). An exception is the
analogous ethyl adduct, O^6-ethylguanine, which is efficiently
repaired by the homogeneous methyltransferase, with the
formation of an S-ethylcysteine residue (Sedgwick and
Lindahl, 1982). The location of the structural gene for the
enzyme on the *E.coli* genetic map is presently unknown.
However, the induction of the methyltransferase is governed
by a regulatory gene, *ada*+, which maps at 47 min on the
standard map (Sedgwick, 1982). The *ada*+ gene, which also
controls the expression of an inducible DNA glycosylase

(see below), has recently been cloned in a multicopy plasmid.
This should allow a more detailed definition of its function.

The biochemical properties of the O^6-methylguanine-DNA
methyltransferase, in particular its poor ability to act on
single-stranded alkylated DNA, provide an explanation for
the property of alkylating agents such as MNNG and MNU to
cause multiple mutations in the vicinity of replication forks
(Lindahl et al., 1982a). This is because O^6-methylguanine
residues in unwound DNA regions near the replication fork
would remain selectively unrepaired. In this regard, it is
also important to note that the cellular mismatch repair
system is unable to correct misreplication caused by the
presence of O^6-methylguanine in the template DNA (Karran and
Marinus, 1982).

REPAIR OF O^6-METHYLGUANINE IN HUMAN CELLS
    O^6-Methylguanine is removed from DNA in human cells in
a rapid reaction strictly limited by the cellular level of
an expendable repair activity (Medcalf and Lawley, 1981;
Sklar et al., 1981). Thus, the process appears directly
analogous to that occurring in E.coli. Since the repair
capacity of many mammalian cells is relatively low, a
sensitive competition method has been devised to measure
removal of O^6-methylguanine, using small amounts of cells.
The rapid but limited repair of O^6-methylguanine in human
fibroblasts has been confirmed by this method (Teo and
Karran, 1982).

    Several groups have studied O^6-methylguanine repair in
mammalian cell-free systems, employing the methodology
developed by us for work with E.coli. Bogden et al. (1981)
first showed that the methyltransferase activity of mammalian
cells (mouse liver) conveys the methyl group to a protein
cysteine residue, exactly as in E.coli. This finding has
been confirmed by other groups (Mehta et al., 1981;
Waldstein et al., 1982). We have recently investigated
the human enzyme and defined some of its salient
properties (Harris et al., 1982). It is a small protein of
mol. wt. 20,000 ± 2,000. The transferase and acceptor
activities seem to be contained within the same protein,
as judged from the lack of resolution of these activities
by chromatography. While this point will only be finally
settled by purification of the human enzyme to homogeneity,
as has already been done for the E.coli methyltransferase,
the biochemical properties of the bacterial and human

activities are so similar that it appears overwhelmingly likely that the human methyltransferase is also a suicide enzyme. In particular, low concentrations of the human enzyme displayed the same unusual, very rapid but limited reaction with alkylated DNA as the *E.coli* enzyme.

While the biochemistry of the methyl transfer process appears to be the same in human cells as in *E.coli*, the two systems differ with regard to their inducibility. The O^6-methylguanine-DNA methyltransferase of *E.coli* is readily induced to a 100-fold higher level by treatment of cells with low doses of MNNG and MNU (Cairns *et al.*, 1981; Demple *et al.*,1982). In contrast, extensive attempts to induce human fibroblasts in an analogous fashion caused no increase in O^6-methylguanine-DNA methyltransferase activity (Karran *et al.*,1982a), Similarly, treatment with MNU or MNNG does not induce improved repair of O^6-methylguanine in mouse and rat liver or in human lymphoma cells (Margison, 1981; Pegg and Perry, 1981; Sklar *et al.*, 1981). However, an induction of O^6-methylguanine-DNA methyltransferase activity can be achieved in rat liver by exposure to a variety of hepato-toxins, for example carbon tetrachloride (Pegg and Perry, 1981). This interesting induction of a repair function by necrosis and cellular damage differs entirely from the adaptation phenomenon in *E.coli*, both by being a much smaller effect and by not being specifically responsive to an alkylation signal. Consequently, the term "adaptive response" for this nonspecific induction in mammalian cells seems misleading and should be avoided. The above body of work does not really support a recent claim by Waldstein *et al.* (1982) that a three-fold adaptive increase in O^6-methyl-guanine-DNA methyltransferase activity could be achieved by treatment of HeLa cells with MNNG.

Recently, several mammalian cell lines, anomalously sensitive to alkylating agents, have been found to be unable to repair O^6-methylguanine. Interestingly, many tumor-derived cells fall into this category. These have been referred to as Mer⁻ (Day *et al.*, 1980) or mex⁻ (Sklar and Strauss, 1981). While the mex⁻ phenotype was characterized as inability to repair O^6-methylguanine *in vivo*, Mer⁻ was originally defined in host-cell reactivation experiments with alkylated adenovirus. Therefore, it is presently unclear if all Mer⁻ cells are also mex⁻, although considerable overlap exists. We have compared extracts and protein fractions from mex⁺ and mex⁻ human lymphoid cell lines, and shown that while mex$^+$ cells contain readily detectable amounts of O^6-methylguanine-DNA methyltransferase, the enzyme activity is absent in mex$^-$ cells (Harris *et al.*, 1982). Similar results have been obtained by Sklar and Strauss (pers. commun.) Thus, measurements of this enzyme activity in cell-free extracts affords an easy method to define human cells as mex$^+$ or mex$^-$. It should be noted, however, that it is not presently known if the alkylation-sensitive mex$^-$ phenotype is entirely due to the inability to remove O^6-methylguanine from DNA, or if (as in *E.coli*) expression of a second repair enzyme, responsible for the removal of lethal lesions, has been switched off simultaneously with that of O^6-methylguanine-DNA methyltransferase.

REPAIR OF KILLING LESIONS
     The quantitatively major DNA lesion introduced by methylating agents is 7-methylguanine. This appears to be a relatively harmless alteration, retaining the coding properties of unsubstituted guanine. 7-Methylguanine persists in the cellular DNA for long periods of time, both in bacteria and in mammalian cells. It may ultimately be removed by cleavage of the 7-methylguanine-deoxyribose bond, either by spontaneous hydrolysis or by an accessory activity of certain 3-methyladenine-DNA glycosylases (Cathcart and Goldthwait, 1981; Karran *et al.*, 1982b). An alternative, minor, but potentially more dangerous pathway of elimination is by conversion of 7-methylguanine to a substituted formamidopyrimidine residue in DNA, generated by alkali-catalyzed opening of the imidazole ring of the methylated purine. The latter secondary alkylation product has recently been shown to behave as a non-coding lesion in experiments on DNA synthesis *in vitro* (J. Laval, pers. commun.). However, a separate DNA glycosylase exists which can catalyze the removal of this particular DNA lesion, both in bacteria and in mammalian cells, so its potential lethal effect is presumably minimized *in vivo* (Chetsanga and Lindahl, 1979; Margison and Pegg, 1981).

     The second most common DNA methylation product, 3-methyl-adenine, is a lethal lesion of importance. *E.coli* mutants unable to repair 3-methyladenine are extremely sensitive to alkylating agents (Karran *et al.*, 1980; Evensen and Seeberg, 1982). However, wild-type *E.coli* as well as mammalian cells remove this lesion very rapidly *in vivo* by the action of a DNA glycosylase. The necessity for rapid excision of this form of damage to avoid cell killing may reflect the fact that the methyl group of 3-methyladenine protrudes into the narrow groove of the double-helix, which is normally free of methyl groups (Lawley and Warren, 1976).

This reasoning focuses attention on the minor but analogous methylation lesion 3-methylguanine. In *E.coli*, this adduct is not removed by the constitutively expressed 3-methyladenine-DNA glycosylase, while the situation in mammalian cells is presently unclear. Consequently, we have shown that in previously unexposed *E.coli* there is more 3-methylguanine than 3-methyladenine present in the cellular DNA shortly after treatment with a methylating agent (Karran *et al.*, 1982b). This is because more than 95% of the 3-methyladenine is repaired very rapidly after treatment, while this is not the case for 3-methylguanine. Further data that implicate 3-methylguanine as a highly relevant killing lesion come from recent studies on the adaptive response in *E.coli*. Jeggo *et al.* (1978) made the important observation that adaptation to killing by MNNG required DNA polymerase I. This indicates that an excision-repair process is involved. In contrast, the repair of the mutagenic lesion O^6-methyl-guanine, which proceeds by methyl group transfer, clearly is not dependent on DNA polymerase I (Karran *et al.*, 1982c). Recently, a DNA glycosylase has been found to be induced during the adaptive response (Karran *et al.*, 1982b; Evensen and Seeberg, 1982). This enzyme, which removes 3-methyl-adenine from DNA, has a broader substrate specificity than the constitutively expressed 3-methyladenine-DNA glycosylase. In particular, the induced enzyme can also excise 3-methyl-guanine (Karran *et al.*, 1982b; Thomas *et al.*, 1982). Thus, the satisfactory situation exists in this model system that increased resistance to cytotoxicity by alkylating agents *in vivo* is associated with induction of a DNA glycosylase, which acts on a potentially lethal lesion.

ALKYLATION OF DNA BY S-ADENOSYLMETHIONINE

In intracellular methyl transfer reactions, S-adenosyl-methionine (AdoMet) is frequently employed as methyl donor. This reactive high-energy compound has recently been shown to act as a weak alkylating agent at physiological concentrations, methylating DNA by a nonenzymatic process (Lindahl *et al.*, 1982b; Rydberg and Lindahl, 1982; Barrows and Magee, 1982). Consequently, a low degree of continuous background alkylation of DNA would be expected to occur in cells. This unfortunate side reaction of AdoMet provides an obvious explanation for the existence of effective cellular repair mechanisms directed against DNA alkylation damage, and the apparently universal occurrence of such repair.

There is presently some disagreement on the spectrum of alkylation products produced by AdoMet with DNA. We (Rydberg and Lindahl, 1982) observed formation of 7-methylguanine and 3-methyladenine, but no O^6-methylguanine (<1% of the amount of 7-methylguanine). This is the product distribution expected of an alkylating agent reacting by an S_N2 mechanism, and model experiments with methylsulfonium compounds support such a mechanism for AdoMet (Coward and Sweet 1971). We concluded that AdoMet acts in a fashion similar to alkylating agents such as methyl methanesulfonate and dimethyl sulfate, and that the background DNA methylation by intracellular AdoMet would correspond to that achieved by continuous exposure of living cells to $2 \cdot 10^{-8}$ M methyl methanesulfonate. In contrast, Barrows and Magee (1982) detected formation of 7-methylguanine and O^6-methylguanine (8% of the former lesion), but no 3-methyladenine. The formation of 7-methylguanine (but not O^6-methylguanine) was qualitatively confirmed by incubation of DNA with non-radioactive AdoMet. Since the amount of DNA alkylation observed, under very similar experimental conditions, was about 5-fold higher than in the experiments of Rydberg and Lindahl (1982), and only unpurified radioactive AdoMet was employed, it seems possible that the formation of O^6-methylguanine could be ascribed to a contaminating alkylating agent. In fact, such reactive contaminants, which are resistant to destruction by an AdoMet-hydrolysing enzyme, have been observed by us in certain batches of commercially obtained radioactive AdoMet (unpublished observations). There is, however, general agreement that AdoMet can methylate DNA nonenzymatically. It is interesting that feeding of the carcinogenic methionine analogue ethionine to rats leads to the accumulation of large amounts of the AdoMet analogue S-adenosylethionine in the target liver cells (Swann *et al.*, 1971). This implies that ethionine might exert its carcinogenic effect by DNA alkylation.

REFERENCES
Barrows LR, Magee PN (1982) Nonenzymatic methylation of DNA by S-adenosylmethionine *in vitro*. Carcinogenesis 3:349

Bogden JM, Eastman A, Bresnick E (1981) A system in mouse liver for the repair of O^6-methylguanine lesions in methylated DNA. Nucleic Acids Res 9:3089

Cairns J, Robins P, Sedgwick B, Talmud P. (1981) The inducible repair of alkylated DNA. Prog Nucleic Acid Res Mol Biol 26:237

Cathcart R, Goldthwait DA (1981) Enzymatic excision of 3-methyladenine and 7-methylguanine by a rat liver nuclear fraction. Biochemistry 20:273

Chetsanga CJ, Lindahl T (1979) Release of 7-methylguanine residues whose imidazole rings have been opened from damaged DNA by a DNA glycosylase from *E.coli*. Nucleic Acids Res 6:3673

Coward JK, Sweet WD (1971) Kinetics and mechanism of methyl transfer from sulfonium compounds to various nucleophiles. J Org Chem 36:2337

Day RS, Ziolkowski CHJ, Scudiero DA, Meyer SA, Mattern MR (1980) Human tumor cell strains defective in the repair of alkylation damage. Carcinogenesis 1-21

Demple B, Jacobsson A, Olsson M, Robins P, Lindahl T (1982) Repair of alkylated DNA in *E.coli*; Physical properties of O^6-methylguanine-DNA methyltransferase. J Biol Chem 257, in press

Evensen G, Seeberg E (1982) Adaptation for alkylation resistance involves the induction of a DNA glycosylase. Nature 296:773

Harris A, Karran P, Lindahl T (1982) O^6-Methylguanine-DNA methyltransferase of human cells : Structural and kinetic properties and absence in cells sensitive to alkylating agents. Submitted for publication

Jeggo P, Defais M, Samson L, Schendel P (1978) The adaptive response of *E.coli* to low levels of alkylating agents; The role of PolA in killing adaptation. Mol gen Genet 162:299

Karran P, Lindahl T, Griffin BE (1979) Adaptive response to alkylating agents involves alteration in situ of O^6-methylguanine residues in DNA. Nature 280:76

Karran P, Lindahl T, Ofsteng I, Evensen G, Seeberg E (1980) *E.coli* mutants deficient in 3-methyladenine-DNA glycosylase. J Mol Biol 140:101

Karran P, Arlett CF, Broughton BC (1982a) An adaptive response to the cytotoxic effects of MNU is apparently absent in normal human fibroblasts. Biochimie, in press

Karran P, Hjelmgren T, Lindahl T (1982b) Induction of a DNA glycosylase for N-methylated purines is part of the adaptive response to alkylating agents. Nature 296:770

Karran P, Marinus MG (1982) Mismatch correction at
  O^6-methylguanine residues in *E.coli* DNA. Nature 296:868
Karran P, Stevens S, Sedgwick B (1982c) The adaptive
  response to alkylating agents; The removal of O^6-methyl-
  guanine from DNA is not dependent on DNA polymerase I.
  Mut Res 104:67
Lawley PD, Warren W (1976) Removal of minor methylation
  products 7-methyladenine and 3-methylguanine from DNA of
  E.coli treated with dimethyl sulphate. Chem Biol Interact
  12:211
Lindahl T (1982) DNA repair enzymes. Ann Rev Biochem 51:61
Lindahl T, Demple B, Robins P (1982a) Suicide inactivation
  of the *E.coli* O^6-methylguanine-DNA methyltransferase.
  Submitted for publication.
Lindahl T, Rydberg B, Hjelmgren T, Olsson M, Jacobsson A
  (1982b) Cellular defense mechanisms against alkylation
  of DNA. In Lemontt JF, Generoso WM (eds): "Molecular
  and cellular mechanisms of mutagenesis", New York:
  Plenum Publ Corp, p89
Margison GP (1981) Effect of pretreatment of rats with MNU
  on the repair of O^6-methylguanine in liver DNA.
  Carcinogenesis 2:431
Margison GP, Pegg AE (1981) Enzymatic release of 7-methyl-
  guanine from methylated DNA by rodent liver extracts.
  Proc Natl Acad Sci USA 78:861
Medcalf ASC, Lawley PD (1981) Time course of O^6-methyl-
  guanine removal from DNA of MNU-treated human fibro-
  blasts. Nature 289:796
Mehta JR, Ludlum DB, Renard A, Verly WG (1981) Repair of
  O^6-ethylguanine in DNA by a chromatin fraction from rat
  liver: Transfer of the ethyl group to an acceptor protein.
  Proc Natl Acad Sci USA 78:6766
Newbold RF, Warren W, Medcalf ASC, Amos J (1980)
  Mutagenicity of carcinogenic methylating agents is
  associated with a specific DNA modification. Nature
  283:596
Olsson M, Lindahl T (1980) Repair of alkylated DNA in
  E.coli: Methyl group transfer from O^6-methylguanine to a
  protein cysteine residue. J Biol Chem 255:10569
Pegg AE, Perry W (1981) Stimulation of transfer of methyl
  groups from O^6-methylguanine in DNA to protein by rat
  liver extracts in response to hepatotoxins.
  Carcinogenesis 2:1195
Rydberg B, Lindahl T (1982) Nonenzymatic methylation of DNA
  by the intracellular methyl group donor S-adenosyl-L-
  methionine is a potentially mutagenic reaction.EMBO J 1:211

Sedgwick B (1982) Genetic mapping of *ada* and *adc* mutations affecting the adaptive response of *E.coli* to alkylating agents. J Bact 150:984

Sedgwick B, Lindahl T (1982) A common mechanism for repair of O^6-methylguanine and O^6-ethylguanine in DNA. J Mol Biol 154:169

Sklar R, Brady K, Strauss B (1981) Limited capacity for the removal of O^6-methylguanine and its regeneration in a human lymphoma line. Carcinogenesis 2:1293

Sklar R, Strauss B (1981) Removal of O^6-methylguanine from DNA of normal and xeroderma pigmentosum-derived lymphoblastoid lines. Nature 289:417

Swann PF, Pegg AE, Hawks A, Farber E, Magee PN (1971) Evidence for ethylation of rat liver DNA after administration of ethionine. Biochem J 123:175

Teo IA, Karran P (1982) Excision of O^6-methylguanine from DNA by human fibroblasts determined by a sensitive competition method. Carcinogenesis 3, in press

Thomas L, Yang CH, Goldthwait DA (1982) Two DNA glycosylases in *E.coli* which release primarily 3-methyl-adenine. Biochemistry 21:1162

Waldstein E, Cao EH, Setlow RB (1982) Adaptive increase of O^6-methylguanine-acceptor protein in HeLa cells following MNNG treatment. Nucleic Acids Res 10:4595

13th International Cancer Congress, Part B
Biology of Cancer (1), pages 251-260
© 1983 Alan R. Liss, Inc., 150 Fifth Avenue, New York, NY 10011

CELLULAR ASPECTS OF DNA REPAIR

R. Sklar, B. Strauss, K. Ayres, K. Larson, V.
Lindgren and D. Sagher
Department of Microbiology
The University of Chicago
Chicago, Illinois 60637

Although the case for control and inducibility of DNA
repair pathways is now easily made in E. coli (Evensen,
Seeberg 1982), the situation is not quite so clear with the
eukaryotes. There are reports of increases in the activity
of repair enzymes (or proteins) as a result of pretreatment
regimens, mostly with alkylating agents (e.g. Montesano et
al. 1980), but as compared to the bacteria the factors of
increase are relatively low: three to fourfold as compared
to hundredfold changes in E. coli. The question is whether
the relatively small increases seen in mammalian eukaryotic
systems are similar in nature to the induced increases in
bacteria; more precisely: are the control systems in eukaryotes working in the same way as the prokaryotes? The
findings are complicated by the changes in enzyme activity
observed during the cell cycle. DNA polymerase and enzymes
involved in DNA repair such as uracil N glycosylase increase
their activity by two to three times as cells enter the S
phase (Gupta, Sirover 1981). Since these differences are of
the same order of magnitude as reported for inducibility in
mammalian cells (Waldstein et al. 1982a), it is important
that the relation (if any) of the effect to cell proliferation be established. Treatment with alkylating agents
increases the capacity of rat liver to remove O^6-
methylguanine [O^6MeG] (see Montesano 1980). The phenomenon
is complex but one factor is certainly proliferation since
pretreatment with a variety of inflammatory agents whose
sole (obvious) common feature is that they stimulate proliferation, also increases the capacity of livers to remove
O^6MeG (Pegg, Perry 1981).

In both bacteria and mammalian cells, an acceptor protein removes the O^6MeG produced in DNA by treatment of cells with alkylating agents such as N-methyl-N'-nitro-N-nitrosoguanidine (MNNG) or N-methyl nitrosourea (MNU) by transferring the CH_3 to one of the cysteines of the protein (Lindahl 1982). As a result of this methyl transfer the protein is inactivated. Pretreatment with MNNG increases O^6MeG acceptor activity in some, but not all, mammalian cell systems (see Waldstein et al. 1982a,b). We think that studies on the control of O^6MeG removal reaction will provide important insights into the mechanisms by which cells control repair reactions and have therefore devoted some time to the problem. Our experiments have been done exclusively with human lymphoblastoid cells.

CHARACTERISTICS OF O^6-METHYLGUANINE REMOVAL IN VIVO

The removal of O^6MeG from cells is extremely rapid. Over 40% of the O^6MeG produced by a nonsaturating dose of MNNG is removed within 5-10 minutes (Sklar et al. 1981). The kinetics of in vivo removal are not those of a simple bimolecular reaction and may be complicated either by the regeneration of new acceptor protein (Waldstein et al. 1982b) or by some other factor. As might be expected from the in vitro studies, the O^6MeG removal reaction is readily saturated in comparison to the relative nonsaturability of the 3MeA (3-methyladenine) removal reaction at these doses (Sklar et al. 1981). This saturation is due to inactivation of acceptor protein since cells treated with a subsaturating dose have not recovered their ability to remove O^6MeG two hours, or even longer after the pretreatment. Relatively long periods, equivalent to a cell generation are required to regenerate O^6MeG acceptor activity, even at pretreatment doses which leave some residual acceptor activity (Fig. 1). Other investigators have reported much faster regeneration times (Waldstein et al. 1982a) and it should be interesting to learn what accounts for the difference. Residual O^6MeG groups remaining in the DNA after pretreatment and which inactivate acceptor protein as it is formed have been suggested as one explanation.

MEX⁻ AND MER⁻ CELLS

Not all lymphoblastoid lines are able to remove O^6MeG

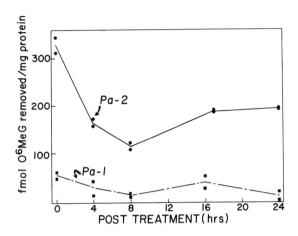

Fig. 1. Removal of O^6MeG from DNA by cell extracts: Recovery after pretreatment. Cell lines Pa1 and Pa2 were obtained by EBV transformation of cells from the same blood sample of a (human) male. Cells were pretreated with 0.68 μM MNNG and incubated in medium for the times indicated. The cells were washed and sonicated and the O^6MeG acceptor activity determined in a reaction mix containing 690 fmol of O^6MeG in DNA. Zero (0) time not pretreated.

with equal efficiency. A class of lines is deficient and we have termed such cells Mex⁻ (methyl excision minus). This deficiency is at least partially specific since extracts of Mex⁻ cells are able to remove other alkylated purines (Table 1). At the time the existence of Mex⁻ cells was being discovered, Day and Ziolkowski (1979) reported a class of Mer⁻ cells, unable to reactivate adenovirus treated with MNNG. Although Day first supposed some other lesion to be responsible, he has subsequently found that Mer⁻ cells are deficient in O^6MeG removal (Day et al. 1980). The work of Day's group has centered on fibroblasts, tumor-derived cells and human fibroblasts transformed with SV40. Our studies have exclusively employed EBV transformed lymphoblastoid lines. The Mer⁻ and Mex⁻ designations describe similar

Table 1. Removal of Alkylated Purines by Cell Extracts.

pmol removed/mg protein

Strain	3-Methyladenine	1-Methyladenine	7-Methylguanine
ROT-5	1.62	0.2	0.21
(Mex$^+$)	2.05	0.4	0.21
L6 (Mex-)	2.8	0.34	0.36
	2.5	0.24	0.32

characteristics but we do not know the genetic basis for this phenotype and it is likely that different changes are responsible. The report that untreated extracts of Mer$^-$ cells contain acceptor activity (Waldstein et al. 1982b) whereas we find no detectable activity in extracts of the Mex$^-$ lines L6 and HOCH2 indicates that different changes may be responsible for the effects in the separate lines. For example, Mer$^-$ (and "intermediate" Mex$^-$) lines might be equivalent to the inducible-deficient ada E. coli mutants (Jeggo 1979) whereas the "absolute" Mex$^-$ cells might represent some other change.

When first discovered, we supposed that all Mex$^-$ lines fit into a single deficient category. It is now clear that this is not so: stable intermediate states do exist (Ayres et al. 1982). Furthermore, no Mex$^-$ normal fibroblast line has been reported. Mer$^-$ characteristics tend to be associated with transformed lines (Day et al. 1980) but the Burkitt lymphoma lines Raji and Daudi are among the most Mex$^+$ cells we have seen. Variation in the capacity of organs (Goth, Rajewsky 1974) and of cell type within organs of the same animal (Lewis, Swenberg 1980) for O^6MeG removal are well known so it is clear that the production of acceptor protein is under developmental control. We have no idea, however, if the variation between Mex$^+$ and Mex$^-$ cells is due to the operation of the same developmental mechanisms as, for example, separate parenchymal and nonparenchymal cells of the rat liver (Lewis, Swenberg 1980).

The Mex$^-$ characteristic is not due to a difference in the germ line of Mex$^+$ and Mex$^-$ strains. Mex$^+$ fibroblasts and Mex$^-$ lymphoblasts can be obtained from the same individual (Shiloh et al. 1982). A high proportion of SV40 transformed cells as well as cultures derived from tumors are deficient in O^6MeG removing activity although the parent cells can remove O^6MeG (Day et al. 1980). We have recently obtained Mex^+ and Mex^- cultures from separate transformations of the same blood sample (Fig. 1). The blood was obtained from a male and our karyotypes indicate a modal chromosome number of 46 and the presence of a single Y among the chromosomes of both Mex^+ and Mex^- lines suggesting that X-inactivation is not responsible for the Mex^- characteristic: e.g. Mex^- cells do not derive from +/- heterozygotes by inactivation of an X-linked gene.

CELL KILLING AND O^6MeG REMOVAL

The original description of Mer^- cells was in terms of the lack of host cell reactivation of MNNG treated adenovirus (Day, Ziolkowski 1979). Insofar as lack of removal of O^6MeG is the only deficiency in Mer^- (Mex^-) cells, these data would identify the lesion as inactivating for adenovirus. There are good arguments for supposing O^6MeG to be lethal for cells as well. Mex^- cells are in general more sensitive to MNNG than are their Mex^+ counterparts. Furthermore the differences in sensitivity of Mex^+ and Mex^- to MMS are much less than their sensitivity to MNNG in a way which quantitatively correlates with the relative amount of O^6MeG among the alkylation adducts produced by the two compounds (Shiloh, Becker 1981). It is peculiar therefore that O^6MeG is not lethal in bacteria (Jeggo et al. 1978), and that O^6-ethylG does not block DNA synthesis (Muller et al. 1981). O^6MeG is a (if not the) mutagenic lesion (see, for example, Sklar, Strauss 1980). However, in bacteria, different inducible processes protect against killing and mutation, and protection against killing requires the operation of a normal polA allele (Jeggo et al. 1978). Somewhat similar observations have been made with mammalian cells. A HeLa line, supersensitive to mutagenesis and to killing by alkylating agents has produced a revertant still hypersensitive to mutagenesis but resistant to killing (Baker et al. 1979). Adaptation of CHO (Chinese hamster ovary) cells to protection against both killing and SCE induction (Samson, Schwartz 1980) does not provide protection against mutation (Schwartz, Samson 1981) as might be expected since these CHO cells have been reported to be deficient in O^6MeG removal capacity (Goth-Goldstein 1980). All these results seem to indicate that the O^6MeG lesion is related to, but not the final determinant of, lethality.

HYBRIDIZATION STUDIES

We have recently completed a set of cell hybridization experiments designed to throw light on the control mechanisms determining O^6MeG removal capacity (Ayres et al. 1982). Mex$^+$ and Mex$^-$ were fused and subjected to selection. The resulting hybrids were karyotyped, analyzed for their ability to remove O^6MeG and 3MeA and for their sensitivity to MNNG as compared to the parental strains (Ayres et al. 1982).

The ability of cells to remove 3MeA is related to the number of chromosome sets. The hybrids have the same capacity for 3MeA removal per mole of G as do the parental lines, i.e. twice as much per hybrid, 4N, cell. In contrast, the O^6MeG removal capacity of the hybrids per mole G is very close to being exactly intermediate between the two parental strains, i.e. the Mex$^+$ x Mex$^-$ hybrid has about the same capacity per cell as the Mex$^+$ parent. There seems to be no dominance of either Mex$^+$ or Mex$^-$ characteristic. This independence is seen also in crosses of Mex$^-$ (intermediate) with Mex$^-$ (low) or with Mex$^+$. The O^6MeG removal capacity per mole G is intermediate, e.g. the introduction of Mex$^-$ chromosomes has no effect on the acceptor activity due to the Mex$^+$. This intermediate state of the hybrids is also seen in the inactivation studies in which the hybrids are found to be inactivated at doses intermediate to those required to kill the Mex$^+$ and Mex$^-$ parents (Ayres et al. 1982) as though some lesion "X" in the DNA was inactivating and the unchanged removal capacity per cell in the hybrids was unable to cope with the increased amount of "X" produced in the 4N amount of DNA.

Although the sensitivity of the ROT5 x L6 hybrid is almost exactly in between that of the parental strains, which is what would be expected if O^6MeG were a lethal lesion, strain Tk-/-, which is an intermediate Mex$^-$ as far as O^6MeG removal capacity is concerned, has the sensitivity of the most Mex$^-$ strain in our collection (Ayres et al. 1982). This lack of correlation between O^6MeG removal and survival means that some factor in addition to O^6MeG is required to produce cell inactivation. On the other hand, the correlation between O^6MeG production or removal and cell sensitivity is so close (see above) that it is difficult to avoid the supposition that the two are related. In bacteria, alkylation produces both O^6MeG, the mutagenic lesion, and 3MeA, a lethal lesion. The removal reactions for both lesions are controlled by the same gene (Evensen, Seeberg 1982). In mammalian cells the identity of the lethal lesion is not yet clear. Most Mex⁻ strains are deficient in the removal of both lesions but states are possible in which removal of either the mutagenic or lethal lesion is turned off, producing either a hypermutable, insensitive strain (Baker et al. 1979) or a hypersensitive strain of normal mutability. The autonomous nature of the chromosomes in hybrids suggests that regulation does not occur via a diffusible inhibitor. If the Mex⁻ characteristic is a result of two separable gene products it implies the existence of something like a bacterial operon structure in these mammalian cell lines.

In bacteria, the requirement for a polA product to provide protection from the lethal effects of alkylation suggests the need for excision and resynthesis (Jeggo et al. 1978). This implies the production of apurinic sites, endonucleolytic cleavage and repair. Daphna Sagher in this laboratory has just shown that several polymerases pause, or stop, at apurinic sites (Fig. 2). Failure to remove AP sites or to heal the breaks produced by AP endonuclease would be expected to lead to chromatid breaks and chromosome imbalance producing cell death. Although the exact nature of the "second reaction" causing cell death is not as clear as seems to be the case in bacteria, we predict that it is related to an excision repair pathway and is under the control of the Mex element and possibly physically linked to it.

CONCLUSIONS AND SUMMARY

DNA repair reactions are under cellular control. In bacteria, the reactions removing O^6-methylguanine and 3-methyladenine are inducible. It is not clear whether similar inducibility occurs in human lymphoblastoid cells. Nonetheless, the ability to manufacture the O^6-methylguanine acceptor protein does seem to be controlled by some chromosomal mechanism which is superimposed on the structural gene. This control system may affect reactions other than

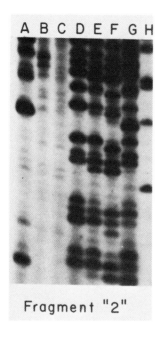

Channels A-C use control DNA. Channels D and H use control DNA with dideoxy A and T sequence standards.
A,G: polymerase alpha
B,F: T4 DNA polymerase
C,E,D,H: DNA pol I Klenow fragment

Fragment "2"

Fig. 2. Termination of DNA synthesis at apyrimidinic (AP) sites. AP M13 DNA was primed with a restriction fragment and used for in vitro DNA synthesis as described by Moore et al. (1981). The bands indicate positions of termination of synthesis.

the removal of O^6-methylguanine. Insofar as this is so, transformed human lymphoblastoid cells have a system reminiscent of that found in bacteria.

Acknowledgment

    The experimental work reported from this laboratory was supported by grants from the National Institutes of Health (GM 07816, CA 19265) and the Department of Energy (EY75 S-0202040). RS was a trainee on a program in Environmental Biology (Mutagenesis and Carcinogenesis) supported by the National Cancer Institute (CA 09273).

REFERENCES

Ayres K, Sklar R, Larson K, Lindgren V, Strauss B (1982). Regulation of the capacity for O^6-methylguanine removal from DNA in human lymphoblastoid cells studied by cell hybridization. Molec Cell Biol 2:904.

Baker R, Van-Voorhis W, Spencer L (1979). HeLa cell variants that differ in sensitivity to monofunctional alkylating agents, with independence of cytotoxic and mutagenic responses. Proc Natl Acad Sci USA 76:5249.

Day R, Ziolkowski C (1979). Human brain tumour cell strains with deficient host cell reactivation of N-methyl-N'-nitro-N-nitrosoguanidine damaged adenovirus 5. Nature 279:797.

Day R, Ziolkowski C, Scudiero D, Meyer S, Lubiniecki A, Giraradi A, Galloway S, Bynum G (1980). Defective repair of alkylated DNA by human tumour and SV40-transformed human cell strains. Nature 288:724.

Evensen G, Seeberg E (1982). Adaptation to alkylation resistance involves the induction of a DNA glycosylase. Nature 295:773.

Goth R, Rajewsky M (1974). Persistence of O^6-ethylguanine in rat brain DNA: Correlation with nervous system-specific carcinogenesis by ethylnitrosourea. Proc Natl Acad Sci USA 71:639.

Goth-Goldstein R (1980). Inability of Chinese hamster ovary cells to excise O^6-alkylguanine. Cancer Res 40:2623.

Gupta P, Sirover M (1981). Stimulation of the nuclear uracil DNA glycosylase in proliferating human fibroblasts. Cancer Res 41:3133.

Jeggo P (1979). Isolation and characterization of Escherichia coli K-12 mutants unable to induce the adaptive response to simple alkylating agents. J Bacteriol 139:783.

Jeggo P, Defais M, Samson L, Schendel P (1978). The adaptive response of E. coli to low levels of alkylating agent: the role of polA in killing adaptation. Mol Gen Genet 162:299.

Lewis J, Swenberg J (1980). Differential repair of O^6-methylguanine in DNA of rat hepatocytes and nonparenchymal cells. Nature 288:185.

Lindahl T (1982). DNA repair enzymes. Ann Rev Biochem 51:61.

Montesano R, Bresil H, Planche-Martel G, Margison G, Pegg E (1980). Effect of chronic treatment of rats with dimethylnitrosamine on the removal of O^6-methylguanine from DNA. Cancer Res 40:452.

Moore P, Bose K, Rabkin S, Strauss B (1981). Sites of termination of in vitro DNA synthesis on ultraviolet- and N-acetylaminofluorene-treated φX174 templates by prokaryotic and eukaryotic DNA polymerases. Proc Natl Acad Sci USA 78:110.

Muller R, Drosdziok W, Rajewsky M (1981). Enzymatic synthesis of double-stranded DNA containing radioactively labeled O^6-ethylguanine as the only modified base. Carcinogenesis 2:321.

Pegg A, Perry W (1981). Stimulation of transfer of methyl groups from O^6-methylguanine in DNA to protein by rat liver extracts in response to hepatotoxins. Carcinogenesis 2:1195.

Samson L, Schwartz J (1980). Evidence for an adaptive DNA repair pathway in CHO and human skin fibroblast cell lines. Nature 287:861.

Schwartz J, Samson L (1981). Induction of mutation in CHO cells after chronic pretreatment with MNNG. J Supramol Struct & Cell Biol Supp 5 No 570:209.

Shiloh Y, Becker Y (1981). Kinetics of O^6-methylguanine repair in human normal and ataxia telangiectasia cell lines and correlation of repair capacity with cellular sensitivity to methylating agents. Cancer Res 41:5114.

Shiloh Y, Tabor E, Becker Y (1982). Repair of O^6-methylguanine in human fibroblast cell strains: deficient repair capacity of lymphoblastoid cell lines does not reflect a genetic polymorphism. Mutation Res in press.

Sklar R, Strauss B (1980). The role of the uvrE gene product and of inducible O^6-methylguanine removal in the induction of mutations by N-methyl-N'-nitro-N-nitrosoguanidine in Escherichia coli. J Mol Biol 143: 343.

Sklar R, Strauss B (1981). Removal of O^6-methylguanine from DNA of normal and xeroderma pigmentosum-derived lymphoblastoid cell lines. Nature 289:417.

Sklar R, Brady K, Strauss B (1981). Limited capacity for the removal of O^6-methylguanine and its regeneration in a human lymphoma line. Carcinogenesis 2:1293.

Waldstein E, Cao E, Setlow R (1982a). Adaptive increase of O^6-methylguanine acceptor protein in HeLa cells following N-methyl-N'-nitro-N-nitrosoguanidine treatment. Nucleic Acids Res 10:4595.

Waldstein E, Cao E, Setlow R (1982b). Adaptive resynthesis of O^6-methylguanine-accepting protein can explain the differences between mammalian cells proficient and deficient in methyl excision repair. Proc Natl Acad Sci USA 79:5117.

13th International Cancer Congress, Part B
Biology of Cancer (1), pages 261–266
© 1983 Alan R. Liss, Inc., 150 Fifth Avenue, New York, NY 10011

CHROMATIN AND DNA REPAIR AFTER TREATMENT WITH SIMPLE
ALKYLATING AGENTS; RELATION TO CARCINOGENESIS.

Walter G. Verly

Biochimie, Faculté des Sciences,
Université de Liège, Sart Tilman B6,
4000 Liège I, Belgium.

Methyl- and ethyl-nitrosoureas, dimethyl- and diethyl-
nitrosamines may be taken as examples of simple alkylating
agents which are carcinogenic. The alkylnitrosoureas are
direct carcinogens : they react with DNA in vitro. The
dialkylnitrosamines are indirect carcinogens : they must be
activated metabolically to yield the ultimate carcinogens
which react with DNA. These simple carcinogens alkylate the
nitrogens and the oxygens in DNA.

The alkylated nitrogens are mostly the N-7 of guanines
and N-3 of adenines. The alkylation brings a positive charge
whose delocalization is responsible for the loss of the
alkylated purine by hydrolysis of the glycosyl bond with
the deoxyribose of the polynucleotide backbone. Moreover,
cells contain enzymes, called DNA glycosylases, which cata-
lyze the hydrolysis of the same glycosyl bonds, accelerating
the loss of the alkylated purines. The departure of the
purine leaves in DNA an apurinic site or AP site. AP sites
are very common lesions in DNA exposed to simple alkylating
agents.

Oxygen alkylation in DNA occurs on phosphates, 0-6 of
guanines, and pyrimidines. A good correlation exists between
the carcinogenic activity of a simple alkylating agent and
the alkylation of oxygens. Alkylation of guanine 0-6 seems
particularly important, but the relevance of the alkylation
of pyrimidine oxygens has not yet been sufficiently assessed.

Several theories try to explain the carcinogenic action
of 0^6-alkylguanine. 0^6-Alkylguanine can pair with cytosine,
but it can also mispair with thymine and be mutagenic; one
rationalizes that a mutation in the promoter region might

awake an oncogene. Another theory is that the target guanine belongs to a methylated CG pair and that alkylation of guanine 0-6 prevents methylation of cytosine in the new strand when DNA replicates; methylation is completely lost after two cycles of DNA replication and undermethylation of the promoter might awake an oncogene.

The fate of these theories or any others to explain how alkylation of guanine 0-6 leads to cancer is of no consequence for the present discussion, the only important point is that disappearance of 0^6-alkylguanine before DNA replicates seems to prevent malignant transformation. DNA does not loose spontaneously 0^6-alkylguanine, but, in vivo, 0^6-methyl- and 0^6-ethylguanine disappear from the DNA of many cells. If alkylation of guanine 0-6 is the principal cause of cancer induced by simple alkylating agents, the probability of a cell malignant transformation will, in principle, depend on several parameters : the level of guanine 0^6-alkylation of the cell DNA; the activity of the repair system which removes the potentially carcinogenic lesion; the delay before the cell DNA replicates since, to be useful, the repair must be completed before the replication fork passes over the modified base.

This paper deals with the repair of two major lesions that appear in DNA of cells exposed to simple alkylating agents : AP sites and 0^6-alkylguanine.

REPAIR OF AP SITES :

Enzymes that recognize specifically AP sites in DNA and nick the damaged strand near the lesions have been found in bacterial, animal and plant cells (Verly et al. 1973). These enzymes are called AP endodeoxyribonucleases (or simply AP endonucleases).

Thibodeau and Verly (1980) have studied the cellular localization of the AP endonucleases in rat liver. The apparent activity tested on an added DNA containing AP sites is mostly located in the nucleus, although some activity is found in the cytoplasm. The cytoplasmic activity is shared between mitochondria, membranes and cytosol. In the nucleus, most of the apparent activity is in the nuclear sap and some in nuclear membranes and native chromatin. However, if chromatin is dissociated with heparin-Sepharose and the complex extracted with 0.5 M KCl, the activity of the non-histone protein solution is 10 to 50 times higher than the apparent activity of the undissociated chromatin (César and Verly 1982). The final conclusion is that more than 90% of the cell AP endonuclease is in chromatin; in native chromatin, this activity is masked 'in the sense that it is unable to work on an added foreign DNA perhaps because the enzyme, firmly integrated in the chromatin structure, is oriented to scan the chromatin DNA. Partial digestion with micrococcal nuclease has shown that the chromatin AP endonuclease is present in the cores as well as in the linkers of the nucleosomes (Bricteux and Verly 1982).

The chromatin AP endonuclease has been purified. Two isozymes are separated on hydroxyapatite chromatography : one is eluted with 0.2 M phosphate, the other with 0.3 M phosphate. The 0.2 M/0.3 M isozyme ratio in chromatin extracts depends on the method of preparation; when protease inhibitors are used at all steps and the time to the end of the hydroxyapatite chromatography is kept at a minimum, the proportion of the 0.2 M isozyme can be lower than 5% (Bricteux et al 1982). The 0.2 M isozyme is thus mostly an artifact and it seems that the 0.3 M species is the true chromatin enzyme. This enzyme has been completely purified (César 1982); it has a molecular weight of 42,000; it hydrolyzes the phosphodiester bridge 5' to the AP sites leaving 3'-hydroxyl and 5'-phosphate ends (César and Verly 1982).

The nuclear sap enzyme has not yet been completely purified. It is eluted from hydroxyapatite with 0.2 M phosphate so that it is different from the main chromatin AP endonuclease. Cytosol and nuclear sap enzymes have the same physical properties so that they are probably the same protein, but the AP endonuclease is 200 times more concentrated in the nuclear sap than in the cytoplasm.

The membrane AP endonuclease is different from the chromatin and nuclear sap enzymes; it is an intrinsic membrane protein that cannot be removed by repeated washings with 0.25 M NaCl. Electron microscopic examination of microsomes prepared from rat liver shows the ribosomes attached on the outside of the vesicles; since these vesicles are active on an added DNA containing AP sites, the membrane AP endonuclease is likely located on the cytoplasmic side of the endoplasmic reticulum.

To summarize, rat liver contains several different AP endonucleases and each one is located in a particular cell compartment. It is likely that the only AP endonuclease used for the repair of nuclear DNA in the living cell is the

chromatin enzyme. Thibodeau and Verly (1980) have speculated
that the AP endonucleases in other cell compartments might
be precursors of the chromatin enzyme. To take account of
all the experimental data, they proposed the following model
the precursor is synthesized on free ribosomes and, because
of a hydrophobic end, attaches to the cytoplasmic side of the
endoplasmic reticulum; this membrane enzyme is carried in the
nucleus as on a conveyor belt by the membrane system; a protease, cutting away the hydrophobic end, releases the nuclear
sap enzyme; very little nuclear sap enzyme leaks into the
cytoplasm, most of it is modified to go into the chromatin.
It is possible that this model is not unique for the AP endonuclease and that nuclear DNA repair enzymes are generally
synthesized as precursors. This hypothesis is relevant to
oncology since lack of maturation of these enzyme precursors
would cause DNA repair deficiencies with their increased
probability of cancer.

Goffin and Verly (1982) have repaired in vitro DNA
containing AP sites with enzymes extracted from rat liver
chromatin : the AP endonuclease nicks the damaged strand 5'
to the AP site; a 5'-3' exonuclease excises the AP site in
an oligonucleotide (Zocchi 1982); DNA polymerase fills the
gap and ligase closes the last break. It is not however
because all the enzymes necessary to repair naked DNA containing AP sites are found in chromatin, that the in vitro
model represents what happens in vivo; it is probably more
complicated in the living cell because of the complex structure of chromatin. Repair of DNA in reconstituted chromatin
should be explored.

REPAIR OF O^6-ALKYLGUANINE :

Rat liver has a repair activity responsible for the
disappearance, from DNA, of O^6-methylguanine and O^6-ethyl-
guanine which are potentially carcinogenic. The cellular
localization of this activity again shows that most of it is
in chromatin; some is also found in nuclear sap and cytoplasm
(Renard and Verly 1980, 1982). It is not yet known whether
the cytoplasmic and nuclear sap enzymes are different from
the chromatin enzyme. All the results reported hereafter
were obtained with the chromatin enzyme.

The preparation of chromatin enzyme is obtained in the
following way : cell nuclei are prepared from rat liver;
chromatin is prepared from the purified nuclei and dissociated

with heparin-Sepharose; the complex is eluted with 0.3 M KCl
to get the chromatin protein solution which is dialyzed
against a suitable buffer. The substrate is prepared by
alkylating DNA either with $(H^3$-methyl)nitrosourea or with
$(H^3$-ethyl)nitrosourea. The alkylated DNA is incubated with
the chromatin proteins and, at the end of the incubation,
DNA and protein are separated by isopycnic centrifugation in
CsCl gradients. In the non-incubated controls, all the radioactivity is in the DNA band; after incubation, part of the
radioactivity is found in the protein band. The same observation is made with ethylated DNA (Mehta et al. 1981) and
methylated DNA (Lemaître et al. 1982). Protein and DNA are
subsequently analyzed separately; the example of the repair
of ethylated DNA will be followed.

The DNA is enzymatically hydrolyzed to nucleosides
which are separated by HPLC. In the non-incubated control,
there is a peak of O^6-ethyldeoxyguanosine. This peak has
nearly disappeared after incubation with the chromatin proteins; the other peaks have barely changed and no new peak
has appeared (Mehta et al. 1981).

A radioactivity equivalent to that lost by DNA as
O^6-ethylguanine is found in the protein fraction. Trypsin
digestion followed by HPLC analysis gives two radioactive
peaks. Hydrolysis of these oligopeptides with pronase and
aminopeptidase yields radioactive S-ethylcystein (Mehta et
al. 1981). The repair is thus a transethylation from O^6-ethyl-
guanine in DNA onto two cysteins of acceptor proteins. Similar results are obtained when methylated DNA is repaired
(Mehta et al. 1982).

The reaction rate is faster with O^6-methylguanine than
with O^6-ethylguanine, but the same limiting component (likely the acceptor protein) is used up in the repair of both
lesions : when this limiting component is exhausted by a
preliminary incubation with methylated DNA, no repair of
O^6-ethylguanine lesions can be observed when ethylated DNA
is added, and vice versa (Lemaître et al. 1982).

The repair is not a simple one-step reaction between
O^6-ethylguanine in DNA and the cystein of the acceptor protein; such a bimolecular reaction should depend on a second
order kinetic constant which is not found. At least a two-
step reaction must be considered in which the overall reaction is catalyzed by a transalkylase. It is still a matter
of debate whether, in mammalian cell chromatin, the transalkylase and acceptor functions belong to the same or

different polypeptides (Renard et al. 1982).

Bricteux S, Habraken Y, Verly W.G (1982). Apurinic/apyrimidinic endodeoxyribonucleases of rat liver chromatin (submitted for publication).

Bricteux S, Verly WG (1982) (unpublished)

César R (1982) (unpublished)

César R, Verly WG (1982). The apurinic/apyrimidinic endodeoxyribonuclease of rat liver chromatin (submitted for publication).

Goffin C, Verly WG (1982). Excision of apurinic sites from DNA with enzymes isolated from rat liver chromatin. Eur J Biochem (in press).

Lemaître M, Renard A, Verly WG (1982). A common chromatin factor involved in the repair of O^6-methylguanine and O^6-ethylguanine lesions in DNA. FEBS Lett (in press).

Mehta JR, Ludlum DB, Renard A, Verly WG (1981). Repair of O^6-ethylguanine in DNA by a chromatin fraction from rat liver : transfer of the ethyl group to an acceptor protein. Proc Natl Acad Sci (US) 78:6766.

Mehta JR, Ludlum DB, Lemaître M, Verly WG (1982) (unpublished).

Renard A, Verly WG (1980). A chromatin factor in rat liver which destroys O^6-ethylguanine in DNA. FEBS Lett 114:98.

Renard A, Verly WG (1982). Repair of O^6-ethylguanine lesions in isolated cell nuclei; presence of the activity in the chromatin proteins (submitted for publication).

Renard A, Verly WG, Mehta JR, Ludlum DB (1982). Properties of the chromatin repair activity against O^6-ethylguanine lesions in DNA. Kinetics and mechanism of the reaction (submitted for publication).

Thibodeau L, Verly WG (1980). Cellular localization of the apurinic/apyrimidinic endodeoxyribonucleases in rat liver. Eur J Biochem 107:555.

Verly WG, Paquette Y, Thibodeau L (1973). Nuclease for DNA apurinic sites may be involved in the maintenance of DNA in normal cells. Nature 244:67.

Zocchi G (1982) (unpublished).

13th International Cancer Congress, Part B
Biology of Cancer (1), pages 267–275
© 1983 Alan R. Liss, Inc., 150 Fifth Avenue, New York, NY 10011

CANCER-PRONE HEREDITARY DISEASES IN RELATION TO DNA REPAIR

Hiraku Takebe[1], Takashi Yagi[1] and Yoshiaki Satoh[2]

[1]Radiation Biology Center, Kyoto University, Kyoto 606 and [2]Department of Dermatology, Tokyo Medical and Dental University, Tokyo 113, Japan

Patients with some hereditary diseases have been known to develop cancers more often than others. These diseases are called as "cancer-prone hereditary diseases". Among them, xeroderma pigmentosum (XP) has been shown to be associated with DNA repair defects. Patients with this disease are defective or reduced in the capacity to repair DNA damage caused by ultraviolet radiation exposure from sunlight.

Repair of DNA damage, or DNA repair, was discovered in bacteria and the basic mechanisms were understood in 1964. Strains of Escherichia coli extremely sensitive to ultraviolet light were shown to be defective in DNA repair. Normal bacterium can repair DNA damage by taking out (excising) the damaged region and by replacing it by normal newly synthesized DNA. This is "excision repair", the most common and well understood type of DNA repair.

In 1968, Cleaver found that this type of repair is also present in human cells by discovering the defective excision repair in the cells derived from xeroderma pigmentosum patients. Since XP had been well known to be associated with skin cancer, possible involvement of DNA repair in carcinogenesis drew attention of the investigators in cancer research.

XERODERMA PIGMENTOSUM

Xeroderma pigmentosum is most extensively studied clinically and experimentally among the cancer-prone hereditary diseases. Table 1 gives the age distribution, skin

cancers of XP patients in Japan and DNA repair capacities of
the cells cultured from them. DNA repair capacities were
measured by the amounts of unscheduled DNA synthesis (UDS)
after UV irradiation relative to those in normal cells. The
ages represent the time of biopsy and, therefore, may not
reflect the age of onset or time of first diagnosis.

Table 1. Age Distribution, Skin Cancers and
DNA Repair of XP Patients in Japan

Ages	No. of Patients	UDS (% of Normal)			
		< 5	5-30	30-60	60 <
0-9	71(25)	62(23)	6(2)	3	0
10-19	46(28)	32(23)	7(3)	2(1)	5(1)
20-29	20(14)	3(3)	3(3)	3(2)	11(6)
30-39	13(7)	0	2(1)	3(2)	8(4)
40-49	13(8)	0	2(1)	3(2)	8(5)
50 ≦	21(16)	0	2(1)	4(4)	15(11)
Total	184(98)	97(49)	22(11)	18(11)	47(27)

Number of patients with skin cancers in parentheses

The characteristics of XP patients in Table 1 are
essentially similar to those reported previously with less
number of the patients (Takebe et al., 1977, Takebe, 1982).
More than half of the patients had very low repair capacities
in their cells and none of them survived more than 30 years.
An inverse correlation between repair capacity measured by
UDS and clinical symptom appear to exist with a few exceptions.

Genetic complementation tests of the cells of some of
the patients revealed the unique nature of XP patients in
Japan in comparison with their counterparts in other countries
as shown in Table 2.

Group C, the most frequently found in other areas, is
represented by only two families so far in Japan and the
majority of the patients belong to either group A or variant.
This explains the distribution of the patients in Table 1
depending on the amount of UDS, the lowest and the highest
groups being far more than the intermediate groups.

Table 2. Genetic Groups of XP Patients

Area	Complementation Group							Variant
	A	B	C	D	E	F	G	
Japan	27	0	3	1	0	4	0	21
USA	3	1	5	0	0	0	0	2
Europe	10	0	14	8	2	0	2	5
Egypt	7	0	12	0	0	0	0	5

Compiled at 16th International Congress of
Dermatology, Tokyo, May, 1982

Skin Cancers

Among the patients listed in Table 1, we collected more
detailed clinical records of 141 patients. Table 3 summarizes
average ages of the patients and of the onset of skin cancers
depending on the levels of DNA repair capacity and genetic
complementation groups. Clearly, patients with very low DNA
repair capacity belonging to the complementation groups A and
C are younger and have developed skin cancers earlier than
those with higher DNA repair capacity.

Table 3. Age Distribution and Onset of
Skin Cancers in Different Groups

Group	Patients*	Av. Age	Cancer Onset Av. Age
A and less than 5 % UDS	61(29)	11.0	9.4
C	3(3)	15.0	10.7
F	4(1)	49.0	(64)
Other Intermediate UDS Levels	32(12)	28.4	36.2
Variants and over 60 % UDS	41(25)	41.2	33.1

*Number of Patients with Skin Cancers in Parentheses

Other Cancers

Four XP patients had cancers of internal organs among the
70 ptients with skin cancers. They are listed in Table 4.

As suggested by Cairns (1981), frequency of the XP patients with cancers other than of skin should be higher than control groups if one assumes that cancers are due to mutagenesis, since XP cells are found to be sensitive to many mutagens. We have not been successful to obtain confirmed negative information on most of the XP patients concerning the internal cancers, particularly for those died without autopsy records. Consequently, it is still difficult to estimate the frequency of internal cancers in XP patients. Kraemer (1982) collected 10 non-skin cancers in XP patients in North America by retrospective studies, and he also pointed out the limitation of this type of study. He suspected (personal communication), however, that some of the non-skin cancers were of uncommon types such as glioblastoma of brain in children, which, incidentally, was also found in Japan.

Table 4. Cancers of Internal Organs
in XP Patients

Died of glioblastoma of brain, 9 yr (Compl. Group A)
Died of bile duct cancer, 65 yr (Compl. Group F)
Died of stomach cancer, 53 yr (Variant)
Transitional cell carcinoma of bladder, 68 yr (Variant)
Two other non-skin cancers (uterus and eye) were recorded,
but not included in the patients listed in Tabel 3

OTHER CANCER-PRONE HEREDITARY DISEASES PRESUMABLY ASSOCIATED WITH DNA REPAIR DEFICIENCY

Three other hereditary diseases of autosomal recessive inheritance have been known to be associated with high incidence of cancer. They are ataxia telangiectasia, Bloom's syndrome and Fanconi's anemia. Cells derived from the patients with these diseases have been shown to be sensitive to some agents causing DNA damages. Direct proof of the repair defects in these cells has not been conclusive and the involvement of DNA replication might be possible at least partially. Table 5 gives the characteristics of these diseases and the sensitivities of the cells to some of the agents. Lack of induced mutation by ionizing radiations in ataxia telangiectasia cells despite high sensitivity in lethal effects (Arlett, 1979) appears to be contradictory to somatic cell mutation theory of cancer. Chromosome aberrations (rearrangements and deletions) may play an important role in producing cancers in these diseases since all of these 3 diseases are associated with chromosome instability. Possible involvement of mutator characteristics of dominantly expressed procancer mutant genes in autosomal dominant cancer-prone diseases has been suggested by Sasaki (1982), supporting the importance of chromosome changes rather than point mutations in carcinogenesis. There are ample evidence indicating that DNA repair is involved in chromosome aberrations and, therefore, the role DNA repair plays in carcinogenesis could be related to the formation of chromosome aberrations.

Table 5. Autosomal Recessively Inherited Cancer-Prone Diseases and Cellular Sensitivity

Disease	Sun Sensitivity of Skin	Spont. Chrom. Aberr.	Spont. SCE	Sensitivity of Cells and Chrom.			
				UV	X	MMC	MMS
Xeroderma pigmentosum	+	–	–	++	–	–	–
Ataxia telangiectasia	+	+	–	–	++	–	–
Bloom's syndrome	+	+	++	+	+	+	–
Fanconi's anemia	–	++	–	+	–	++	–

++: very high or extremely sensitive, +: high or sensitive
–: same as normal
XP variant: + to UV
X: X- or gamma-rays, MMC: mitomycin C, MMS: methylmethane sulfonate

POPULATION AT HIGH RISK OF CANCER IN RELATION TO DNA REPAIR

Frequency of the patients with autosomal recessively inherited cancer-prone diseases may be less than 1/10,000 altogether, in any part of the world. But if the frequency of patients with a disease is 1/40,000, the gene frequency is 1/200, and the frequency of the heteroqygote carrier of the gene should be approximately 1 %. Swift et al (1976, 1979) presented the epidemiological evidence of higher incidence of malignancy in ataxia telangiectasia heterozygotes and of skin cancer in XP heterozygotes. Consequently, these heterozygotes consist of a genetically high risk group for

cancer, and the contribiution of DNA repair genes could be a
few per cent in general population (Takebe et al, 1981).
Bridges (1982), however, postulated that there could be more
DNA repair genes which are non-viable as homozygotes and might
exist in the heterozygous state undetected. If such genes
also enhance the incidence of cancer in heterozygotes, the
effect of DNA repair genes on current cancer incidence may
be more profound than our previous estimate.

DIFFERENCE IN DNA REPAIR BETWEEN HUMAN AND MOUSE CELLS

The mouse is the most widely used test animal in cancer
research. Although it has been known that human and mouse
cells are different in DNA repair characteristics considerably, apparently contradicting reports have been presented
on excision repair capacity of mouse cells by several investigators. Unscheduled DNA synthesis (UDS) after UV irradiation,
which has been assumed to represent the excision repair capacity, varied in different strains or in different cell passages.

Reduced Excision Repair in Mouse Cells

Using the cells originating from embryos of BALB/c,
C3H/He and C57BL/10, we confirmed the varying UDS levels in
different cell passages, but no differences were noted among
three strains used. Despite high levels of UDS at certain
passages, host-cell reactivation of UV-irradiated herpes
simplex virus in mouse cells was as low as that in XP cells
belonging to complementation group A in all passages. This
indicates that mouse cells are always defective in excision
repair as XP cells, and the normal UV sensitivity as normal
human cells should be due to DNA repair other than excision
repair (Yagi, 1982, Yagi et al., submitted).

The reduced excision repair in mouse cells was also
demonstrated by measuring the disappearance of T4-endonuclease
V susceptible sites in DNA after UV irradiation. By this
method, mouse cells were shown to have approximately 25 %
capacity compared with normal human cells.

Limitation of the Use of UDS as the Measure of Excision Repair

Our results strongly indicated that the use of UDS as

the measure of excision repair capacity might lead to misunderstanding of the mechanisms. Even in XP cells, cells derived from group F patients usually show very low (10 % of normal level) UDS, but are considerably resistant to UV by different assays. This was found to be due to slow and long-lasting excision repair in these cells (Hayakawa et al., 1981). Other XP cells, however, were found to have UDS levels which represented excision repair capacity consistently.

Apparently high UDS levels in some passages of mouse cells were found to be caused by smaller intracellualr dTTP pool size than human cells or mouse cells at different passages (Yagi et al., submitted).

CONCLUDING REMARKS

Involvement of DNA repair in carcinogenesis has been convincingly demonstrated in xeroderma pigmentosum. Recent report of higher frequency of cellualr transformation by UV in XP cells than in normal cells (Maher et al., 1982) supports the idea. But questions raised by Cairns (1981) have not been answered yet, even in XP, concerning cancers which might be caused by environmental factors other than UV. Also roles of DNA repair in other cancer-prone diseases are not clear.

Difference in DNA repair between human being and mouse should be taken into account when mouse data are to be extrapolated to human. We did not discuss "post-replication repair" and "SOS repair" in this paper, partially because we are not working on them directly, and partially because the presence of SOS repair in mammalian cells has not been solidly demonstrated. Post-replication repair should be more predominant in mouse cells than in human cells and further comparative studies would reveal what is same and what is different between human and mouse.

ACKNOWLEDGMENTS

The authors wish to thank to Drs. Y. Fujiwara, M. Ikenaga, M. Inoue and M. S. Sasaki who provided data on XP in Japan. This work was supported by Grant-in-Aid for Cancer Research from Ministry of Education, Science and Culture, and by Grant No. 82-07 from National Center of Nervous, Mental and Muscular Disorders of the Ministry of Health and Welfare.

REFERENCES

Arlett CF (1979). Survival and mutation in gamma-irradiated human cell strains from normal or cancer-prone individuals. In Okada S et al (eds): "Radiation Research: Proc 6th Intern Cong Radiat Res", Tokyo: Maruzen, p 596.

Bridges BA (1982). Some DNA repair-deficient human syndromes and their implications for human health. In Sugimura T et al (eds): "Environmental Mutagens and Carcinogens," Tokyo/ New York: Univ. Tokyo Press/Alan R. Liss, p 47.

Cairns J (1981). The origin of human cancers. Nature 289:353.

Cleaver JE (1968). Defective repair replication of DNA in xeroderma pigmentosum. Nature 218:652.

Hayakawa H, Ishizaki K, Inoue M, Yagi T, Sekiguchi M, Takebe H (1981). Repair of ultraviolet radiation damage in xeroderma pigmentosum cells belonging to complementation group F. Mutation Res 80:381.

Kreamer KH (1982). Diseases of environmental-genetic interaction: Preliminary report on a retrospective survey of neoplasia in 268 xeroderma pigmentosum patients. In Sugimura T et al (eds) "Environmental Mutagens and Carcinogens," Tokyo/New York: Univ. Tokyo Press/Alan R. Liss, p 603.

Maher VM, Rowan LA, Silinskas KC, Kateley SA, McCormick J (1982). Frequencey of UV-induced neoplastic transformation of diploid human fibroblasts is higher in xeroderma pigmentosum cells than in normal cells. Proc Natl Acad Sci USA 79:2613.

Sasaki MS (1982). Genetically determined chromosome instability in man. In Sugimura T et al (eds) "Environmental Mutagens and Carcinogens," Tokyo/New York: Univ. Tokyo Press/Alan R. Liss, p 475.

Swift M, Chase M (1979). Cancer in families with xeroderma pigmentosum. J Natl Cancer Inst 62:1415.

Swift M, Sholomon L, Perry M, Chase M (1976) Malignant neoplasms in the families of patients with ataxia telangiectasia. Cancer Res 36:209.

Takebe H (1982). Genetic aspects of repair deficiency and skin cancer. In Helene M et al (eds) "Trends in Photobiology," New York: Plenum Press, p 229.

Takebe H, Ishizaki K, Yagi T (1981). Genetic aspects of DNA repair deficiency. Gann Monograph on Cancer Res, 27:13.

Takebe H, Miki Y, Kozuka T, Furuyama J, Tanaka K, Sasaki MS, Fujiwara Y, Akiba H (1977). DNA repair characteristics and skin cancers of xeroderma pigmentosum patients in Japan. Cancer Res 37:490.

Yagi T (1982). DNA repair ability of cultured cells derived from mouse embryos in comparison with human cells. Mutation Res 96:89.

CONGRESS SYMPOSIA

IMMUNOLOGICAL ASPECTS OF CARCINOGENESIS Della
Porta, G., Italy, Chairman; Kripke, M., USA, Co-
Chairwoman; Snoqualmie Room

Immunological Aspects of Ultraviolet
Carcinogenesis. *Kripke, M. L., Frederick, MD
USA.

The Use of Antibodies to Detect Carcinogen - DNA
Adducts In Vivo and In Vitro. *Poirier, M. C.,
Bethesda, MD USA.

Cell Surface Antigens of Chemically Induced
Sarcomas of Inbred Mice. *DeLeo, A. B., New York,
NY USA. (By Title Only)

The Major Histocompatibility System and
Malignancies. *Jersild, C., Aalborg, Denmark.

The Epidemiology of Immune Factors in
Carcinogenesis. *Kinlen, L., J., Oxford, England.
(By Title Only)

Please note: Papers that are listed as "By Title
Only" were presented at the 13th International
Cancer Congress, but are not included in these
volumes.

13th International Cancer Congress, Part B
Biology of Cancer (1), pages 279–287
© **1983 Alan R. Liss, Inc., 150 Fifth Avenue, New York, NY 10011**

IMMUNOLOGICAL ASPECTS OF ULTRAVIOLET CARCINOGENESIS

Margaret L. Kripke

Cancer Biology Program
NCI-Frederick Cancer Research Facility
Frederick, MD   21701

The role of immunological factors in carcinogenesis has been debated and addressed experimentally for nearly twenty years. There are factions that argue that the immune system plays a major role in the development of neoplasia, and other factions that argue that it plays little or no role at all. Our present knowledge seems to indicate that both sides probably are correct. On the one hand, there is clear evidence that some tumors have no detectable tumor-associated antigens, especially cancers that arise spontaneously (Hewitt, 1977) and that the occurrence of these tumors cannot be explained entirely by immunoselection. There is also clear evidence that, in many cases, the immune status of the host does not seem to influence greatly the outcome of carcinogenesis, for example, in chemical carcinogenesis in nude mice (Stutman, 1973). On the other hand, there are other systems in which the immune system seems to be a determining factor in the development of neoplasia, such as in Burkitt's lymphoma (Klein, 1971), feline leukemia (Essex et al., 1973), and probably also in Kaposi's sarcoma and lymphomas associated with the newly described Acquired Immunodeficiency Syndrome (Marx, 1982).

Until recently, the primary examples in which the immune system appears to play a role in tumor induction were systems in which viruses are implicated in the etiology of the disease. Evidence for such a role of the immune system in chemical and physical carcinogenesis, which undoubtedly accounts for a significant fraction of human cancers, is less convincing. However, in the past few years, a new system has been described that does not involve conventional oncogenic viruses and that illustrates very dramatically the importance of the immune system in carcinogenesis. In this system, skin cancers are induced in mice by repeated exposure to ultraviolet (UV) radiation. The system is particular interesting not only because it illustrates the extent to which immunological factors can be involved in neoplasia given the appropriate circumstances, but also because it involves an environmental agent that has been implicated in the induction of human skin cancers.

ANTIGENICITY OF UV RADIATION-INDUCED SKIN CANCERS

The first suggestion that immunological factors might be involved in UV carcinogenesis in mice came from studies on the antigenic properties of UV radiation -induced fibrosarcomas and squamous carcinomas. These tumors resemble those induced by chemical carcinogens in that they have individually specific tumor-specific transplantation antigens (Graffi et al, 1967). Transplantation of these primary skin cancers into mice of the same inbred strain resulted in tumor growth only in a few instances. Most of the primary tumors failed to survive in syngeneic recipients, and this failure was shown to be due to immunological rejection of the transplanted tissue (Kripke, 1974). This finding that the UV radiation-induced skin cancers were so antigenic that they were rejected by normal animals raised the intriguing question of how these tumors could survive immunological destruction in the primary host.

Studies addressing this question produced the unexpected finding that mice that had been exposed to a short course of UV radiation were unable to reject transplants of these highly antigenic tumors, even when they were implanted into unirradiated sites. This demonstrated that exposure of the animals to UV radiation produced a systemic alteration that interfered with their ability to carry out immunological rejection. Furthermore, this alteration occurred before primary skin cancers could be detected, which indicated that it was not related to the growth of a primary tumor (Kripke, Fisher, 1976).

IMMUNOLOGICAL ALTERATIONS IN UV-IRRADIATED MICE

One approach to analyzing the nature of this systemic alteration in UV-irradiated mice was to investigate the ability of such animals to carry out other immune responses.

Such studies demonstrated that many immune reactions occur normally in UV-irradiated animals, which, nonetheless, are unable to reject UV radiation-induced tumors (reviewed in Kripke, 1981). Most importantly, these mice are able to reject transplanted allogeneic tumors and even some syngeneic tumors induced by chemicals or viruses (Kripke et al, 1979), indicating that the systemic alteration is selective for only certain antigens and is not caused by generalized immunosuppression.

The UV radiation-induced systemic alteration was shown to be immunological in nature, however, as demonstrated by the finding that it could be passively transferred with lymphoid cells to animals that had not been exposed to UV radiation. In these experiments, lymphoid cells from normal and UV-irradiated mice were used to reconstitute lethally X-irradiated syngeneic recipients. Mice that received normal lymphoid cells were able to reject transplants of UV radiation-induced tumors, whereas those reconstituted with lymphoid cells from the UV-irradiated donors were unable to reject such transplants. Reconstituting X-irradiated recipients with a mixture of cells from normal and UV-irradiated donors rendered them susceptible to tumor growth also. This implied that a suppressor mechanism was involved (Fisher, Kripke, 1977).

Subsequent studies demonstrated that T lymphocytes in the lymphoid cell suspension are responsible for the suppressive activity. After exposure of mice to UV radiation, these suppressor T lymphocytes can be found in the spleen and lymph nodes. They are capable of inhibiting the immunological rejection of syngeneic UV radiation-induced skin cancers, but not other types of tumors (Fisher, Kripke, 1978; Spellman, Daynes, 1977; 1978).

INDUCTION OF THE UV RADIATION-INDUCED SUPPRESSOR T LYMPHOCYTES

One of the most interesting questions raised by the finding of suppressor T lymphocytes in UV-irradiated mice is how exposure of the skin to UV radiation can lead to this alteration in the regulatory cells of the immune system. Because these wavelengths of radiation do not penetrate the deeper tissues in mice, the radiation cannot be acting directly on T lymphocytes that are contained within the lymphoid organs. Thus, the initial events leading to the induction of the suppressor cells must occur in the skin, and several

intermediate steps may be required to induce the proliferation
of the specific subpopulation of suppressor T lymphocytes.

A required step in this process must be the formation of
new antigens in the skin after exposure to UV radiation. This
requirement is deduced from the fact that a specific subpopulation of suppressor lymphocytes appears after UV irradiation. The antigen(s) responsible for triggering the
appearance of these cells must be produced endogenously in the
skin as a consequence of the irradiation. The nature of these
antigens is unknown, and there is little direct evidence for
their existence. However, they must resemble the antigens
that subsequently appear on UV radiation-induced tumors,
because it is the immune response against these tumors that is
inhibited by the suppressor T lymphocytes.

Evidence for other steps in this pathway has been accumulating for the past several years. Studies have shown that
UV-irradiated mice have at least two other immunological
alterations: One involves the contact hypersensitivity
response to haptens applied directly on UV-irradiated skin
(Toews et al, 1980); the other involves delayed and contact
hypersensitivity reactions to antigens that enter through
unirradiated sites (Jessup et al, 1978; Noonan et al, 1981).
Both alterations can lead to activation of the suppressor cell
pathway in response to certain antigens, and both probably
involve an initial alteration in the activity of cells of the
macrophage-monocyte-Langerhans cell lineage. A current
hypothesis is that these cells, which are involved in the
uptake, processing, and presentation of antigens to
lymphocytes, are affected either directly or indirectly by UV
radiation in a way that results in activation of the
suppressor cell pathway, rather than in activation of an
effective immune response (Greene et al, 1979). This
hypothesis is consistent with evidence from other systems
suggesting that the way in which an antigen is first
encountered by T lymphocytes determines what type of immune
response is generated (Feldmann, 1973).

Based on these studies of contact hypersensitivity, the
following pathways can be envisioned for the induction of the
tumor-specific suppressor cells by UV irradiation. First, the
initial exposures of the skin to UV radiation disturb the
Langerhans cells in the epidermis and alter their antigen-
presenting activity. Antigens that are produced in the skin
as a consequence of UV irradiation would then encounter this

altered mode of antigen presentation, resulting in activation of suppressor T lymphocytes with specificity for these antigens. Second, with continued exposures to UV radiation, an alteration occurs in the function of splenic macrophages that also causes the induction of suppressor cells in response to certain antigens (Greene et al, 1979). This systemic alteration in antigen presentation also could activate the suppressor cell pathway for the antigens associated with UV irradiation. When the suppressor T lymphocytes reach a sufficiently high concentration, they are able to prevent the immunological rejection of those tumors that express the appropriate UV radiation-associated antigens.

THE ROLE OF THE UV RADIATION-INDUCED IMMUNOLOGICAL ALTERATIONS IN CARCINOGENESIS

Tests of the relevance of these UV radiation-induced alterations in immune function in UV radiation carcinogenesis in mice have been carried out recently. Experiments by deGruijl, van der Leun (1982) demonstrated that UV radiation carcinogenesis in hairless mice is accelerated in animals that have been exposed previously to UV radiation at a separate site. This finding supports the concept that the systemic effects of exposure to UV radiation can influence the development of primary skin cancers, in addition to controlling the growth of transplants of UV radiation-induced tumors.

Recent studies by Fisher, Kripke (1982) have demonstrated, in addition, that the UV radiation-induced suppressor T lymphocytes can determine the outcome of UV radiation carcinogenesis in the primary host. In one approach, mice were lethally X-irradiated and reconstituted with lymphoid cells from normal mice, UV-irradiated mice, or a mixture of these two populations. Four weeks later, they were grafted with UV-irradiated skin in which tumors had not yet developed. Few tumors developed in the skin grafted to mice that had received only normal lymphoid cells. In contrast, many more tumors developed in the skin grafted to mice that had received lymphoid cells from UV-irradiated donors or a mixture of lymphoid cells from UV-irradiated donors and normal mice. Thus, even though the skin grafts had received equal doses of UV radiation before grafting, the subsequent appearance of most primary tumors in the grafts depended on the presence in the host of UV radiation-induced suppressor T lymphocytes.

In a second approach, groups of mice were given intravenous injections of T lymphocytes from either UV-irradiated
or normal animals on four occasions, beginning at the
initiation of a course of carcinogenic UV irradiation. Mice
that received T lymphocytes from UV-irradiated donors
developed more tumors than uninjected mice or mice given
normal T lymphocytes. Furthermore, the skin cancers began to
appear after week 20 in the mice injected with the UV
radiation-induced suppressor T lymphocytes, but only after
week 40 in the other two treatment groups. This result
implies that newly transformed cells are eliminated or held in
check by immunological means during the long latent period of
UV radiation carcinogenesis and that these transformed cells
can develop into visible tumors only after the accumulation of
an effective number of suppressor T lymphocytes.

CONCLUSIONS

Clearly, the immune system plays an important and probably
decisive role in UV radiation carcinogenesis in mice. It is also
clear from studies of other tumor systems that this represents
an extreme example of the extent to which immunological
factors may influence the carcinogenic process. One reason
for this undoubtedly is because of the very high degree of
antigenicity of these tumors, which ensures the involvement of
the immune system in tumor development. In systems in which
the carcinogen produces tumors that are weakly antigenic, the
participation of the immune system would be commensurately
less. A second reason may relate to the fact that these
tumors arise in the skin. This organ has special immunological
capabilities and is anatomically designed to carry out
immunological surveillance functions against foreign chemicals
and microorganisms. Antigenic tumors developing in this
milieu may have less opportunity for escape than tumors
arising in the parenchyma of other organs.

Although this tumor system may represent a unique case
in terms of the participation of immunological processes, it
illustrates several general conclusions in a very dramatic
way: First, the system provides a very striking
demonstration of the importance of studying the primary host
in attempting to understand the relationship between cancer
and the immune system. In the UV radiation carcinogenesis
system, what appears to be the most superficial treatment,
exposure to UV radiation, turns out to have systemic

consequences that have a profound influence on the immunological relationship between tumor and host. Thus, studying the immune response to tumors that are transplanted into normal animals is not equivalent to studying the immune response in carcinogenesis, because the former study neglects the unknown and potentially important effects of the carcinogen on the immune system.

Second, the general level of immunological responsiveness of the host does not necessarily reflect the ability of the host to respond to its autochthonous tumor. For example, the UV-irradiated animal is capable of carrying out many immunological functions in a normal manner but yet is incapable of rejecting its own highly antigenic tumor. Thus, it is not always possible to predict the nature or extent of the interaction between host and tumors based on tests of general immunological function.

Third, this tumor system illustrates the importance of immunological regulatory pathways in controlling tumor immunity, as well as other types of immune responses. Thus, manipulation of the immune response to tumor antigens will not be possible in a predictable way without a detailed understanding of how this regulation occurs. One benefit of the UV radiation carcinogenesis system is that it has provided a new tool with which to analyze these immunological pathways.

ACKNOWLEDGEMENT

Research sponsored by the National Cancer Institute, DHHS, under contract No. N01-CO-75380 with Litton Bionetics, Inc. The contents of this publication do not necessarily reflect the views or policies of the Department of Health and Human Services, nor does mention of trade names, commercial products, or organizations imply endorsement by the U.S. Government.

REFERENCES

de Gruijl FR, van der Leun JC (1982). Systemic influence of pre-irradiation of a limited skin area on UV-tumorigenesis. Photochem Photobiol 35:379.
Essex M, Cotter SM, Carpenter JL (1973). Feline virus-induced tumors and the immune reponse: Recent developments. Am J Vet Res 34:809.

Feldmann M (1973). Induction of B-cell tolerance by antigen-specific T-cell factor. Nature (New Biol) 242:82.

Fisher MS, Kripke ML (1977). Systemic alteration induced in mice by ultraviolet light irradiation and its relationship to ultraviolet carcinogenesis. Proc Natl Acad Sci USA 74:1688.

Fisher MS, Kripke ML (1978). Further studies on the tumor-specific suppressor cells induced by ultraviolet radiation. J Immunol 121:1139.

Fisher MS, Kripke ML (1982). Suppressor T lymphocytes control the development of primary skin cancers in ultraviolet-irradiated mice. Science 216:1133.

Graffi A, Horn KH, Pasternak G (1967). Antigenic properties of tumors induced by different chemical and physical agents, In Harris RJC (ed): "Specific Tumor Antigens" Copenhagen: Munksgaard, p 204.

Greene MI, Sy MS, Kripke ML, Benacerraf B (1979). Impairment of antigen-presenting cell function by ultraviolet radiation. Proc Natl Acad Sci USA 76:6592.

Hewitt HB (1977). The choice of animal tumors for experimental studies of cancer therapy. Adv Cancer Res 27:149.

Jessup JM, Hanna N, Palaszynski E, Kripke ML (1978). Mechanisms of depressed reactivity to dinitrochlorobenzene and ultraviolet-induced tumors during ultraviolet carcinogenesis in BALB/c mice. Cell Immunol 38:105.

Klein G (1971). Immunologic aspects of Burkitt's lymphoma. Adv Immunol 14:187.

Kripke ML (1974). Antigenicity of murine skin tumors induced by ultraviolet light. J Natl Cancer Inst 53:1333.

Kripke ML (1981). Immunologic mechanisms in UV radiation carcinogenesis. Adv Cancer Res 34:69.

Kripke ML, Fisher MS (1976). Immunologic parameters of ultraviolet carcinogenesis J Natl Cancer Inst 57:211.

Kripke ML, Thorn RM, Lill PH, Civin CI, Fisher MS, Pazmino NH (1979). Further characterization of immunologic unresponsiveness induced in mice by UV radiation: Growth and induction of non-UV-induced tumors in UV-irradiated mice. Transplantation 28:212.

Marx J (1982) Research News: New disease baffles medical community. Science 217:618.

Noonan FP, Kripke ML, Pedersen GM, Greene MI (1981). Suppression of contact hypersensitivity in mice by ultraviolet radiation is associated with defective antigen presentation. Immunol 43:527.

Spellman CW, Daynes RA (1977). Modification of immunologic potential by ultraviolet radiation II. Generation of suppressor cels in short-term UV-irradiated mice. Transplantation 24:120.

Spellman CW, Daynes RA (1978). Properties of ultraviolet light-induced suppressor lymphocytes within a syngeneic tumor system. Cell Immunol 36:383.

Stutman O (1973). Tumor development after 3-methylcholanthrene in immunologically deficient athymic-nude mice. Science 183:534.

Toews GB, Bergstresser PR, Streilein JW (1980). Epidermal Langerhans cell density determines whether contact hypersensitivity or unresponsiveness follows skin painting with DNFB. J Immunol 124:445

13th International Cancer Congress, Part B
Biology of Cancer (1), pages 289–298
© 1983 Alan R. Liss, Inc., 150 Fifth Avenue, New York, NY 10011

THE USE OF ANTIBODIES TO DETECT CARCINOGEN - DNA ADDUCTS
IN VIVO AND IN VITRO

Miriam C. Poirier, Ph.D.

Laboratory of Cellular Carcinogenesis and Tumor Promotion
National Cancer Institute
Bethesda, Maryland 20205

Since most chemical carcinogens modify macromolecules,
and since carcinogenesis involves expression of heritable
changes, the formation of binding products (adducts) be-
ween chemical carcinogens and DNA has been implicated as a
necessary, if not sufficient, step in the carcinogenic process (Miller 1970; Miller 1978). Studies directed toward
determining the structural and functional consequences of
carcinogen-DNA adduct formation have recently been advanced
by the development of immunological assays able to detect
femtomole quantities of these adducts in DNA isolated from
biological samples. Antisera against either protein-bound
nucleoside adducts or carcinogen-modified DNA's have been
utilized in sensitive radioimmunoassays (RIA) and enzyme-
linked immunosorbent assays (ELISA) as well as immunofluorescence and electron microscopy (Poirier 1981; Müller 1981).
This report will concentrate on quantitative and morphological information obtained with antisera elicited in rabbits
against the major deoxyguanosine adducts of 2-acetylamino-
fluorene (2-AAF, an experimental carcinogen), benzo[a]pyrene
(BP, an environmental pollutant) and cis-diamminedichloro-
platinum(II) (cis-DDP, a chemotherapeutic drug).

The use of immunological probes for carcinogen-DNA
interactions has certain advantages over other procedures.
Antibodies are specific for a particular three-dimensional
structure, cross-react with neither the carcinogen nor DNA
alone, distinguish between different adducts of the same
carcinogen and can be used to investigate the conformation
of unknown adducts on DNA. In the most sensitive immunoassays utilizing carcinogen-DNA adduct antisera the limit of

detectability (one adduct adduct in 10^7 nucleotides) is
frequently better than that obtainable with radiolabeled
carcinogens. RIA and ELISA are versatile, the cost is low,
the reproducibility is excellent and many samples can be
rapidly assayed simultaneously. These procedures have been
employed to investigate the effects of carcinogen exposure
on DNA in cultured cells and intact animals administered a
carcinogenic protocol (Poirier 1981). In association with
morphological procedures such as immunofluorescence (Poirier,
Stanley 1982) and electron microscopy (Paules 1981), carcinogen-DNA adduct antisera have been been utilized to localize
adducts in particular cells, subcellular compartments and
DNA molecules in vivo and in vitro (Poirier 1981).

MATERIALS AND METHODS

     Procedures relevant to the antisera elicited against
guanosin-(8-yl)-acetylaminofluorene (G-8-AAF) and DNA
substituted with trans-(7R)-N^2-(10- 7β, 8α, 9α-trihydroxy-
7,8,9,10-tetrahydrobenzo[a]pyrene -yl)-deoxyguanosine
(BP-DNA) or cis-DDP are contained in Poirier 1977; Poirier
1979; Poirier, Williams 1980; Poirier, Santella 1980;
Poirier, True, Laishes 1982a and b; Poirier, Stanley 1982;
Poirier, Lippard 1982. Procedures for RIA (Poirier 1977,
1979), ELISA (Hsu 1980) and immunofluorescence (Poirier,
Stanley 1982) have been described previously.

RESULTS

Antisera Specific For (guan-8-yl) Adducts of 2-AAF

     Rabbit antiserum specific for deoxyguanosin-(8-yl)-2-
acetylaminofluorene (dG-8-AAF) and deoxyguanosin-(8-yl)-2-
aminofluorene (dG-8-AF), the major adducts observed in vivo
and in vitro upon interaction of DNA with the aromatic amine
2-acetylaminofluorene, has been employed in sensitive immunoassays (RIA and ELISA) to monitor the formation and removal
of these adducts in cultured cells and intact animals. Anti-
G-8-AAF cross-reacts with both C-8 adducts and can be used
in RIA's with [^{3}H]G-8-AAF and [^{3}H]G-8-AF tracers allowing for
quantitation of these two adducts in a mixture by profile
analysis and comparison with appropriate standard curves
(Poirier, Williams 1980; Poirier 1982a). The standard curve
50% Inhibition for this antiserum is at 0.05 picomoles for

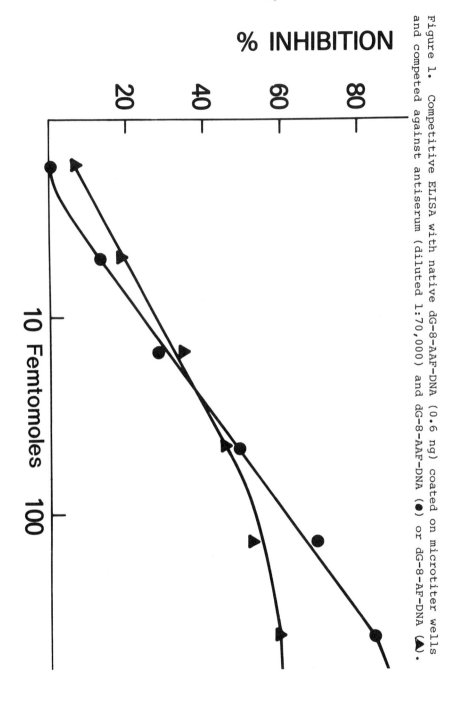

Figure 1. Competitive ELISA with native dG-8-AAF-DNA (0.6 ng) coated on microtiter wells and competed against antiserum (diluted 1:70,000) and dG-8-AAF-DNA (●) or dG-8-AF-DNA (▲).

RIA, (Poirier 1979), and in the range of 20-50 femtomoles
for ELISA (Hsu 1980 and Figure 1). In both assays it is
possible to include up to 50 μg of control DNA in the standard curve tubes or wells allowing comparison with the same
quantitity of unknown DNA, and extending the limits of sensitivity for the ELISA to about 0.1 femtomole adduct per μg
DNA.

A variety of cultured cells from different tissues and
species have been exposed to 10^{-5} M N-acetoxy-acetylamino-
flourene (N-Ac-AAF) and the DNA assayed for C-8 adducts by
RIA. Binding levels were in the range of 100-200 fmoles/μg
DNA. The deacetylated adduct was found to predominate
($\geq$90% of C-8 adducts) in all cells except primary rat
hepatocytes (Table 1 and Poirier, Williams 1980). The
validity of the RIA approach in performing such studies was
confirmed by concomitant HPLC analysis of DNA-binding products (M.C. Poirier and F.A. Beland, unpublished observations.) These data (Table 1) suggested that specific
patterns of AAF-DNA binding are determined at the cellular
level. Subsequently repair experiments were devised to
follow the removal of adducts, and experimental techniques
were developed to modify the quantity and type of adduct
formed (Poirier 1979; Poirier, Williams 1980).

Table 1.   Proportions of acetylated and decetylated C-8
           adducts in N-Ac-AAF-exposed cells from different
           tissues and species.

Species	Cells	% dG-8-AAF	% dG-8-AF
Mouse	Balb/c epidermal	3.0	97
	Sencar epidermal	8.0	92
	Balb/c fibroblast	5.0	95
	Sencar fibroblast	5.0	95
Human	YDF dermal fibroblast	4.5	95.5
Rat	Epidermal	9.0	91
	Fibroblast	5.4	94.5
	Hepatocyte	80.0	20

RIA has been employed to study adduct formation in
liver and kidney DNA during feeding of 0.02 or 0.04% 2-AAF
to male Wistar-Furth rats either continuously up to 2
months or for a specific time followed by an interval for

repair (Poirier 1982a and b). The formation of C-8 adducts in liver DNA increased from 80 fmoles/μg DNA at 24 hr to a plateau of approximately 230 fmoles/μg DNA at 30 days and thereafter. During the first week of continuous feeding about 80% of the total C-8 adducts in the liver DNA were deacetylated (dG-8-AF) but the proportion of dG-8-AF increased to 100% by 30 days on the AAF-containing diet (Table 2). In rats fed 2-AAF for 3 or 7 days followed by control diet for one month, the adduct levels in the liver were reduced by 90% indicating that repair processes were functioning efficiently. When dietary administration of 2-AAF was for 28 days, the adduct levels were higher (than after 3 or 7 days), the rate of removal or repair remained constant and therefore the quantity of adducts remaining on the DNA after one month on control diet were substantial (Poirier 1982b). At this time dG-8-AF was persistent and there was no dG-8-AAF detectable in liver DNA (Table 2). Adduct profiles in kidney DNAs from the same animals indicated formation and removal similar to that occurring in liver but the binding levels were several-fold lower than those observed in liver (Poirier 1982a and b).

Table 2. Proportions of acetylated and deacetylated C-8 adducts in liver DNA of male rats fed 0.02% 2-AAF.

Days of Feeding			
AAF Diet	Control Diet	% dG-8-AAF	% dG-8-AF
7	0	20	80
15	0	20	80
25-31	0	0-3	97-100
60	0	3	97
7	7	-	100
7	28	-	100
28	7	0-3	97-100

Antisera Elicited Against BP-DNA

BP-DNA was prepared by reaction of calf thymus DNA with the anti isomer, (±) 7β, 8α- dihydroxy - 9α, 10α -epoxy - 7,8,9,10 - tetrahydrobenzo(a)pyrene (BPDE I), and utilized as immunogen (Poirier, Santella 1980). This is the major adduct formed upon interaction of BP and DNA in vivo (Weinstein 1978). The resulting antisera, anti-BP-DNA, have a higher affinity for BP-DNA than for the isolated BPdG adduct (suggesting antibody recognition of the DNA backbone) and do not cross-react with deoxyguanosine, DNA or the carcinogen alone. The ability of this antiserum to recognize BPdG in intact (non-hydrolyzed) DNA makes it particularly useful for morphological studies.

Qualitative studies have been performed at the cellular level by examining cultured mouse epidermal cells exposed to BPDE-I in vitro, by indirect immunofluorescence (Poirier, Stanley 1982). Generalized nuclear fluorescence punctuated with discrete bright spots was observed in BPDE-I-exposed cells with specific antiseum, but normal serum, absorbed specific serum, and non-exposed cells did not yield fluorescence. Specific fluorescence was abolished by treatment of fixed, permeabilized cells with DNAase. RNAase treatment removed the particularly intense bright staining localized in spots in the nucleus but did not change overall nuclear fluoresecence. While immunofluorescence was readily seen one hour after BPDE-I-exposure, by 24 hours it could no longer be observed suggesting removal of adduct during that time to levels undetectable by this technique (Poirier, Stanley 1982).

Antisera Specific For cis-DDP-Modified DNA

To further expand this immunotechnology with the intention of monitoring human exposure, rabbit antibodies have been elicited against DNA modified with the chemotherapeutic drug cis-diamminedichloroplatinum(II) (cis-DDP, Poirier, Lippard 1982). By ELISA the antiserum is specific for cis-DDP-DNA with no cross reactivity towards either the drug cis-DDP or unmodified DNA alone. The ELISA standard curve in the range of 20-60 femtomoles for 50% Inhibition, varies with the assay conditions. Quantitation of DNA adducts has been achieved in cultured murine L1210 leukemia cells exposed to cis-DDP (Table 3); a dose of 5×10^{-4} M resulted in 8 femtomoles platinum bound per μg DNA while 2×10^{-5} M yielded 0.27 femtomoles/μg DNA. DNAs from untreated cells or cells exposed to trans-DDP or phenylalanine-mustard (another cross-linking agent) were not recognized by the anti-cis-DDP-DNA (Table 3). DNAs from tumor ascites cells extracted from L1210 tumor bearing mice injected with 10 mg/kg cis-DDP contained 1.5-2 femtomoles/μg DNA when measured in the ELISA. These experiments constitute the first evidence that antigenic determinants present on cis-DDP-DNA synthesized in vitro are stereochemically similar to some or all of the cis-DDP-DNA adducts formed in vivo.

Table 3. Adducts of cis-DDP in DNA of cultured L1210 cells or ascites fluid of L1210 tumor-bearing mice exposed to cis-DDP.

	Exposure	Dose	fmoles adduct μg DNA
Cultured Cells[a]	None		0
	cis-DDP	5×10^{-4} M	8.0
	cis-DDP	2×10^{-5} M	0.27
	trans-DDP	5×10^{-4} M	0
	L-PAM	1×10^{-2} M	0
Mouse Ascites[b]	cis-DDP	10 mg/kg	1.9
			2.1

[a]Cells were exposed to cis-DDP or other chemical agent for 1 hr.
[b]Each value represents one animal in which the duration of exposure was 5 hr.

CONCLUSIONS AND FUTURE APPROACHES

Studies with carcinogen-DNA adduct antisera have been directed toward quantitation of the extent of in vivo covalent DNA binding and removal, and determination of the structural and functional consequences of specific DNA adduct formation. These studies have employed antibodies to investigate the nature and extent of binding of 2-AAF, BP and cis-DDP to deoxyguanosine in the DNA of biological samples by RIA, ELISA and immunofluorescence.

Anti-G-8-AAF has been utilized to monitor C-8 adducts in cultured cells and intact animals. Since experimental techniques have been developed to modulate the quantity and type of C-8 adducts formed in the BALB/c epidermal culture system (Poirier, Williams 1980) ongoing investigations have focused upon the effects of such changes during primary epidermal cell transformation. With the low levels of carcinogen exposure required to insure cell viability in transformation assays the increased sensitivity of the ELISA is a requirement for adduct determination. Studies with RIA have demonstrated the predominance and persistence of the deacetylated C-8 adduct in most cell culture systems and in animals fed a carcinogenic regimen of 2-AAF. In contrast, in in both systems the acetylated C-8 adduct undergoes relatively rapid removal. The kinetics of addition and removal are complex in livers of rats chronically-fed 2-AAF, and future studies are utilizing a combination of biochemical and morphological approaches to elucidate the mechanism involved.

The applications for immunofluorescence and electron microscopy pioneered with the anti-BP-DNA have only recently been validated. Immunofluorescence should provide a means to investigate nuclear localization of carcinogen in exposed cells and to explore binding in different strata of whole tissues. Electron microscopy may yield information concerning the location of a carcinogen molecule with respect to DNA gaps and breaks, and may allow us to observe the effect of a carcinogen on replication complexes.

cis-DDP-DNA adducts have been determined in cultured cells and intact animals by quantitative ELISA with anti-cis-DDP-DNA. Since analysis of platinum bound to DNA has previously been accomplished with atomic absorption spectroscopy the structures of specific adducts formed in vivo or in vitro have been unknown. These immunoassay studies have shown that antigenic determinants present on cis-DDP-DNA prepared in vitro have immunologic identity with some or all of cis-DDP-DNA adducts formed in vivo. Thus it is likely that adducts formed in DNA of tissues and cells of chemotherapy patients may also be recognized by this antibody. Currently clinical studies are underway to assay DNA extracted from circulating nucleated cells of individuals receiving cis-DDP chemotherapy to investigate the possibility that adducts may be measurable in the cis-DDP-DNA ELISA.

This technology provides a powerful tool with which to probe for the mechanisms of chemically-induced cancer in model systems including cultured cells and whole animals. Sensitive immunoassays may also be useful in detecting DNA damage in individuals exposed to chemical carcinogens through life-style, occupation or chemotherapy.

Hsu IC, Poirier MC, Yuspa, SH, Yolken RH, Harris CC (1980). Utrasensitive enzymatic radioimmunoassay detects femtomoles of acetylaminofluorene-DNA adducts. Carcinogenesis 1:455.

Miller JA (1970). Carcinogenesis by chemicals: an overview (G.H.A. Clowes Memorial Lecture). Cancer Res 30:559.

Miller EC (1978). Some current perspectives on chemical carcinogenesis in humans and experimental animals. Cancer Res 38:1479.

Muller R, Rajewsky MF (1981). Antibodies specific for DNA components structurally modified by chemical carcinogens. J Cancer Res Clin Oncol 102:99.

Paules RS, Poirier MC, Mass MJ, Weinstein IB, Grunberger D, Yuspa SH, Kaufman DG (1981). Electron microscopic visualization of benzo[a]pyrene-DNA adducts using highly-specific antibody probes. Proc Am Assoc Cancer Res 22:86 (abstract 341).

Poirier MC (1981). Antibodies to carcinogen-DNA adducts. J Natl Cancer Inst 67:515.

Poirier MC, Yuspa, SH, Weinstein IB, Blobstein S (1977). Detection of carcinogen-DNA adducts by radioimmunoassay. Nature 270:186.

Poirier MC, Dubin MA, Yuspa SH (1979). The formation and removal of specific acetylaminofluorene-DNA adducts in mouse and human cells measured by radioimmunoassay. Cancer Res 39:1377.

Poirier MC, Williams GM, Yuspa SH (1980). Effect of culture conditions, cell type and species of origin on the distribution of acetylated and deacetylated deoxyguanosine C-8 adducts of N-acetoxy-2-acetylaminofluorene. Mol Pharmacol 18:581.

Poirier MC, Santella R, Weinstein IB, Grunberger D and Yuspa SH (1980). Quantitation of benzo[a]pyrene-deoxyguanosine adducts by radioimmunoassay. Cancer Res 40:412.

Poirier MC, True B, Laishes BA (1982a). The formation and removal of (guan-8-yl)-DNA-2-acetylaminofluorene adducts in liver and kidney of male rats given dietary 2-acetylaminofluorene. Cancer Res 42:1317.

Poirier MC, True B, Laishes BA (1982b). Determination of 2-acetylaminofluorene adducts by immunoassay. In Beland FA, Kadlubar FF (eds): Second International Conference on Carcinogenic and Mutagenic N-Substituted Aryl Compounds. Environmental Health Perspectives, in press.

Poirier MC, Stanley JR, Beckwith JB, Weinstein IB, Yuspa SH (1982). Indirect immunofluorescent localization of benzo[a]pyrene adducted to nucleic acids in cultured mouse keratinocyte nuclei. Carcinogenesis 3:345.

Poirier MC, Lippard SJ, Zwelling LA, Ushay HM, Kerrigan D, Thill CC, Santella R, Grunberger D, Yuspa SH (1982). Antibodies elicited against cis-diamminedichloroplatinum

(II)-modified DNA are specific for cis-diammineplatinum-DNA adducts formed in vivo and in vitro. Proc Natl Acad Sci, in press.

Weinstein, IB, Jeffrey A, Leffler S, Pulkrabeck P, Yamasaki H, Grunberger D (1978). Interactions between polycyclic aromatic hydrocarbons and cellular macromolecules. In Gelboin HV, Ts'O PO (eds): "Polycyclic Hydrocarbons and Cancer", Volume 2, New York: Academic Press, pp. 4-36.

13th International Cancer Congress, Part B
Biology of Cancer (1), pages 299–308
© **1983 Alan R. Liss, Inc., 150 Fifth Avenue, New York, NY 10011**

THE MAJOR HISTOCOMPATIBILITY SYSTEM AND MALIGNANCIES.

Casper Jersild, M.D.,Ph.D.

Ass.Medical Director
Regional Bloodtransfusion Center
Aalborg Hospital, DK-9000 Aalborg, Denmark.

Introduction.

Initial studies of HLA antigens in disease were stimulated by the discovery of H-2 linked genetic control of susceptibility to oncogenic virus infections in mice (Lilly,
Boyse, Old, 1964). In man the studies of Hodgkins' disease
(Amiel, 1967) and Acute Lymphocytic Leukemia (Kourilsky et
al, 1967) were, however unable to demonstrate a strong association to any specific HLA antigen then studied. Other malignant diseases were subsequently investigated, and similarly only weak or absent associations to HLA were found. In
contrast, several non-malignant disease entities did show significant association to HLA, the most remarkable one being
that of HLA-B27 with Anchylosing Spondylitis (Brewerton et
al, 1973; Schlosstein et al, 1973).

The ability of the host to mount a specific immunological respons is probably decisive in determining disease susceptibility. The demonstration of specific immune response
(Ir) genes within the Major Histocompatibility Complex (MHC)
region in mice (McDevitt et al, 1972) and guinea pig (Benacerraf, 1975) added a new and important aspect to HLA studies in disease. The Ir-genes in mice are located within the I-
region of the MHC, called H-2, and the I-region also exerts
the genetic control of reactivity in the Mixed Leukocyte Culture (MLC). A similar MLC locus was soon defined in man, and
was shown to be independent of the then known serologically
defined HLA antigens (HLA-A,B, and C). When techniques to define specific MLC determinants, now called HLA-D antigens,
became available (Dupont et al, 1973; van den Tweel et al,1973;

Mempel et al, 1973; Jørgensen et al, 1973) it was soon demonstrated that in Multiple Sclerosis the HLA-D antigen, DW2, showed a much stronger association to the disease than to any other HLA-A,B,or C antigen (Jersild et al, 1973). Later also other diseases, notably those of possible autoimmune nature, were shown to be much stronger associated with some HLA-D antigens, findings which favoured the concept of human Ir-genes, the genetic control of which were postulated to be closely linked to the HLA-D locus.

The participation of MHC products in defence mechanisms were further demonstrated by Zinkernagel and Doherty (1974). In a series of experiments in Lymphocytic Choriomeningitis (LCM) virus infected mice, they demonstrated that LCM virus specific cytolytic T-lymphocytes (CTL) only were able to lyse virus infected target cells that had at least one H-2K or -D antigen in common with the CTL. Although compatibility for one out of four H-2 antigens thus is sufficient for the interaction between CTL and target cell to occur, it was later demonstrated that the diversity of specific CTL's increased in H-2 heterozygous mice, the overall cytolytic capacity being almost twice as great as in homozygotes (Doherty and Zinkernagel, 1974). The H-2K/D or analogous class I (se below) antigens of the MHC thus restricts T-cell recognition of foreign antigens, detailed knowledge with respect to combined presentation of MHC and antigen as well as T-cell receptor requirements however are still lacking.

In 1974 Allen found the genetic control of the polymorphism of Factor B of the alternative pathway of complement to be closely linked to HLA. Deficiency of complement C2 (Fu et al, 1974) as well as the genetic polymorphism of C2 was subsequently shown to be HLA linked. Also the complex genetic control of C4 was shown to reside within HLA, this complement factor being related to the blood group antigens Chido and Rodger (O'Neill et al, 1978). The central role of the complement system in amplification of immunological reactions makes these findings especially interesting and applicable to the study of the HLA system in disease.

The HLA system - present status.

This short description of the present status of the HLA system has no intention of being complete; more extensive up-to date comprehensive reviews can be found elsewere (Svejgaard et al, 1979; Terasaki, 1980).

The MHC in man is composed of several series of antigens, the majority of which are highly polymorphic. They are all under the genetic control of several closely linked loci, located on the short arm of chromosome No.6. The MHC molecules can be divided into three classes on the basis of their structure and function. Both class I and class II antigens show a two chain structure, containing four domains, indicating possible homologies between them.

The class I antigens, or the classical HLA-ABC antigens, have the following two chain structure: an α-chain with a MW of approximately 45.000 containing three domains α_1, α_2, and α_3, where the last one spans the membrane; the β-chain, with a MW of 11.000, is non-covalently bound to the α-chain, and does not penetrate the membrane, has been identified as β_2-microglobuline. It is coded for outside the MHC region, on chromosome No.15, is not polymorphic, and shows considerable homology in domaine structure with immunoglobulin. The class I antigens are found on all nucleated cells.

The class II antigens are primarily located on B-lymphocytes and monocytes. This group of antigens include HLA-D and DR series. HLA-D antigens are detected by MLC technique, using homozygous typing cells (HTC) or primed lymphocyte typing (PLT), and these antigens correspond to the serologically detectable HLA-DR (D-Related) antigens. The DR antigens have more recently been characterized chemically and shown to be composed of two polypeptide chains, α and β, with a MW of 23.000 and 40.000 respectively (papain solubilization). The chains are non-covalently linked, and both penetrate the membrane. Two domains have been found in both the α and β chain, the α_2 and β_2 domains showing homology to immunoglobulin domains. The major polymorphism has been located to the α_1 domain, but

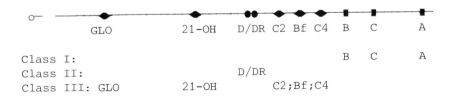

Fig.1. The HLA Chromosomal Region on Chromosome No.6.

polymorphism within the other domains has been observed, and may relate to the supertypic characteristics (MT, MB, and TE systems), indicating that genetic control of these complex antigens are controlled by more than one locus (Tanigaki and Tosi, 1982).

The class III antigens comprise several of the early complement factors (Factor B, C2, and C4); a locus giving rise to 21-hydroxylase deficiency; and the enzyme Glyoxylase (GLO), the genetic polymorphism of which is controlled by a locus within the HLA region.

Mapping of the different loci within the HLA region (Fig. 1) has been possible from the studies of large numbers of families, including those with informative recombinations of the HLA markers (Hawkins et al, 1980).

HLA markers in malignancies.

Studies have been conducted in several ways: (i)Comparative analysis of HLA antigen frequencies in unrelated groups of patients and normal unrelated controls of same ethnic group. (ii)For malignancies showing a familial occurence, linkage analysis between HLA and disease. (iii)Detailed analysis of HLA markers on tumor cells, including quantitative as well as qualitative determination of specificity. All aspects of these studies have been the subject of several international meetings ("HLA and Disease", Edts: Dausset J, Svejgaard A. Munksgaard, Copenhagen, 1977; "HLA and Malignancy",Edt: Murphy GP. Allan R Liss, New York, 1977; J.Immunogenetics, Vol.7, 1980; Transpl.Proc., Vol.13 No.3, 1981). Furthermore a continuous registration of all published and many unpublished data occur in the HLA-Disease Registry of Copenhagen, a WHO sponsored data file headed by A.Svejgaard and LP Ryder. The reports from this registry is regularly published ("HLA and Disease Registry.Third Report", Edts. Ryder LP, Andersen E, Svejgaard A. Munksgaard, Copenhagen 1979).

(i) Studies of HLA antigen frequencies.

In studies of malignancies it is of the utmost importance to distinguish between prospective and retrospective patient materials. Whereas the consecutively collected patient material in a prospective study will give information about

factors of importance for susceptibility, the retrospective
study will have added other variables to the material, namely
those associated with survival, and evaluation of susceptibility factors in such a material is not possible. In several
of the initial studies of malignancies these problems in as-
certainment were not sufficiently controlled, and later it was
shown to be of importance in Hodgkins' disease, carcinoma of
the breast (Falk, Osoba 1977), and acute lymphoblastic leukemia (Lawler et al, 1974; Rogentine et al, 1973; Cohen et al,
1977).

The most well established association to HLA is that of
Hodgkins' disease. Table I shows the combined results for all
studies. There is a small, but significant increase in the
frequencies of HLA-A1 and B8, relative risks 1.38 and 1.23
respectively. Also HLA-B5 and B18 antigens seem slightly increased, but a significant heterogeneity exists among the 25
studies reported. In carefully controlled prospective studies
only the increased frequency of HLA-A1 can be found. Subdividing patients according to histology has only been reported
in smaller groups of patients, and lack of HLA-B17 observed
among the nodular sclerosing type. In a more recent analysis
of data from the Danish lymphogranuloma study group LYGRA,
the significantly decreased frequency of HLA-B17 was found
in 48% of the 612 prospectively entered cases with the nodular sclerosing type.The lymphocyte predominance type (20%)
showed a significant increase in A1 and a non-significant increase in B8, but normal frequency of B17. The mixed cellula-

Table I. *Relative Risks of HLA antigens in Hodgkins' Disease.**)

| Antigen | Number of | | Relative | Significans | |
	Studies	Patients	Controls	Risk	R.R.	Heterog.
Hodgkins' Disease						
A1	25	2669	13694	1.38	$<10^{-10}$	–
B5	25	2668	13600	1.33	$1.6*10^{-5}$	$2.3*10^{-2}$
B8	25	2670	13692	1.23	$4.7*10^{-5}$	–
B18	20	2306	11424	1.30	$1.4*10^{-3}$	$2.2*10^{-2}$
Hodgkins' Disease, prospective						
A1	6	741	3446	1.37	$6.0*10^{-4}$	–
Hodgkins' Disease, Nodular Sclerosis						
B17	2	298	3409	.36	$1.8*10^{-3}$	–

*)*from:* 'HLA and Disease Registry. Third Report.' Edts. Ryder LP,
Andersen E, Svejgaard A. Munksgaard, Copenhagen 1979.

rity type of disease (32%) were characterized·by a combination of these deviations, the A1 and B8 antigens being significantly increased and B17 significantly decreased (Madsen M, Kissmeyer-Nielsen F, Lamm LU et al, personal communication).

Increased reactivity in MLC was found for HLA-B8 positive patients and normal controls by Falk and Osoba (1977), and this increased reactivity seems in their studies associated with prolonged survival. However, the preliminary analysis of survival data in the LYGRA study in Denmark indicate that the deviations of A1, B8, and B17 are even more pronounced among the 24% of cases which did not survive three years, as compared to the whole group of prospective cases. Also, in those surviving for more than three years, these antigens seem less deviating (Madsen M, Kissmeyer-Nielsen F, Lamm LU, et al, personal communication). These observations fit findings in other diseases of HLA associations, being even stronger in the most severely ill group of patients, e.g. multiple sclerosis and DW2 (Jersild et al, 1973).

Extensive studies in patients with acute lymphatic leukemia have been published, and show an increased frequency of HLA-A2 and B12, the relative risks being 1.39 and 1.24 respectively. The increased frequency of B12 is not significant, and there is a significant heterogeneity in the combined estimate from the 15 different studies. The association with A2 thus seems to be the primary, the slight increase in B12 being the result of the well known linkage disequilibrium between these two antigens.

In prospective studies an evaluation of antigens in long term survivors of ALL has been studied. Initial reports by Lawler et al (1973) described A9 and B27 associated with survival, these findings being partly confirmed by Cohen et al (1977). However Rogentine et al (1973) as well as Dausset (1977) reported an increased frequency of A2 in this patient group. These findings are difficult to evaluate since a number of HLA related secondary phenomena could influence survival, e.g. stimulation of anti-HLA antibodies during the course of platelet transfusions in A2 positive versus A2 negative patients.

Only in a few malignancies have HLA-D or -DR typings been included, and most of these studies have been negative. More recently, however, DeWolf et al (1981) have shown that HLA-DR5 occurs significantly more frequent among 26 renal carcinoma patients (54%) compared to 124 normal controls (20%). Also in

thyroid carcinoma Panza et al (1982) have reported a significantly increased frequency of HLA-DR1 in the 20 patients studied.

(ii) Familial occurence of malignancies.

Study of HLA markers in families with several members affected with retinoblastoma have shown that occurence of tumor
within families does not segregate with HLA (Gallie et al,
1977). Lynch et al (1977) reported similar findings in a study of 7 families with two or more cases of carcinoma of the
breast, and 5 families with the cancer family syndrome, characterized by increased frequency of adenocarcinoma and multiple primary malignant neoplasms usually with an early age
onset. They were unable to identify a single HLA antigen or
haplotype segregating with tumor occurence in these families.

(iii) HLA antigens on tumor cells.

It is well known that HLA typing of patients with acute
leukemias may be difficult, many of the typing sera showing
'extra' reactions. Before concluding that these extra reactions represent 'new' or 'alien' HLA antigens expressed on the
leukemic or tumor cell, following considerations should be
kept in mind: The specificity of a typing reagent is defined
by the technique used, the sensitivity of the cells to complement lysis, and the 'normal' distribution of lymphocyte subpopulations in the cell preparation. Deviation of any of these
factors may lead to false positive reactions, as well as differences between normal and tumor cells in number of normal
antigen molecules and their spatial relationship to other components of the cell membrane. Antibody activity in typing reagents to differentiation antigens or public specificities
being better represented on tumor cells than on normal cells
can also explain some of these extra reactions (for review
se Festenstein and Schmidt, 1981).

From a theoretical point of view changes in expression
of HLA antigens on tumor cells including 'alien' antigens,
may represent an escape mechanism for the MHC restricted immune surveillance, a topic which recently has been excellent-
ly reviewed by Demant and Festenstein,(1980).

Conclusions.

The majority of malignant diseases show no association
to HLA, a finding which may not surprise if lack of heredity
of these diseases is taken into consideration. Important information has, however, been obtained in Hodgkins' disease,
where differences in the weak but significant HLA associations
may support the histological classification of subtypes, and
indicate at least two different pathogenetic mechanisms in
this disease. HLA-D and -DR typings has not been extensively
applied in the studies, and may together with more recent discovered HLA-linked genetic markers of complement factors, add
information which is likely to give a more refined classification of genetic risk factors in malignancies. Since products
of the MHC is so intimately involved in cell to cell signals
within the immune system, as well as in the effector phase of
immune processes, it seems important not only to investigate
these products phenotypically, but also to characterize them
at the molecular level in membranes of normal as well as tumor
cells.

References.

Allen FHJr (1974). Linkage of HL-A and GBG. Vox Sang 27:382.
Amiel JL (1967). Study of leukocyte phenotypes in Hodgkin's
    disease. In Curtoni ES, Nattiuz PL, Tosi RM (edts): "Histo-
    compatibility Testing 1967", Copenhagen:Munksgaard, p 79.
Benacerraf B (1975). Immune response genes. Scand J Immunol
    4:381.
Brewerton DA, Caffrey M, Hart FD, James DCO, Nicholls, Stur-
    rock RD (1973). Anchylosing spondylitis and HL-A 27. Lan-
    cet i:904.
Cohen E, Singal DP, Khurana U, Gregory SG, Cox C, Sinks L,
    Henderson E, Fitzpatrick JE, Higby D (1977).In Murphy GP(ed):
    "HLA and Malignancy", New York:Allan R Liss, p 65.
Dausset J (1977). HLA and Association with Malignancy: A cri-
    tical View". In Murhpy GP(ed):"HLA and Malignancy", New
    York:Allan R Liss, p 131.
Dausset J, Svejgaard A (1977)(edts)"HLA and Disease", Copen-
    hagen:Munksgaard.
Demant P, Festenstein H (1980). Histocompatibility Antigens,
    Tumors and Viruses. J.Immunogenet. 7:1.
DeWolf WC, Lange PH, Shepherd R, Martin-Alosco S, Yunis EJ
    (1981). Association of HLA and Renal Cell Carcinoma. Hum.
    Immunol. 2:41.

Doherty PC, Zinkernagel RM (1975). Immune surveillance and the role of major histocompatibility antigens. Nature (London) 256:50.

Dupont B, Jersild C, Hansen GS, Nielsen LS, Thomsen M, Svejgaard A (1973). Typing for MLC-determinants by means of SD-homozygote and LD-homozygote test cells. Transpl.Proc.5:1543.

Falk J, Osoba D (1977). The HLA system and survival in malignant disease: Hodgkins' disease and carcinoma of the breast. In Murphy GP(ed):"HLA and Malignancies",New York:Allan R Liss, p 205.

Festenstein H, Schmidt W (1981). Variation in MHC antigenic profiles on tumor cells and its biological effects. Immunol. Rev.60:85.

Fu SM, Kunkel HG, Brusman HP, Allen FHJr, Fotino M (1974) Evidence for linkage between HL-A histocompatibility genes and those involved in the synthesis of the second component of complement. J.Exp.Med. 140:1108.

Gallie BL, Dupont B, Whitsett C, Kitchen FD, Ellsworth RM, Good RA (1977). Histocompatibility typing in spontaneous regression of retinoblastoma. In Murphy GP(ed):"HLA and Malignancies", New York:Allan R Liss, p 229.

Hawkins BR, Danilovs JA, O'Neill GR (1980). Analysis of recombinant families. Joint report". In Terasaki PI(ed):"Histocompatibility Testing 1980", Los Angeles:Regents Univ.Calif. p 148.

Jersild C, Fog T, Hansen GS, Thomsen M, Svejgaard A, Dupont B (1973). Histocompatibility determinants in multiple sclerosis with special reference to the clinical course. Lancet ii:1221.

Jersild C, Rubinstein P, Day NK (1976). The HLA system and inherited deficiencies of the complement system. Transpl. Rev. 32:43.

Jørgensen F, Lamm LU, Kissmeyer-Nielsen F (1973). Mixed lymphocyte cultures with inbred individuals: An approach to MLC typing. Tissue Antigens 3:323.

Kourilsky FM, Dausset J, Feingold N, Dupuy JM, Bernard J (1967). Etude de la repartition des antigenes leucocytaires chez des malades atteints de leucemie aigue en remission. In Dausset J, Hamburger J, Mathé G (edts):"Advances in Transplantation", Copenhagen:Munksgaard, p 515.

Lawler SD, Klouda PT, Smith PG, Till MM, Hardisty RM (1974). Survival and the HLA system in acute lymphoblastic leukemia. Brit Med J 1:547.

Lilly F, Boyse EA, Old LJ (1964). Genetic basis of susceptibility to viral leukemogenesis. Lancet ii:1207.

Lynch HT, Terasaki PI, Guirgis HA, et al (1977). HLA in breast cancer-prone families and the cancer family syndrome. In Murphy GP(ed):"HLA and Malignancies", New York:Allan R. Liss, p 149.

Madsen M, Kissmeyer-Nielsen F, Lamm LU et al (1982). Personal communication.

McDevitt HO, Dead BD, Schreffler DC, Klein J, Stimpfling JH, Snell GD (1972). Genetic control of immune response: Mapping of the Ir-1 locus. J Exp Med 135:1259.

Mempel W, Grosse-Wilde H, Baumann P, Netzel B, Steinbauer-Rosenthal I, Scholz S, Bertrams J, Albert ED (1973). Population genetics of MLC response: Typing for MLC determinants using homozygous and heterozygous reference Cells. Transpl. Proc. 5:1529.

O'Neill GJ, Yang SY, Tegoli J, Berger R, Dupont B (1978). Chido and Rodger's blood groups are distinct antigenic components of human complement C4. Nature(London) 273:668.

Panza N, Vecchio LD, Maio M, Felice MD, Lombardi G, Minozzi M, Zappacosta S (1982). Strong association between an HLA-DR antigen and thyroid carcinoma. Tissue Antigens 20:155.

Rogentine GN, Trapani RJ, Yankee RA, Henderson ES (1973). HLA antigens and acute lymphocytic leukemia: The nature of the HL-A2 association. Tissue Antigens 3:470.

Ryder LP, Andersen E, Svejgaard A (1979). "HLA and Disease Registry. Third Report", Copenhagen:Munksgaard.

Schlosstein L, Terasaki PI, Bluestone R, Pearson CM (1973). High association of an HL-A antigen, W27, with anchylosing spondylitis. New Engl J Med 288:704.

Svejgaard A, Hauge M, Jersild C, Platz P, Ryder LP, Staub Nielsen L, Thomsen M (1979)."The HLA System. An Introductory Survey". Monographs Hum Genet, Vol7, 2nd revised edt.

Tanigaki N, Tosi R (1982). "The genetic control of human Ia alloantigens: A three-loci model derived from the immunochemical analysis of "supertypic" specificities. Immunol. Rev. 66: 5.

Terasaki PI, Park MS, Bernoco D, Opelz G, Mickey MR (1980). Overview of the 1980 International Histocompatibility Workshop. In Terasaki PI(ed):"Histocompatibility Testing 1980", Los Angeles:Regents Univ Calif, p 1.

Tweel JGvd, Blusse AvOA, Keuning JJ, Goulmy E, Termijtelen A, Bach ML, Rood JJv (1973). I.Lymphocytes from cousin-marriages offspring as typing cells. Transpl.Proc 5:1535.

Zinkernagel RM, Doherty RM (1974). Activity of sensitized thymus derived lymphocytes in lymphocytic choriomeningitis reflects immunological surveillance against altered self components. Nature(London) 251:547.

CONGRESS SYMPOSIA

EFFECTOR AND REGULATORY IMMUNOLOGICAL MECHANISMS IN
CANCER Nossal, G., Australia, Chairman; Henney,
C. H., USA, Co-Chairman; Playhouse

Cellular Regulation of Tumor Immunity, An Overview.
*Stutman, O., New Yrok, NY USA.

Natural Killer Cells in Cancer. *Klein, E.,
Stockholm, Sweden.

Properties of the Sirs Suppressor Pathway. *Aune,
T. M. and Pierce, C. W., St. Louis, MO USA.

Suppressor Cells in Cancer. *Iverson, M. and
Green, D. R., New Haven, CT USA. (By Title Only)

Regulation of Tumor-Specific Immune Response by T
Cell Products. *Tada, T., Okumura, K., Yamada, S.,
Kitahara, T., Karasuyama, H., Ochi, A. and
Yamauchi, K., Tokyo, Japan.

Please note: Papers that are listed as "By Title
Only" were presented at the 13th International
Cancer Congress, but are not included in these
volumes.

13th International Cancer Congress, Part B
Biology of Cancer (1), pages 311–323
© 1983 Alan R. Liss, Inc., 150 Fifth Avenue, New York, NY 10011

CELLULAR REGULATION OF TUMOR IMMUNITY, AN OVERVIEW

Osias Stutman, M.D.

Head, Cellular Immunology Section
Memorial Sloan-Kettering Cancer Center
1275 York Avenue, New York, New York 10021

THREE LEVELS OF TUMOR-HOST INTERACTION

At least three critical interactions may take place between the tumor and the defense mechanisms of the host: 1)
The possible early recognition of the malignant change in
situ, and some form of reaction to it, hopefully eliminating
such abnormal cells (i.e. the immunological surveillance
view, preventing tumor development); 2) The complex immunological responses of the host to the developing tumor, once
it has attained a certain critical mass in situ; with all
the putative effector and regulatory circuits to be discussed in this Symposium, involving different types of responses, some of which may benefit the host and some which appear
to be beneficial for the tumor (i.e. the domain of tumor
immunology proper, which is the post factum response triggered by the developing tumor) and 3) The immunological
mechanisms, if any, which effect metastatic spread of the
tumor, which also includes interactions between different
components of the host's defense mechanisms, as well as
selection of tumor cell variants.

By definition, the appearance of "tumor immunity" as in
(2) above, means that "surveillance" as in (1) above has
failed. Similarly, the appearance of metastatic spread as
in (3) above, means that in spite of the ongoing response
as in (2) above, such response was ineffective in preventing
the progression of the tumor to the clinically dangerous
metastatic stage.

I am using the term "immunological" as it applies to

the putative anti-tumor defense mechanisms, in a rather
loose manner, since it certainly includes the "para-immunological" cell-mediated responses in the sense proposed by
Woodruff (1980), such as natural cell-mediated cytotoxicity
(NCMC) as well as macrophage-mediated responses, as opposed
to the "conventional" cell-mediated immune responses mediated
by thymus-dependent (T) cells (Stutman, 1980, 1981).

The fact that an immunological and para-immunological
defense mechanism against tumor development and progression
can be detected under certain circumstances, has also prompted studies aimed at defining the "escape" mechanisms of
surveillance or of tumor immunity (as in 1 and 2 above), or
the "subversion" of the immune response of the host by the
tumor (see Klein, 1975; Plescia et al., 1975; Naor, 1979,
for some examples of proposed mechanisms of escape). The
mechanisms for escape/subversion of the defense systems
have been variously attributed to immunodepression by the
oncogenic agents themselves (Prehn, 1963; Burnet, 1970),
blocking factors produced by the host or the tumor (Hellstrom and Hellstrom, 1974; Kamo and Friedman, 1977) and
more recently to suppressor cells (Naor, 1979; Greene, 1980).
G. Klein (1980) indicated that "The current tendency to at-
tribute the absence of expected immunological reactions to
suppressors is a new occupational hazard in the field of
tumor immunology...." By "suppressors" Klein means suppressor cells. I think that such an "occupational hazard" has
been quite endemic in the tumor immunology field, even before
suppressor cells were discovered, and could be applied to
the temporary waves of enthusiasm (or "band-wagons" in col-
loquial American) which all of the different proposed escape
mechanisms have generated. I think that the critical point
in the above comment by Klein is not the "occupational hazard"
component, but rather the "absence of expected," since high
expectations from the different branches of the immune system, whether conventional or not, have dominated this area
of research. For example, the brunt of immunological surveillance was first placed on the T cell system (Burnet,
1970; Klein, 1975), subsequently on macrophages (Alexander,
1976; Adams and Snyderman, 1979) and presently on natural
killer cells (Herberman and Holden, 1979; Herberman et al.,
1980; Roder et al., 1981). While tumor immunity appears to
be mediated by all of the above in some sort of combination
and down-regulated by either the humoral antibody system
(Hellstrom and Hellstrom, 1974) or by specific and non-specific suppressor cells and similar mechanisms (Naor, 1979;

Greene, 1980; Stutman, 1982). In some tumor-bearing hosts, there is evidence of antibody-dependent, complement-indepen- dent, cell-mediated cytotoxicity (ADCC), as the main effector system against the tumor (Shin et al., 1978). Probably, one of the best examples of a combination of effector mechanisms being active as a possible surveillance devise is represented by the Epstein-Barr (EB) virus induced lymphoproliferative diseases in humans, where the transformed B cells appear to be affected by HLA-restricted cytotoxic T cells (Rickinson et al., 1981), while EBV-carrying cells that have entered the lytic cycle are particularly sensitive to spontaneous or activated natural killer (NK) cells and ADCC (Blazar et al., 1980; Pearson et al., 1978), with an uncontrolled growth of the transformed cells in patients with immunode- ficiencies, such as the X-linked lymphoproliferative syn- drome and in immunodepressed renal transplant patients (Klein and Purtilo, 1981). Another good example is that of the ultraviolet (UV) radiation induced carcinogenesis in rodents (Kripke, 1981; Urban et al., 1982). In this rather unique system, the sarcomas induced by the radiation are highly antigenic, usually do not grow in normal animals and require immunodepression or UV-irradiation of the host for success- ful transplantation (Kripke, 1981). The few progressive variants which grow in normal syngeneic mice appear to have lost the antigenic determinants recognized by T cells and not by either NK cells or non-specific T cell cytotoxicity (Urban et al., 1982). Furthermore, suppressor T cells are induced in this system, which interfere with the development of the specific T cell immunity, allowing the development and growth of the tumor in the original, UV-irradiated host (Kripke, 1981), with the effects of UV, probably on antigen- presenting accessory cells, being the critical inducer of the suppressor mechanisms (Kripke, 1981). Finally, a third example from the immunological studies with virus-induced murine mammary tumors, has shown that in spite of a variety of specific host responses to viral components, the tumors do appear in these animals, and that such a situation is accompanied by the development of specific suppressor T cells, which prevent the interaction of helper T cells with the precursors for cytotoxic T cells, producing as a con- sequence a limited cytotoxic T cell response (Stutman, 1982). In these studies, the correlation of in vitro with in vivo responses was usually not easy (Stutman, 1982) and even the putative role of the suppressor T cells could be ques- tioned (Stutman, 1982). In the latter case, it was shown that adult thymectomy produced a disappearance of the sup-

pressor T cell component, allowing excellent in vitro cytotoxic T cell responses which however, did not affect overall
tumor incidence in these animals, who were technically without suppressor T cells (Stutman, 1982). The observed effect
of thymectomy on suppressor T cells in this system, may suggest, at first glance, that such phenomenon may explain the
puzzling effect of early thymectomy actually decreasing
mammary tumor incidence in the virus-infected mice (see
Stutman, 1982 for appropriate references), however, it was
found that only thymectomy at 6 days of age, but not at 30
or later (as done in the suppressor cell experiments) had
any effect in reducing overall tumor incidence (Stutman,
1982). Thus, I was forced to indicate that in many cases
one could not avoid the feeling "...of forcing the in vitro
data to fit the in vivo results...", giving as an example
the thymectomy data discussed above (Stutman, 1982). Imagine
the discussion that could have accompanied the description
of the effect of thymectomy on suppressor T cells in the
in vitro assays, if the experiments on the effects of adult
thymectomy on tumor development would have not been performed!

Four conclusions can be derived from the three examples
described above: 1) That in some instances the separation of
level 1 (surveillance) from the level 2 (tumor immunity)
may not be easy; 2) That different effector mechanisms may
be operative within the same system; 3) That down-regulation
(i.e. suppression) is not enough to explain successful growth
of antigenic tumors and 4) That the above examples may apply
only to tumors that show strong (or easily detectable) antigenicity.

Due to space limitations, I will not discuss the third
of the tumor-host interactions, i.e. metastasis and progression. It is apparent that the main facotr in this process
is biological diversity, even of clonal populations with
the development of sub-populations with metastatic potential
within the parent tumor (Fidler and Hart, 1982). The actual
role of the host, and of the defense mechanisms of the host,
in this diversification is still undefined (Fidler and Hart,
1982).

Finaly, although at first glance it may seem that there
is a large corpus of knowledge concerning immune cell-mediated effector mechanisms and their regulation, especially
at the effector cell level, or that the properties of the

malignant cell phenotype are being progressively defined, our understanding of the interphase between the host and the growing tumor itself, is still quite incomplete. Suffice it to cite as examples the regional differences in growth of neoplastic cells in inbred animals (Auerbach and Auerbach, 1981) or the phenomenon of "concomitant immunity". Concomitant immunity is the observed resistance to a second tumor graft in animals with progressive growth of the primary tumor (Ehrlich, 1906; Bashford et al., 1908; the term was coined by Bashford and used extensively in studies with tumors as well as with parasites and other infectious organisms, see Nelson, 1974). This phenomenon was re-discovered sixty years later (Mikulska et al., 1966; Gershon et al., 1967) and still remains unexplained, regardless of the regulatory mechanisms proposed to explain the experimental facts (Hellstrom et al., 1970; Youn et al., 1973; Vaage, 1973; Naor, 1979).

THE PROBLEMS WITH CONVENTIONAL ANTI-TUMOR IMMUNITY

One of the problems of specific tumor immunology, either as a surveillance device or developing as a consequence of the appearance of the tumor, is that it requires "antigens" for its triggering; and, unfortunately, not all tumors are antigenic or have unique determinants that can be recognized by immunological methods (Klein and Klein, 1977). In addition, as I have indicated in previous reviews (Stutman 1975; 1977 a,b; 1981), and drawing upon some similarities of the responses to highly antigenic infectious agents, it seems that the specific immune component is incapable of detecting small amounts of antigen, and only recognizes the invaders once they attain a critical mass (see Nelson, 1974); however, in the case of some infections (as perhaps some tumors, see above), once the T cell response has developed, it may be quite efficient in eliminating large numbers of infected cells or bacteria. Thus, it seems that, as was elegantly demonstrated by Andrews (1974), the immune system can detect visible in situ tumors, only if its attention is focused by using the trick of autografting the tumor-bearing skin back in place. Under such conditions, the tumors are rejected, while they grow well when the grafting is not performed; such rejection does not take place in immunodepressed animals (Andrews, 1974). Thus, as I indicated some time ago (Stutman, 1980), the hope of some of the immunotherapists that the enhanced immune response could clean up the small tumor burden that remains after surgery, probably cannot be performed by the conventional immune response.

From the standpoint of surveillance proper (as in point 1 in the previous section), the conventional cellular immunity mediated by T cells has the additional inconvenience of requiring time consuming priming (assuming that it can detect the in situ transformed cells), a problem that also applies to the activation of macrophages for cytotoxicity (Meltzer et al., 1982; see also Stutman, 1981 for further discussion of this point). Thus, with the exception of natural cell-mediated cytotoxicity(NCMC), which includes NK (Roder et al., 1981) and natural cytotoxic or NC cells (Stutman et al., 1981), which exist at relatively high levels in the absence of apparent priming, and that can deal preferentially with small numbers of tumor cells, there is no apparent cell-mediated mechanism which can act as a surveillance device (see Stutman, 1981, for further discussion). I will return to this point in the next section.

IN VIVO AND IN VITRO CORRELATIONS

One of the problems of the analysis of the role of conventional or unconventional immune (or cell-mediated) responses against neoplasia has been the correlation of the in vitro findings with the in vivo behavior of the transplanted or spontaneous tumors (see Stutman, 1982 for further discussion). In many cases, the in vivo behaviour was "unexpected" based on the levels of in vitro immunity detected. Besides the more vague explanations based on various "escape/subversion" mechanisms, there are some inherent problems to both methods.

For example, activated macrophages (i.e. cells with nonspecific tumoricidal activity) can be recovered from animals with certain infections for very long periods after infection (Meltzer et al., 1982). The activation stimuli are derived from the infection and from the host's immune response to the infection, and are usually localized at the site of infection (Meltzer et al., 1982). However, despite this chronicity, the actual regulatory mechanisms for induction and control of macrophage activation are operative for only brief periods, as judged from the in vitro studies (Meltzer et al., 1982). For example, lymphokine-activated macrophages lose their cytotoxic activity within approximately 24 hrs, although they remain viable but inactive

(Meltzer et al., 1982). Thus, the in vivo persistence of activated macrophages is due to the combination of the presence of the initiating agent, the ongoing host immune response which includes lymphokine production for macrophage activation and a constant replacement of the responsive resting macrophages for activation (as well as replacement of the specific immune response cells involved). The "replacement" part of this sequence is the one that cannot be included in the in vitro testing (Meltzer et al., 1982). Thus, the in vivo experiments contain, besides the replacement capacity of the effector cells (which can be affected in many different ways by the tumor-bearing state), the problem of appropriate delivery of the cells to the tumor sites, as well as the actual levels of effectors at the different sites. One may even postulate, taking a "neo-surveillance" stand, that, assuming that indeed such a thing as surveillance is operative, whatever its mechanisms, that actual tumor development may take place on the "weak spots" of the surveillance system, which may be related to low levels of local effectors, poor delivery or recruitment of new effectors, etc. Thus, it seems that the in vitro testing, with all of its analytical strengths, is not sufficient for the analysis of the complexities of the tumor-host interaction. Furthermore, as we showed in the murine mammary tumor system, immunological events taking place in spleen or even in the draining lymph nodes, may have little relevance to tumor behaviour (Stutman, 1982).

IN VIVO FUNCTIONS OF NK AND NC CELLS?

As indicated previously, NK and NC cells appear to be ideally fit for mediating immune surveillance in situ in a true Burnetian sense. These cells do not need priming for function, exist in relatively high frequencies in normal hosts, can handle in vivo small numbers of tumor cells and are present in circulation (see Roder et al., 1981 for review on NK and Stutman et al., 1981 for review on NC). In addition, their cytotoxic capacity for lymphoid and non-lymphoid tumors does not seem to require the presence of conventional tumor-associated transplantation antigens; although the NK-NC effector cells seem to show recognition for some surface structures which determine resistance or susceptibility to lysis (Roder et al., 1981; Stutman et al., 1981). In addition, it seems that the repair capacity of the lytic damage by the target cell proper may play a role in defining resistance-susceptibility to killing by

NK-NC cells (Collins et al., 1981). While there is good
evidence that NK-NC cells may be involved in preventing
growth of small inocula of transplanted tumor cells (Roder
et al., 1981; Stutman et al., 1981), the actual in vivo
function as a surveillance mechanism is not so well established. However, I should indicate that the current interpretation of the "normal" incidence of spontaneous and
induced tumors in athymic nude mice (Stutman, 1978 for detailed review), by normal meaning no major differences between the athymic nudes and their controls in tumor incidence or type, has been the normal or high levels of NK-NC
cells in nude animals (Roder et al., 1981; Stutman et al.,
1981; Herberman and Ortaldo, 1981).

Space limitations do not allow me to expand too much on
the available in vivo studies on the effect of NK or NC activity on tumor development (see Wigzell, 1982 for brief
review). However, I will present one example with NK cells,
which unfortunately does not fit with the expectations,
since it shows no clear correlation between the basal levels
of NK activity, or whether such activity can be augmented
by interferon or interferon inducers (Roder et al., 1981)
on spontaneous and induced lymphomas in different mouse
strains. Table 1 shows these results.

TABLE 1. LACK OF CORRELATION BETWEEN BASAL NK ACTIVITY AND
SUSCEPTIBILITY TO LYMPHOMA DEVELOPMENT IN DIFFERENT
INBRED MOUSE STRAINS

Strain	Lymphoma incidence (percent)*		NK activity**
	Spontaneous	MCA-induced***	
AKR	100 (330)	100 (150)	Low (I)
RF/J	20 (510)	93 (110)	Int.,High (I)
129/J	20 (500)	33 (260)	Low (I)
PL/J	10 (500)	40 (340)	Low (NI)
I/St	5 (550)	5 (350)	Low (NI)
A/J	10 (550)	5 (550)	Low (I)

*Lymphoma indicence presented as percent of total animals
under study; in parentheses, mean latency period in days.
**NK activity in spleen or blood, tested against YAC-1 target
cells in 4 or 18 hr ^{51}Cr-release assays. (I) means that augmentation of NK activity is inducible by in vivo or in vitro
treatment with interferon or poly-IC. Low activity is defined by 15% or less cytotoxicity at 100:1 effector:target
ratios in a 4 hr assay; High activity is defined for values

TABLE 1 FOOTNOTES CONTINUED:

of 35% lysis or higher under the same conditions.
***Induction was done using the Duran-Reynals et al. (1978)
protocol of skin painting with methylcholanthrene for the
PL/J, I/St and A/J studies. The values for spontaneous
and induced lymphomas in AKR, RF are from Duran-Reynals
et al., (1978), data on 129 is from Mayer et al. (1980).

It is apparent from Table 1 that spontaneous or induced
lymphoma development does not correlate well with the basal
levels of NK activity in a given strain, nor with the capacity to augment such low levels with interferon or interferon inducers. Some low NK strains, which usually are
as low or lower than the popular "NK deficient" beige mice
(Roder et al., 1981) do not show increased risk for lymphoma
development.

I will not repeat here our past criticism of the experimental support of immunological surveillance as mediated
by T cells (Stutman 1975; 1977 a,b; 1978), macrophages
(Stutman, 1981) or natural cell-mediated cytotoxicity effectors, i.e. NK-NC (Stutman, 1981). However, in spite
of the type of data in Table 1 and some of the studies reviewed by Wigzell (1982) concerning in vivo relevance of
NK-NC cells, it is apparent, based on the properties of
these natural effector cells, that for the first time there
is actually a mechanism which may act as a true surveillance
device, independently of the strong antigens of certain
tumor systems (Klein and Klein, 1977; Klein, 1980; Kripke,
1981; Klein and Purtilo, 1980). Thus, it warrants further
analysis.

CONCLUSION

This disjointed essay certainly aims at introducing
questions and caveats concerning the role of conventional
and unconventional tumor immunity and its regulation in
the behaviour of tumors in vivo. Our comments are based
primarily on the fact that our present knowledge of the
peculiar symbiont represented by the tumor-host interaction
is still rudimentary, in spite of some remarkable advances
in our understanding of regulatory mechanisms in immunity,
as well as the definition of effector functions in cell-
mediated immunity. The page limitations may help to keep
some important areas practically not discussed, and may

also help to generate somewhat dogmatic stances concerning certain aspects of the problem. As Aldous Huxley indicated, "...however elegant and memorable, brevity can never... do justice to all the facts of a complex situation..." (Huxley, 1965), and although this essay is brief, and indeed does not do justice to a complex situation, it is also neither elegant nor memorable.

Acknowledgments: I thank Dr. E.C. Lattime for discussions and collaborative work on NC-NK cells; Ms. Mary Lou Devitt for the care of our experimental animals and Ms. Linda Stevenson for preparation of the manuscript. The experiments described in some of the sections were supported by NIH grants CA-08748, CA-15988 and CA-17818.

REFERENCES

Adams DO, Snyderman R (1979). Do macrophages destroy nascent tumors? J Natl Cancer Inst 62: 1341.

Alexander P (1976). Surveillance against neoplastic cells: Is it mediated by macrophages? Br J Cancer 33: 344.

Andrews EJ (1974). Failure of immunosurveillance against chemically induced in situ tumors in mice. J Natl Cancer Inst 52: 729.

Auerbach R, Auerbach W (1981). Regional differences in the growth of normal and neoplastic cells. Science 215: 127.

Bashford EF, Murray JA, Haaland M, Bowen WH (1908). General results of propagation of malignant new growths. Third Sci Rep Imperial Cancer Res Fund London 3: 262.

Blazar B, Patarroyo M, Klein E, Klein G (1980). Increased sensitivity of human lymphoid lines to natural killer cells after induction of the Epstein-Barr viral cycle by superinfection or sodium butyrate. J Exp Med 151: 614.

Burnet FM (1970). The concept of immunological surveillance. Prog Exp Tumor Res 13:1.

Collins J.L., Patek PQ, Cohn M (1981). Tumorigenicity and lysis by natural killers. J Exp Med 153: 89.

Duran-Reynals ML, Lilly F, Bosch A, Blank KJ (1978). The genetic basis of susceptibility to leukemia induction in mice by 3-methylcholanthrene applied percutaneously. J Exp Med 147: 459.

Ehrlich P (1906). Experimentelle Karzinomstudien an Mausen. Arb Inst Exp Ther Frankfurt 1: 65.

Fidler IJ, Hart IR (1982). Biological diversity in metastatic neoplasms: Origins and implications. Science 217: 998.

Gershon RK, Carter RL, Knodo K (1967) On concomitant immunity in tumor-bearing hamsters. Nature 213: 674.

Greene MI (1980) The genetic and cellular basis of regulation of the immune response to tumor antigen. Contemp Topics Immunobiol 11: 81.

Hellstrom KE, Hellstrom I (1974) Lymphocyte mediated cytotoxicity and blocking serum activity to tumor antigens. Adv Immunol 18: 209.

Hellstrom I, Hellstrom KE, Sjogren HO (1970) Serum mediated inhibition of cellular immunity to methylcholanthrene-induced murine sarcomas. Cell Immunol 1: 18.

Herberman RB, Holden HT (1979) Natural killer cells as anti-tumor effector cells. J Natl Cancer Inst 62: 441.

Herberman RB, Ortaldo JR (1981) Natural killer cells: Their role in defense against disease. Science 214: 24.

Huxley A (1965) "Brave New World Revisited" New York: Perennial Library, Harper & Row Pubs. p. vii.

Kamo I , Friedman H (1977) Immunosuppression and the role of suppressive factors in cancer. Adv Cancer Res 25: 271.

Klein G (1975). Immunological surveillance against neoplasia. Harvey Lectures 69: 71.

Klein G (1980) Theme 10: Summary Tumor Immunol. In Fougereau GJ, Dausset J (eds): "Immunology 80: Progress in Immunology IV," New York: Academic Press, p. 680.

Klein G, Klein E (1977) Immune surveillance against virus-induced tumors and non-rejectability of spontaneous tumors: Contrasting consequences of host versus tumor evolution. Proc Natl Acad Sci USA 74: 2121.

Klein G, Purtilo DT (1980) Symposium on Epstein-Barr virus-induced lymphoproliferative diseases in immunodeficient patients. Cancer Res 41: 4209.

Kripke ML (1981) Immunologic mechanisms in UV-radiation carcinogenesis. Adv Cancer Res 34: 69.

Mayer A, Lilly F, Duran-Reynals ML (1980) Genetically dominant resistance in mice to 3-methylcholanthrene-induced lymphoma. Proc Natl Acad Sci 77: 2960.

Meltzer MS, Occhionero M, Ruco LP (1982) Macrophage activation for tumor cytotoxicity: regulatory mechanisms for induction and control of cytotoxic activity. Fed Proc 41: 2198.

Mikulska ZB, Smith C , Alexander, P (1966) Evidence for an immunological reaction of the host directed against its own actively growing primary tumor. J Natl Cancer Inst 36: 29.

Naor D (1979) Suppressor cells: Permitters and promoters of malignancy Adv Cancer Res 29: 45.

Nelson DS (1974) Immunity to infection, allograft immunity and tumor immunity: Parallels and contrasts. Transplant Rev 19: 226.

Pearson G, Johansson B, Klein G (1978). Antibody-dependent cellular cytotoxicity against Epstein-Barr virus-associated antigens in African patients with nasopharyngeal carcinoma. Int J Cancer 22: 120.

Plescia OJ, Smith AH, Grinwich K (1975) Subversion of immune system by tumor cells and role of prostaglandins. Proc. Natl Acad Sci USA 72: 1848.

Prehn RT (1963). Function of depressed immunologic reactivity during carcinogenesis. J Natl Cancer Inst 31: 791.

Rickinson AB, Moss DJ, Wallace LE, Rowe M, Misko IS, Epstein MA, Pope JH (1981). Long term T cell mediated immunity to Epstein-Barr virus. Cancer Res 41: 4216.

Roder JC, Karre K, Kiessling R (1981). Natural killer cells. Prog Allergy 28: 66.

Shin HS, Johnson RJ, Pasternack GR, Economou JS (1978). Mechanisms of tumor immunity: The role of antibody and non-immune effectors. Prog Allergy 25: 163.

Stutman O (1975). Immunodepression and malignancy. Adv Cancer Res 22: 261.

Stutman O (1977a) Immunodeficiency and cancer. In Green I, Cohen S, McClusky RT (eds): "Mechanisms of Tumor Immunity", New York: J. Wiley and Sons, p. 27.

Stutman O (1977b) Immunological surveillance. In Hiatt HH, Watson HD, Winsten JA (eds): "Cold Spring Harbor Conferences on Cell Proliferation", Book B, New York: Cold Spring Harbor Laboratories, p. 729.

Stutman, O (1978) Spontaneous, viral and chemically induced tumors in the nude mouse. In Fogh J, Giovanella B (eds) "The Nude Mouse in Experimental and Clinical Research", New York: Academic Press, p. 411.

Stutman O (1980) Some thoughts on tumor immunology and immunotherapy. In Steinberg GM, Gery I, Nussenblatt RB (eds): "Proc Immunology and the Eye: Workshop I", Virginia: Information Retrieval Inc, p. 179.

Stutman O (1981) Immunological surveillance and cancer In Waters H (ed): "The Handbook of Cancer Immunology", Vol 7, New York: Garland STPM Press, p. 1

Stutman O (1982) Natural and induced immunity to mouse mammary tumors and the mouse mammary tumor virus (MuMTV). Springer Semin Immunopathol 4: 333.

Stutman O, Lattime EC, Figarella EF (1981) Natural cytotoxic cells against solid tumors in mice: a comparison with natural killer cells. Fed Proc 40: 2699.

Urban JL, Burton RC, Holland JM, Kripke ML, Schrieber H
(1982). Mechanisms of syngeneic tumor rejection. Susceptibility of host-selected progressor variants to various
immunological effector cells. J Exp Med 155: 557.

Vaage J (1973). Concomitant immunity and specific desensiti-
zation in murine tumor hosts. Israel J Med Sci 9: 332.

Wigzell H (1982). Immunosurveillance. In Yohn DS, Blakslee
JR (eds): "Advances in Comparative Leukemia Research 1981"
New York: Elsevier, p. 173.

Woodruff MFA (1980)."The Interaction of Cancer and Host. Its
Therapeutic Significance" New York: Grune & Stratton, p.
121

Youn JK, LeFrancois D, Barski G (1973). In vitro studies on
mechanism of the "eclipse" of cell-mediated immunity
in mice bearing advanced tumors. J Natl Cancer Inst 50:
921.

13th International Cancer Congress, Part B
Biology of Cancer (1), pages 325–334
© **1983 Alan R. Liss, Inc., 150 Fifth Avenue, New York, NY 10011**

NATURAL KILLER CELLS IN CANCER

Eva Klein, M.D.

Department of Tumor Biology
Karolinska Institutet
S-104 01 Stockholm, Sweden

How to interpret the title? What is expected from it?
In order to answer these questions we have to look back at
the discovery of the natural killer - or spontaneous cytotoxicity - phenomenon. It emerged in studies which searched
for tumor specific lymphocyte mediated responses in cancer
patients and simultaneously in animal experiments aimed to
study the details and relevance of cell mediated immunity
against transplanted tumors. Tumor cell lines were used as
targets in most of these assays, based on the assumption
that an interpretation of the results with standard targets
would not be hampered by the variation in their sensitivity to lysis. It was found that lymphocytes of healthy individuals and unprimed animals often exerted lytic effects.
Since tumor lines were the targets, it was proposed that
this activity indicates the existence of a surveillance mechanism acting promptly on transformed cells before the development of an immune response against putative tumor specific surface antigens. Consequently the nature of the lym-
phocyte-target interaction, the target surface moiety recognised by the lymphocytes and the phenotypic characteristics of the reactive lymphocytes have been the subject of
many investigations.

The nomenclature was coined operationally, based on the
lack of immunisation steps similar to the designation used

Acknowledgements. This work was supported by PHS grant
number 1 R01 CA 25184-03 and by grant number 5 R01 CA25250,
both awarded by the National Cancer Institute, DHHS (DHEW)
and by the Swedish Cancer Society.

for naturally occurring antibodies. The conventional designation for lytic cells which appear after immunisation or
are generated in vitro: cytotoxic T lymphocyte (CTL) existed already at that time.

However, the operational limitation originally defined
by the effectors almost unperceivably was extended to the
target and "NK effect" or NK cells" were often used to name
systems, whenever K562 in man or YAC in the mouse were the
targets even if the lymphocytes were experimentally manipu-
lated. With the phenotypic characterisation of the active
populations a third basis for the definition appeared.

What is then our present task? Reactivity of the patients' lymphocytes against their own tumor cells, which is
the relevant function in tumor immunology, does not conform
with the designation natural killing, since they may have
been immunised against these cells. Reactivity against K562
or against other NK sensitive targets may not be of relevance for the response against their own tumor. It seems that
the definition of the reactive subset in the lymphocyte population links the "natural" to the "autoimmune" lytic phenomena. Autologous tumor cells are the targets in the latter
system, while any cell which does not carry antigens against
which the lymphocyte donor is sensitised can be the target
of the "natural" system.

With certain cell lines, membrane properties and not
the recognition of surface antigens seem to be responsible
for the lytic consequence of the majority of target-lympho-
cyte encounters. Experiments with mouse somatic hybrid cell
lines support this assumption. In hybrids between high and
low NK sensitive cells, alloantigens, virally determined
cell surface antigens, and other tumor-related membrane antigens were expressed codominantly but their NK sensitivity
was low (Ährlund-Richter et al. 1980).

We therefore proposed that the NK sensitivity is related to the differentiation of the target, because differentiation traits are usually suppressed in somatic hybrids.
This assumption has received further support by the demonstration of the NK sensitivity of certain stem cells in the
bone marrow and primitive types of teratocarcinoma lines
(Hansson et al. 1981, Stern et al. 1980). Differentiated
cell lines from the same tumor were found to be more resistant.

Some Characteristics of the NK Function

Considerable effort has been directed to the characterisation of natural killer cells on the basis of morphology and cell surface markers. In these experiments K562 or other cell lines selected for sensitivity were used as targets. Papers which deal with the subject are numerous and this reflects the fact that the cells with lytic function are heterogeneous. Variation in lymphocyte separation techniques provided a slightly varied information and consequently led to slightly or largely divergent conclusions about the nature of the active cells, influenced by the bias of the investigator.

The lymphocytes have been studied for cell membrane markers such as nylon adherance, expression of SRBC(E), Fc, and lectin receptors; morphologic features; reactivity with monoclonal antibodies and buoyant density. Taking into consideration these features, the activity of the human blood lymphocytes can be enriched by separating nylon wool passed, large, granular, Fc gamma receptor-positive cells not expressing high avidity E receptors and reacting with the monoclonal antibody OKM1. Due to the quantitative variations in the expression of these markers, each differing independently from the other, it is not possible to separate all active cells and all inactive cells in homogeneous populations.

The phenotypic characteristics of the NK active lymphocyte subsets and the fact that in certain systems they were proven to show selectivity, provided evidence that NK is at least in part a T cell function (Potter and Moore 1979, Kaplan and Calleweart 1978, Masucci et al. 1982 c, Vanky and Klein 1981, Welsh et al. 1979). We proposed therefore previously that the distinction between CTL and NK cells is not as sharp as initially suggested (Klein 1980).

The strength of spontaneous cytotoxicity in the blood lymphocyte population varies in different individuals. This is reflected in the dose-response curves when a constant number of target cells are exposed to a different number of effector cells. The activity of blood lymphocytes collected from tumor patients was found to be lower than that of healthy individuals (Vose et al. 1977). Also in tumor bearing mice the NK activity of the spleen cell population was low (Becker et al. 1976).

Lymphocytes exposed to various in vitro manipulations such as interferon (IFN) treatment or addition of phytohemagglutinin (PHA) during the assay have enhanced the activity (Santoli and Koprowski 1979, Masucci et al. 1982 b). With exceptionally high NK-active donors, neither of these two treatments were found to increase substantially the lytic effect. This suggests that the lytic potential required for the killing of the particular target cell was already maximal. IFN-induced potentiation of cytotoxicity, IFN-activated killing (IAK), occurs in those lymphocyte subsets which also exert the function spontaneously (Berthold et al. 1981). Therefore, the distinction between NK and IAK may be only operational. In contrast, PHA can induce the lytic machinary in lymphocytes which are in a physiologic inactive state, such as the high avidity sheep red blood cells (SRCB) receptor carrying Fcj receptor-negative subset (Masucci et al. 1982 b, Clark et al. 1981).

An important similarity between the natural, IFN-, and lectin-induced cytotoxic potential is its species restriction (Hansson et al. 1978, Stejskal et al. 1973). Thymocytes and activated T cells have an affinity for cells derived from the same or related species and this can be revealed visually because they can form conjugates (Galili et al. 1978). On the first level, the lymphocyte seems to recognise the target cell on the basis of the species relationship. On the second level, the lymphocyte detects the finer alterations on the plasma membrane and this is the basis of immunologic specificity, i.e. epitope recognition. We assume that with exceptional targets the first type of interaction may be sufficient for lysis to occur once the lymphocytes is differentiated to perform this function (Klein 1980).

Lysis of Allogenic, Freshly Isolated Cells by IFN-Treated Blood Lymphocytes

In the search for autotumor-reactive lymphocytes in blood, we found that freshly harvested tumor cells from human sarcomas and carcinomas possess low NK sensitivity or none at all. The cells were lysed by healthy donor lymphocytes only when these belonged to the category with very high NK potential, as indicated by the strong effect on K562 cells. However, cytotoxicity could be induced against tumor biopsy cells in 50% of the cases, by incubation of the lymphocytes for 2-3 h with IFN before the tests (Vanky et al.

1980).

Since allorecognition is a property of the T subsets, our interpretation of the results was that the biopsy cells were killed by alloreactive T cells triggered for lytic function by treatment with IFN. The high proportion of lymphocytes which recognise alloantigens may explain that activation without clonal expansion is sufficient to generate cytolytic populations (Nisbet et al. 1969). Similar results, but with a different interpretation, were reported for leukemias and melanomas (Mukherji et al. 1980, Zarling et al. 1979).

One way to prove that alloantigens are responsible for the lytic effect is to show that lymphocytes (or blasts), from the donor who provided the tumor target cells, have an inhibitory effect when mixed into the cytotoxic assay. Since they also express the alloantigens they ought to compete with the target cells for the effectors. These were indeed the results of our competition experiments performed using the ^{51}Cr release assay (Table 1; Vanky and Klein 1981). The presence of target identical unlabeled cells, and lymphocytes from the target donor lowered the ^{51}Cr release values, but tumor cells from the effector donor or unrelated individuals had only a slight effect and only at high labeled: cold target ratios. In all experiments K562 and Daudi cells, as well as the target cells inhibited. Similar results were reported by Pattengale et al. who showed that the lytic effect of IFN-activated lymphocytes from healthy donors against allogeneic leukemia cells was inhibited by an admixture of K562 cells (Pattengale et al. 1982).

The characterisation of the lymphocyte subsets which act on the allogeneic tumor cells substantiated the cross-competition with K562 and Daudi cells in this lytic system. Lymphocyte subsets separated on the basis of cell density were tested for lysis against both K562 and fresh tumor cells. The relative distribution of the activities was similar, in that they were enriched in the low density fractions as shown for the anti-K562 effect previously (Masucci et al. 1982 a).

Lysis of Autologous, Freshly Isolated Tumor Cells by Blood Lymphocytes

Autologous tumor cells were lysed in short-term in vitro assays in 25% of the cases (Vanky et al. 1980). In cold target competition experiments this effect was not inhibited by admixture of concanavalin (Con A) blasts A of the patient or of allogeneic freshly isolated tumor cells (Table 1). When patients' lymphocytes were the effectors against allogeneic tumor cells, their own tumors did not compete (Vanky and Klein 1982). These findings suggest that in the autotumor reactive systems, tumor and/or organ-specific antigens are recognised, and the various tumors involved in these experiments did not cross-react. This may be either due to a real antigenic difference or because a putative cross-reactivity could not be detected due to the MHC-restriction phenomenon.

As discussed above, the designation of the cytolytic system in which lymphocytes of patients and their own tumor cells participate may not conform operationally with NK, since it may reflect tumor specific sensitisation. On the other hand, the same phenotypically defined subset of lymphocytes which perform the indiscriminate killing of cell lines may act also on the autologous tumor cells in vitro (Masucci et al. 1982 a).

It seeems that in a certain differentiation state T cells are capable of lysing targets in either way and it is the characteristics of the target that are decisive. Apart from those lymphocytes which can respond to both types of trigger signals, other functional subsets may exert only one or the other action.

The relative representation of these functionally different subsets differs individually and also in lymphocyte populations of various sources (blood, spleen, lymph node) and can be shifted temporarily both in vivo and in vitro. Shifts may be caused by direct interactions between different lymphocyte subsets or soluble factors.

If these aspects are considered, the lytic events may be considered as: 1. Natural, activated (e.g. by IFN or lectins); a) antigen restrictive, selective, clonal; b) non-restricted, non-selective, polyclonal. 2. Immune; a) sensitisation specific, restricted, clonal; b) transactivated, restricted, selective, clonal; c) non-restricted, non-selective, polyclonal.

Introduction of the clonality aspects in the designations could help the evaluation and comparison of results obtained in different systems.

Conclusion

Results of the cold target competition assays using freshly isolated tumor cells as targets and the characteristics of cloned killer lines, suggest that at least a proportion of lytic T cells can act on targets due to different cell membrane interaction (Dennert 1980, Hengarten et al. 1982). One is based on the recognition of cell surface epitope by the clonally distributed genetically determined receptors and the other does not seem to involve antigen recognition but may be triggered by the contact between the effector and target cell surfaces, through a yet unknown mechanism. As mentioned above, in the latter only the species seems to be recognised by the effectors.

Considering the general competing capacity of K562 and Daudi the main distinction between the two types of lysis seems to be that one is polyclonal; it is exerted by lymphocytes which carry the relevant antigen receptor; it is clonal.

Both of these lytic events can occur in assay systems designated as NK, IAK, and CTL (Vanky and Klein 1982). Because of the heterogeneity of the lymphocyte population and the various plasma membrane moieties which can be recognised on one target type, even in one essay, the recorded lysis is the sum of concomitant events in which the nature of the effector and target interaction may differ.

In several series of experiments reported in the literature, the natural cytotoxicity of blood lymphocytes was monitored in various categories of patients using K562 cells as target. We assume that the anti-K562 effect is a measure of the cytolytic activation profile of the lymphocyte population. Thus information obtained from such experiments is relevant for a possible effect against the autologous tumor cells. It is, however, an important consideration that fresh tumor cells (and some tumor lines) are not sensitive to the indiscriminating lytic effect. Consequently, they have to carry antigens recognised by the host in order to be damaged by the lymphocytes. The question to be posed, therefore, is whether the tumor cells carry such antigens

before the significance of the cytolytic potential of lymphocyte populations can be judged for the antitumor response. If lymphocytes with specific receptors exist, they are
likely to be represented in all subsets with different functional characteristics including the cytotoxic subset. The
blood lymphocyte population of individuals with a high proportion of cells with lytic potential revealed by its effect
on cell lines (such as K562) may thus lyse their own tumor
cells on the basis of antigen recognition.

Table 1.

Cold target competition on the lytic effect against freshly
isolated tumor cells by blood lymphocytes.[a]

Unlabeled targets[b]		Number of tests	% inhibition of ^{51}Cr release Ratio labeled/Cold Targets		
			5:1	1:1	1:5
Autologous Target - Effector Combination					
autologous	T	10	30 ± 3[c]	67 ± 11	93 ± 7
autologous	L	5	0	9 ± 6	13 ± 8
unrelated	T	15	0	6 ± 5	26 ± 7
unrelated	L	5	7 ± 7	10 ± 5	20 ± 3
Allogeneic Target - Effector Combination[d]					
target identical	T	24	35 ± 6	66 ± 13	92 ± 5
effector "	T	8	8 ± 2	11 ± 3	14 ± 3
unrelated	T	27	6 ± 1	14 ± 4	34 ± 1
target identical	L	7	16 ± 5	72 ± 11	87 ± 18
effector "	L	5	0	4 ± 1	14 ± 2
unrelated	L	21	0	5 ± 2	17 ± 4
K562		20	61 ± 9	82 ± 5	99 ± 1
Daudi		6	33 ± 7	62 ± 3	91 ± 2

a. Specific ^{51}Cr release measured at effector:target ratio
50:1 in 4h cytotoxicity test without cold targets was in all
cases at least 20%.
b. T = Tumor biopsy cells; L = PHA or Con-A blasts.
c. Mean $\pm$ SD.
d. The lymphocytes were pretreated for 2h with 1000 IU/ml
IFN-α

Becker S, Klein E (1976). Decreased "natural killer" effect in tumor bearing mice and its relation to the immunity against oncorna virus-determined cell surface antigens. Eur J Immunol 6:892.

Berthold W, Masucci M G, Klein E, Strander (1981). Interferon treatment elevates the cytotoxic potential of lymphocytes and thereby increases the frequency of functional killer cells. Hum Lymph Diff 1:1.

Clark EA, Sturge JC (1981). Phylogeny of NK cell reactivity against human and nonhuman primate lymphoblastoid cell lines: evolving and conserved target antigens. J Immunol 126:969.

Dennert G, Weiss S, Werner JF (1981). T cells may express multiple activities: Specific allohelp, cytolysis and delayed-type hypersensitivity are expressed by a cloned T line. Proc Natl Acad Sci 78:4540.

Galili U, Galili N, Vanky F, Klein E (1978). Natural species restricted attachment of human and murine T lymphocytes to various cells. Proc Natl Acad Sci 75:2396.

Hansson M, Kiessling R, Andersson B (1981). Human felal thymus and bone marrow contain target cells for natural killer cells. Eur J Cancer 11:8.

Hansson M, Kärre K, Bakács T, Kiessling R, Klein G (1978). Intra- and interspecies reactivity of human and mouse natural killer (NK) cells. J Immunol 121:6.

Hengarten H, Acha-Orbea H, Lang R, Stitz L, Rosenthal KL, Groscurth P, Keller P (1982). Murine clones of cells with NK like activities. In Natural Cell-Mediated Immunity. Herberman RB (ed), in press.

Kaplan J, Calleweart DM (1978). Expression of human T lymphocyte antigens by natural killer cells. J Natl Cancer Inst 69:961.

Klein E (1980). Natural and activated cytotoxic T lymphocytes. Immunol Today 1:IV.

Masucci MG, Bejarano MT, Vanky F, Klein E (1982 a). Cytotoxic and cytostatic activity of human large granular lymphocytes against allogeneic tumor biopsy cells and autologous EBV infected lymphocytes. In Natural Cell-Mediated Immunity. Herberman RB (ed) Academic Press, in press.

Masucci G, Masucci MG, Klein E (1982 b). Activation of human blood lymphocyte subsets for cytotoxic potential. Cell Immunol 69:21.

Masucci G, Masucci MG, Klein E (1982 c). Natural cytotoxicity of human blood lymphocyte subsets separated on the basis of nylon adherençe, SRBC and EA rosetting and characterized with monoclonal reagents. Cell Immunol 69:166.

Mukerji B, Flowers A, Rothman L, Nathanson L (1980). Spontaneous in vitro cytotoxicity against autochthonous human maelanoma cells. J Immunol 124:413.

Nisbet NW, Simonsen M, Zaleski M (1969) The frequency of antigen sensitive cells in transplantation. J Exp Med 129:459.

Pattengale PK, Gidlund M, Nilsson K, Sundström C, Sällström J, Simonsson B, Wigzell H (1982). Lysis of fresh human B-lymphocyte-derived leukemia cells by interferon-activated natural killer (NK) cells. Int J Cancer 29:1.

Potter MR, Moore M (1979). Natural cytotoxic activity of human lymphocyte subpopulations. Immunol 37:187.

Santoli D, Koprowski H (1979). Mechanism of activation of human natural killer cells against tumor and virus infected cells. Immun Rev 44:125.

Stejskal V, Lindberg S, Holm G, Perlmann P (1973). Differential cytotoxicity of activated lymphocytes on allogeneic and xenogeneic target cells. II. Activation by phytohemagglutinin. Cell Immunol 8:82.

Stern P, Gidlund M, Örn A, Wigzell H (1980). Natural killer cells mediate lysis of embryonal carcinoma cells lacking MHC. Nature 285:341.

Vanky F, Argov S, Einhorn S, Klein E (1980). Role of allo-antigens in natural killing. Allogeneic but not autologous tumor biopsy cells are sensitive for interferon-induced cytotoxicity of human blood lymphocytes. J Exp Med 151:1151.

Vanky F, Klein E (1981). Alloreactive cytotoxicity of inter-feron triggered human lymphocytes detected with tumor biopsy targets. Immunogenetics 15:31.

Vanky F, Klein E (1982). Specificity of fresh and activated human cytotoxic lymphocytes. In Natural Cell-Mediated Immunity. Herberman RB (ed), Academic Press, in press.

Vose BM, Vanky F, Argov S, Klein E (1977). Natural cytotoxicity in man: activity of lymph node and tumor-infiltrating lymphocytes. Eur J Immunol 7:753.

Welsh RM, Zinkernagel RM, Hallenbeck LA (1979). Cytotoxic cells induced during choriomeningitis virus infection in mice. II. Specificities of the natural killer cells. J Immunol 122:475.

Zarling JM, Eskra L, Borden EC, Horoszewiecz J, Carter WA (1979) Activation of human natural killer cells cytotoxic for human leukemia cells by purified interferon. J Immunol 123:63.

Ährlund-Richter L, Masucci G, Klein E (1980). Somatic hybrids between a high NK-sensitive lymphoid (YACIR) and several low sensitive sarcoma or L-cell derived mouse lines exhibit low sensitivity. Somatic Cell Gen 6:89.

13th International Cancer Congress, Part B
Biology of Cancer (1), pages 335–344
© 1983 Alan R. Liss, Inc., 150 Fifth Avenue, New York, NY 10011

PROPERTIES OF THE SIRS SUPPRESSOR PATHWAY

Thomas M. Aune, Ph.D., Carl W. Pierce, M.D., Ph.D.

Department of Pathology and Laboratory Medicine, The Jewish Hospital of St. Louis, and Department of Pathology and of Microbiology and Immunology, Washington University School of Medicine, St. Louis, MO 63110

INTRODUCTION

Polyclonal activation of spleen cells with the T cell mitogen, concanavalin A, results in the induction of suppressor cells which are Ly 2^+ T lymphocytes. These suppressor cells act by releasing a soluble suppressor lymphokine, soluble immune response suppressor (SIRS) (Rich and Pierce, 1973; Rich and Pierce, 1974). Suppressor cells or their product, SIRS, nonspecifically inhibit a variety of in vitro immune responses including primary and secondary antibody responses, proliferative responses to mitogens or alloantigens and the generation of cytotoxic T cell responses (Pierce and Aune, 1981). The target of SIRS is the macrophage (Mø) and SIRS-treated Mø suppress immune responses in a fashion analogous to SIRS. SIRS or SIRS-treated Mø suppress responses with a characteristic kinetic pattern. Responses initiate normally for the first three days of culture, are partially suppressed on day 4 and are fully suppressed on day 5 (Tadakuma and Pierce, 1976; Tadakuma and Pierce, 1978). The reason for this is that SIRS-treated Mø release a second factor, Mø-derived suppressor factor, which is responsible for SIRS mediated suppression and is not released from Mø until day 2-3 of culture (Aune and Pierce, 1981b). In contrast to SIRS, addition of Mø-SF at culture initiation blocks both initiation and full expression of the immune response under study. Further, Mø-SF can be added at any point during the culture period up to 2 hrs before assay and fully inhibit responses. Thus, Mø-SF can terminate immune responses within a few hours. Mø-SF also inhibits division by a variety of normal and neoplastic cell lines. These include 3T3 fibroblast, plasmacytoma (MOPC315), thymoma (EL4), masocytoma (P815) or transformed fibroblast (L929) cell lines (Aune and Pierce, 1981a).

PROPERTIES OF MØ-SF

SIRS-treated MØ release approximately equivalent amounts of MØ-SF on days 2 and 3 of the culture period after an initial 24 hr lag period. MØ-SF can also be obtained from the MØ-like cell line RAW264.7 following treatment with SIRS but not from several other MØ-like cell lines (P388D1, J774.2, PU5-1R and J774A.1). Although MØ-SF activity is quite stable under normal conditions it is easily inactivated by a variety of compounds which can serve as electron donors. These include sulfhydryl compounds such as dithiothreitol, 2-mercaptoethanol or cysteine, reducing agents such as sodium borohydryde, or aromatic compounds and aromatic amines such as hydroquinone, phenylenediamine, o-dianisidine or p-aminobenzoic acid. These and other data suggested that MØ-SF may be an oxidizing agent and raised the possibility that MØ-SF may not be a newly synthesized product, but may actually be modified SIRS. For this reason, requirements for MØ-SF production by SIRS-treated MØ were examined. It was found that MØ-SF production was insensitive to inhibitors of protein synthesis, RNA synthesis or prostaglandin synthesis, but was sensitive to catalase or cyanide. Although cyanide sensitivity has multiple explanations, some of which may not reflect upon the relationship between SIRS and MØ-SF, sensitivity to catalase suggested that peroxide was necessary for MØ-SF production. This finding, coupled with the similar mol. wt., heat and pH sensitivities of SIRS and MØ-SF suggested that MØ-SF may be a product of the reaction between SIRS and H_2O_2. This hypothesis was tested and found to be correct. SIRS and MØ-SF activity are simple to distinguish since SIRS only suppresses plaque forming cell (PFC) responses when added at culture initiation whereas MØ-SF suppresses responses when added at any point during the culture period. Using this procedure to distinguish between SIRS and MØ-SF, it was found that as low as 10^{-12}M H_2O_2 could convert SIRS to MØ-SF. Table 1 compares the yield of MØ-SF using similar amounts of SIRS and either MØ or H_2O_2 to convert SIRS to MØ-SF. The similar yields of MØ-SF under these conditions indicate that H_2O_2 is as efficient as MØ at activating

Table 1

CONVERSION OF SIRS TO MØ-SF

SIRS[a] (units)	MØ[b]	H_2O_2	MØ-SF[d] (units)
20	-	-	0
20	+	-	16
20	-	+	22

[a]One unit of SIRS is defined as the amount necessary to suppress PFC responses by 50% when added at culture initiation and assayed on day 5.
[b]RAW264.7 MØ were cultured with 20 units of SIRS as previously described (Aune and Pierce, 1981b).
[c]SIRS was reacted with $10^{-12}M$ H_2O_2 for 15 min, 0-4°C as previously described (Aune and Pierce, 1981c).
[d]MØ-SF activity was tested by addition to SRBC-stimulated spleen cell cultures 24 hr before assay. One unit of MØ-SF activity is defined as the amount necessary to suppress responses by 50 under these conditions.

SIRS and suggests that other mechanisms do not play significant roles in SIRS mediated suppression. Since MØ-SF appears to be activated or oxidized SIRS use of the term MØ-SF has been discontinued in favor of $SIRS_{ox}$ (Aune and Pierce, 1981b,c; Aune and Pierce, 1982c).

ACTIVATION OF THE SIRS PATHWAY BY IFNβ

Agents which inactivate $SIRS_{ox}$ or block its formation also block SIRS mediated suppression. The most effective agents include 2-mercaptoethanol, dithiothreitol, ascorbic acid, iodide, p-aminobenzoic acid and catalase. This suggests that the use of these reagents may be a helpful way to screen for the SIRS pathway in other suppressor systems. Addition of IFNβ (10^7 units/mg protein; 30-50 units/culture) at culture initiation resulted in complete suppression of PFC responses to sheep erythrocytes; addition of 2-mercaptoethanol, catalase, ascorbic acid or iodide completely or partially blocked suppression. These results suggested that IFNβ may suppress PFC responses by activating suppressor T cells and the SIRS pathway. Table 2 shows

Table 2

ACTIVATION OF SUPPRESSOR CELLS BY CON A OR IFNβ

Cell Type	Activator	Suppressor Cells	SIRS
Spleen	Con A	+	+
	IFNβ	+	+
T cells	Con A	+	+
	IFNβ	+	+
B cells	Con A	-	-
	IFNβ	-	-
Ly 1$^+$ T cells	Con A	-	-
	IFNβ	-	-
Ly 2$^+$ T cells	Con A	+	+
	IFNβ	+	+

schematically the activation of suppressor cells by IFNβ or con A and the phenotype of activated suppressor cells. These and other results have shown that either con A or IFNβ activate Ly2$^+$ suppressor T cells and that suppressor cells of both types act by releasing the soluble lymphokine, SIRS (Aune and Pierce, 1982a). T cell hybridomas producing SIRS have been constructed and SIRS has been purified to homogeneity from hybridoma culture supernatant fluids. SIRS exists as two species with mol. wts. of 14,000 and 21,500 (Aune, Webb and Pierce, 1982d); the relationships of these two species of SIRS are being investigated.

INHIBITION OF IFNβ OR SIRS MEDIATED SUPPRESSION BY LEVAMISOLE

A number of immunopharmacological agents have been described in recent years which enhance immune responsiveness in normal and clinically compromised hosts (Hadden, 1981). One of these drugs, levamisole, was tested for its ability to block SIRS- or IFNβ-mediated suppression. At optimal concentrations (10 μg/ml) levamisole completely blocked suppression by either SIRS or IFNβ. Levamisole did not affect the activity of SIRS, IFNβ or SIRS$_{OX}$, the three active mediators in this pathway, but instead inhibited production of SIRS$_{OX}$ by SIRS treated Mø or inhibited conversion of SIRS to SIRS$_{OX}$ by levamisole (Table 3) (Aune and Pierce, 1982b). Experiments analyzing the effects of levamisole on IFNβ- or SIRS-mediated suppression have been

Table 3

EFFECT OF LEVAMISOLE ON $SIRS_{ox}$ PRODUCTION

SIRS (units/ml)	Activator	Levamisole	% Suppression[a]
10	-	-	0
10	MØ	-	70-90
10	MØ	$10\mu g/ml$	0-20
10	H_2O_2	-	70-90
10	H_2O_2	$0.1\mu g/ml$	0-20

[a]$SIRS_{ox}$ samples were added to antigen stimulated cultures on day 4 and PFC assayed on day 5. Results are expressed as % suppression of control responses.

useful for three reasons. First, they strengthen the hypothesis that IFN_β derives its immunosuppressive properties through activation of the SIRS pathway. Second, these experiments provide another means by which the conversion of SIRS to $SIRS_{ox}$ can be analyzed and strengthens the link between SIRS and $SIRS_{ox}$. Finally, they offer an alternate view of immunoenhancing agents; at least some immunoenhancing agents may inhibit suppressor cell or suppressor factor function rather than actually serving as direct immunostimulatory agents. Other immunomodulating agents such as muramyldipeptide, tuftsin or bestatin do not appear to affect the SIRS suppressor pathway.

MECHANISMS OF $SIRS_{ox}$ ACTION

$SIRS_{ox}$ acts rapidly to inhibit cell division by normal or neoplastic cells and antibody secretion. Under appropriate conditions inhibition of cell division is reversible by addition of high concentrations of 2-mercaptoethanol or dithiothreitol. Table 4 shows the effects of $SIRS_{ox}$ on division by the plasmacytoma cell line MOPC315. Cells were cultured with 5-10 units of $SIRS_{ox}$ for 17 hours, counted, treated with $10^{-3}M$ 2-mercaptoethanol and recounted 2 hrs later. Inhibition was largely complete in the presence of either 5 or 10 units of $SIRS_{ox}$. However, addition of $10^{-3}M$ 2-mercaptoethanol to culture treated with 5, but not 10 units $SIRS_{ox}$, caused a rapid increase in cell

Table 4

INHIBITION OF CELL DIVISION BY $SIRS_{OX}$

$SIRS_{OX}$	% Inhibition[a]	2-ME, M	% Inhibition[b]
5	78	10^{-3}	7
10	89	10^{-3}	89

[a]MOPC 315 cells were treated with $SIRS_{OX}$ for 17 hrs and counted.
[b]2-ME was added to inhibited and control cultures and cells were recounted 2 hrs later.

number almost to control values. These and other data indicate that $SIRS_{OX}$ can block cells in the late G_2/M phase of the cell cycle and that addition of 2-mercaptoethanol or dithiotreitol reverses inhibition. Table 4 also shows that the ability to reverse inhibition is very sensitive to the amount of $SIRS_{OX}$ present. An increase in the concentration of $SIRS_{OX}$ by two-fold only increased inhibition by 10% but completely prevented reversal by 2-mercaptoethanol. These data suggest that their is a critical dose-effect relationship between reversible and irreversible inhibition (Aune and Pierce, 1981a).

Inactivation of $SIRS_{OX}$ by electron donors and reversal of $SIRS_{OX}$-mediated inhibition by sulfhydryl reducing agents, such as 2-mercaptoethanol or dithiothreitol, suggest that $SIRS_{OX}$ may be an oxidzing agent which may act by oxidizing or modifying cellular protein sulfhydryl groups necessary for cell division. Modification of cellular protein sulfhydryls can lead to inhibition of cell division and the disruption of a wide variety of intracellular processes (Rebhun, et al., 1976). Although modification of protein sulfhydryl groups is a very efficient way to inhibit a wide variety of enzyme activities, treatment of cells with low concentrations of sulfhydryl modifying agents such as N-ethylmaleimide or organic mercurials results in inhibition of cell division without causing significant inhibition of protein synthesis, DNA synthesis and without causing cell toxicity (Thrasher, 1973; Lehman, 1947). Similarly, DNA and protein synthesis are not directly inhibited by $SIRS_{OX}$ under conditions where cell division is completely inhibited.

To test the hypothesis that inhibition of cell division by $SIRS_{ox}$ may result from modification of certain sulfhydryl groups, protein sulfhydryls were quantitated in control or $SIRS_{ox}$ treated tumor cells using the sulfhydryl specific radiolabeled compounds; ^{3}H-N-ethylmaleimide (^{3}H-NEM) or ^{14}C-p-chloromercuribenzoic acid (^{14}C-PCMB). ^{3}H-NEM detected 1700 pmoles protein sulfhydryl per 10^6 cells in control P815 cells, whereas ^{14}C-PCMB detected 6000 pmoles protein sulfhydryls per 10^6 cells. $SIRS_{ox}$ treated P815 tumor cells contained 20% less protein sulfhydryls when ^{14}C-PCMB was used and 50% less protein sulfhydryls when ^{3}H-NEM was used. Reduction in protein sulfhydryls paralleled inhibition of cell division when compared to the amount of $SIRS_{ox}$. Maximum reduction of protein sulfhydryls was obtained after 3-4 hrs of incubation with $SIRS_{ox}$, was dependent upon activation of SIRS by H_2O_2, and was prevented by inactivation of $SIRS_{ox}$ by DTT (Table 5). Additionally, loss of protein sulfhydryls was partially reversed by 2-mercaptoethanol or dithiothreitol and reversal of sulfhydryl loss paralleled reversal of inhibition when compared to $SIRS_{ox}$ concentration. Table 6 shows that $SIRS_{ox}$ did not lower reduced glutathione levels during this same 4 hr period. These results, coupled with the fact that extended incubation of cells with $SIRS_{ox}$ or addition of excess $SIRS_{ox}$, did not lead to further reduction in protein sulfhydryls suggests that there is some selectivity in the ability of $SIRS_{ox}$ to mediate the loss or oxidation of cellular sulfhydryl groups.

Table 5

MODIFICATION OF PROTEIN SULFHYDRYLS BY $SIRS_{ox}$

Treatment[a]	Sulfhydryls[b] (pmoles/10^6 cells)
-	1520
SIRS	1580
$SIRS_{ox}$	790
$SIRS_{ox}$ + DTT	1470

[a]P815 cells were treated with SIRS or $SIRS_{ox}$ (10 units) for 4 hrs at 37˘C.
[b]P815 cell protein sulfhydryls were labeled with ^{3}H-NEM in the presence of 1% SDS and collected by precipitation with 15% trichloroacetic acid.

Table 6

FAILTURE OF $SIRS_{ox}$ TO MODIFY GLUTATHIONE LEVELS

Treatment[a]	Reduced Glutathione[b] (pmoles/10^6 cells)
Control	1100
$SIRS_{ox}$	1140

[a]P815 cells were treated with $SIRS_{ox}$ for 4 hrs at 37˘C.
[b]P815 cells were solubilized in 1% NP40 and acid soluble
(15% TCA) sulfhydryls determined by reaction with 5,5'
dithiobis(2-nitrobenzoic acid) (DTNB) (Beutler, et al., 1963).

Finally, these results do not address whether $SIRS_{ox}$ is
directly responsible for sulfhydryl modification or whether
$SIRS_{ox}$ may initiate some other pathway directly responsible
for sulfhydryl loss.

SUMMARY

The SIRS suppressor pathway is initiated by
activation of Ly 2^+ T lymphocytes by either con A or IFNβ.
SIRS is a protein which has been purified and exists as two
species with mol. wts. of 14,000 and 21,500. The target of
SIRS is the macrophage and macrophages appear to oxidize or
activate SIRS in a peroxide dependent process. Catalase
blocks SIRS or IFNβ action by consuming H_2O_2 and
levamisole blocks SIRS or IFNβ by preventing activation or
oxidation of SIRS by H_2O_2. Other agents which block SIRS
or IFNβ action include electron donors which can inactivate
$SIRS_{ox}$. $SIRS_{ox}$ is a potent inhibitor of immune responses
and proliferation of normal and neoplastic cells. The
mechanism of $SIRS_{ox}$-mediated inhibition of proliferation
appears to involve oxidation or modification of protein
sulfhydryls. Although the applicability of this pathway to
the regulation of immune responses and cellular proliferation
remains to be determined, both IFNβ and levamisole have been
found to affect a wide variety of cellular processes. The
involvement of both IFNβ and levamisole in the SIRS pathway
suggests that this pathway may be an important host mechanism
for regulating both immune responses and cellular
proliferation in general.

ACKNOWLEDGMENTS

We thank Barbara Wollberg for secretarial assistance and Nancy Fieldhammer for technical assistance. This work was supported in part by grant PCM-811906 from the National Science Foundation, grant 1431 from the Council for Tobacco research and grants RR-05491 and AI-15353 from the National Institutes of Health. Dr. Aune is a recipient of a Junior Faculty Research Award from the American Cancer Society.

REFERENCES

Aune TM, Pierce CW (1981a). Mechanism of action of macrophage-derived suppressor factor produced by soluble immune response suppressor-treated macrophages. J Immunol 127:368.

Aune TM, Pierce CW (1981b). Identification and initial characterization of a nonspecific suppressor factor produced by soluble immune response suppressor treated macrophages. J Immunol 127:1828.

Aune TM, Pierce CW (1981c). Conversion of soluble immune response suppressor to macrophage-derived suppressor factor by peroxide. Proc Natl Acad Sci 78:5099.

Aune TM, Pierce CW (1982a). Activation of a suppressor T-cell pathway by interferon. Proc Natl Acad Sci 79:3808.

Aune TM, Pierce CW (1982b). Inhibition of soluble immune response suppressor or interferon mediated suppression by levamisole. Int J Immunopharm, in press.

Aune TM, Pierce CW (1982c). Preparation of soluble immune response suppressor and macrophage-derived suppressor factor. J Immunol Methods, in press.

Aune TM, Webb DR, Pierce CW (1982d). Purification of soluble immune response suppressor, in preparation.

Beutler E, Duron O, Kelly BM (1963). Improved method for the determination of blood glutathione. J Lab Clin Med 61:882.

Hadden JW (1981). The immunopharmacology of immunotherapy: An update. In Hadden JW, Chedid L, Mullen P, and Spreafico F (eds): "Advances in Immunopharmacology," Oxford: Pergamon Press, p. 327.

Lehman FE (1947). Chemical influence on cell division. Experientia 3:223.

Pierce CW, Aune TM (1981). Mechanism of action of soluble immune response suppressor (SIRS). In Hadden JW, Chedid L, Mullen P, Spreafico F (eds): "Advances in Immunopharmacology," Oxford: Pergamon Press, p. 397.

Rebhun LI, Miller M, Schnaitman TC, Nath J, Mellon M (1976).
Cyclic nucleotides, thiol-disulfide status of proteins and
cellular control processes. J Supra Struct 5:199.

Rich RR, Pierce CW (1973). Biological expressions of
lymphocyte activation. II. Generation of a population of
thymus-derived suppressor lymphocytes. J Exp Med 137:649.

Rich RR, Pierce CW (1974). Biological expressions of
lymphocyte activation. III. Suppression of plaque-forming
cell responses in vitro by supernatant fluids from
concanavalin A-activated spleen cell cultures. J Immunol
112:1360.

Tadakuma T, Pierce CW (1976). Site of action of a soluble
immune response suppressor (SIRS) produced by concanavalin
A-activated spleen cells. J Immunol 120:461.

Tadakuma T, Pierce CW (1978). Mode of action of a soluble
immune response suppressor (SIRS) produced by concanavalin
A-activated spleen cells. J Immunol 120:481.

Thrasher JD (1973). The effect of mercuric compounds on
dividing cells. In Zimmerman AM, Padilla GM, Cameron IL
(eds): "Drugs and the Cell Cycle," New York: Academic
Press, p. 25.

13th International Cancer Congress, Part B
Biology of Cancer (1), pages 345–351
© 1983 Alan R. Liss, Inc., 150 Fifth Avenue, New York, NY 10011

REGULATION OF TUMOR-SPECIFIC IMMUNE RESPONSE
BY T CELL PRODUCTS

Tomio Tada, Ko Okumura, Seiichi Yamada, Toshiki Kitahara
Hajime Karasuyama, Atsuo Ochi, and Katsumi Yamauchi

Department of Immunology, Faculty of Medicine, University
of Tokyo, 7-3-1 Hongo, Bunkyo-ku, Tokyo 113, Japan

Introduction

Some years ago Fujimoto et al. (1976a,b) reported that in mice carrying a growing tumor there existed tumor-specific suppressor T cells which inhibited the development of tumor-specific immunity. They demonstrated that A/J mice immunized with a methylcholanthrene-induced syngeneic tumor, S1509a, developed specific immunity to reject the same tumor upon secondary transplantation, and that this immunological resistance was greatly suppressed by the transfer of spleen cells from syngeneic mice burdened with the growing S1509a. It was found that the cells have an exquisite specificity for the individual tumor cell line, and that their cell surface phenotype is Lyt-$1^-2^+3^+$ and I-J$^+$, similar to that observed with antigen-specific suppressor T cells in other experimental systems (reviewed by Tada and Okumura, 1979). Subsequent studies by Greene et al. (1977, 1978) demonstrated that the effect of suppressor T cells was mediated by a soluble product of splenic T cells of tumor-bearing animals. The molecule termed tumor-specific suppressor T cell factor (TsF) had a molecular weight less than 70,000, carried no immunoglobulin constant structure, and contained determinants controlled by a gene in the H-2 major histocompatibility complex (MHC). Perry et al. (1978) was able to map the gene coding for the structure on TsF in the I-J subregion of MHC, and thus the molecule was considered to be a complex composed of an antigen-specific moiety and an I-J subregion gene product. A similar suppressor factor was demonstrated by Takei et al. (1978), who showed that

TsF suppresses the generation of cytotoxic T cells. These observations prompted us to characterize the molecule both biochemically and functionally, as the production of TsF in tumor-bearing animals would be one of the major factors that limits the specific tumor resistance in tumor bearing hosts. We shall briefly describe the present state of our knowledge about the antigen-specific TsF in general, which lends a clue for understanding of apparent immunological unresponsiveness to the tumor in tumor-bearing hosts.

Suppressor hybridomas and cell lines

In order to characterize the suppressor molecule we produced a number of T cell hybridomas and T cell growth factor(TCGF)-dependent cell lines with suppressor functions. The majority of these clones produced TsF specific for a protein (keyhole limpet hemocyanin, KLH) or a hapten (4-hydroxy-3-nitrophenylacetyl, NP), while others produced antigen-nonspecific suppressor factors. Some other hybridomas produced antigen-specific augmenting T cell factor (TaF) that enhanced the immune response in an antigen-specific fashion. TsF from NP-specific hybridoma could suppress both delayed type hypersensitivity to NP and cytotoxic T cell response to NP-modified self, and thus TsFs discussed here are considered to be similar to those involved in the suppression of tumor immunity. The properties of these T cell hybridomas were described elsewhere (Tada and Nonaka, 1982).

Monoclonal antibodies against MHC products associated with T cell factors

Monoclonal antibodies reactive with MHC products associated with T cell factors (TsF and TaF) were prepared by the fusion of spleen cells producing anti-MHC antibodies with an enzyme-deficient myeloma P3-X63-Ag8-653. To produce anti-I-J^k, we utilized B10.A(3R) spleen cells immune to lymphoid cells of B10.A(5R). To produce anti-I-A which react with TaF, the combination of A.TH (H-2^{t2}) and A.TL (H-2^{t1}) was used (Hiramatsu et al. 1982). In both cases, monoclonals reacting with I-J or I-A positive cell lines were selected, and those reactive with conventional B cell Ia antigens were excluded.

Monoclonal antibodies against T cell products linked to immunoglobulin allotype

A series of monoclonal antibodies which detect T cell determinants linked to immunoglobulin (Ig) allotype genes were produced by fusion of P3-X63-Ag8-653 with SJL (Igh^b) or SJA (Igh^a) spleen cells after reciprocal immunization with partner spleen cells. The basic idea to produce antibodies against alloantigens of T cells was based on the experiment by Owen et al. (1981) who immunized Igh congenic strains with Con A blasts of the partner, and made a number of monoclonals detecting a set of Igh-linked products (Spurll and Owen, 1981). Since these Ig congenic mice of SJL background develop a lymphoproliferative disease where the majority of the proliferating cells are blastic T cells, no special mitogenic stimulation of immunizing cells was necessary. The antibodies were screened for their ability to block the activity of suppressor, helper, proliferating and allospecific killer T cells. Several categories of monoclonals which putatively detect allotype-linked products on functionally different T cells have been established (Okumura et al. manuscript in preparation).

Properties of the recognition structure of cytotoxic T cells

Spleen cells of A/J mice immunized in vivo with a syngeneic T cell leukemia, L1117, developed tumor-specific Tc upon stimulation in vitro with Mitomycin C-treated tumor cells. Such mature cytotoxic T cells were treated either with anti-I-A or anti-I-J monoclonals and complement (C). The cytotoxic activity after the treatment was measured by the ^{51}Cr release from the target cells. No reduction of cytotoxic activity was observed after treatment with any of the anti-Iat monoclonals.

To test the activity of monoclonals against allotype-linked T cell products, cytotoxic T cells were generated in CB-20 (H-2^d, Igh^b), BAB/14 (H-2^d, IgCH^b, V$_H^b$) and BALB/c (H-2^d, Igh^a) by immunizing with C57BL/6 (H-2^b) spleen cells, as no comparable syngeneic tumors were available in these strains. The cytotoxic activity of their spleen cells were assayed by the ^{51}Cr release from EL-4 (H-2^b).

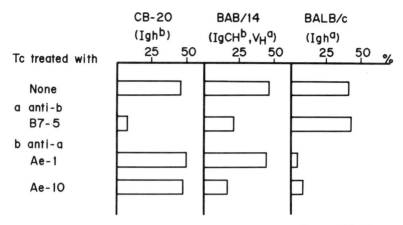

Target: EL-4

Fig. 1. Presence of Igh allotype-linked determinants on allo-specific cytotoxic T cells (Tc). Tc generated in these strains (H-2^d) by stimulation with alloantigens (H-2^b) were treated with monoclonal antibodies putatively specific for allotype-linked products and complement. The treated cells were used for the ^{51}Cr release test using EL-4 (H-2^b) as the target. Note that the elimination of cytotoxic activity of spleen cells with the right allotype. Two of the monoclonals partially reduced the Tc activity of BAB/14 which is a recombinant between V_H and CH gene clusters.

As depicted in Fig. 1, one monoclonal (SJA anti-SJL, a anti-b) could eliminate the cytotoxic activity of CB-20 (Igh^b) but not of BALB/c (Igh^a). There was some effect on Tc of BAB/14 which share the same CH genes with CB-20. With SJL anti-SJA monoclonals (b anti-a), we observed that one monoclonal showed a strict allotype-linked specificity in eliminating the cytotoxic T cells of BALB/c (Igh^a) but not others. Another monoclonal showed some activity on BAB/14 Tc that shares the same V_H with BALB/c. These results suggest that Tc carries Igh-linked product on their cell surface most probably as an antigen-recognition device. No Iat antigens were detected in association with such a structure. Since some of the monoclonals specific for Igh^a allotype-linked products can react with BAB/14 (IgV_H^a), the locus controlling these determinants have to be carefully examined in future studies.

Nature and properties of antigen-recognition units
of antigen-specific regulatory T cells

Monoclonal   anti-Iat   and   anti-T   cell   allotype
antibodies were also used to characterize antigen-specific
TsF and TaF. These T cell factors were prepared from
hybridoma   cell   lines,   and   were   absorbed   with
immunoadsorbents of various monoclonal anti-Iat antibodies.
As depicted in Fig. 2, one anti-I-A (1L9) could absorb TaF
but not TsF, and an anti-I-J (1G8) was capable of reacting
with TsF but not with TaF. Acid eluates from the columns
fully contained either TsF or TaF activity. On the other
hand, one monoclonal anti-I-A (2L2) could absorb both TaF
and TsF activities which can be recovered in the acid
eluates.   These results indicate that TsF and TaF share
some   identical   determinants   while   they   have   their
individual epitopes which are uniquely determined by
separate I subregions.

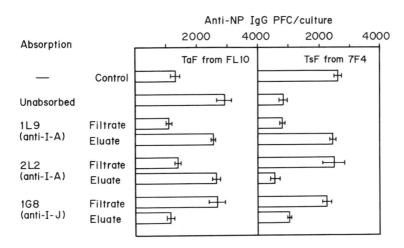

Fig.   2.   Presence   of   common   and   individual   Iat
determinants on TaF and TsF. Extracts from an augmenting
(FL10) and suppressor (7F4) hybridomas were absorbed with
three   different   monoclonal   anti-Iat   immunoadsorbent
columns. After absorption, the filtrates were added to the
in vitro cultures of NP-KLH-primed spleen cells to assess
remaining TaF and TsF activities. Note that 1G8 can absorb
TaF but not TsF, and that 1G8 can absorb TsF but not TaF.
2L2   can   absorb   both   factors   indicating   that   this
determinant is shared by these two distinct factors.

By utilizing various monoclonals putatively specific for allotype-linked structures on T cells, we were able to detect epitopes linked to IgCH which were associated with T cell factors (some monoclonal anti-Tind^d and Tsu^d were kindly provided by Dr. F.W. Owen). TaF and TsF were found to carry different epitopes that are also distinct from those detected on Tc. By biochemical studies using SDS gel, Iat and allotype-linked determinants were found to be present on two separate polypeptide chains (Miyatani et al. in preparation).

We also found that the injection of a small quantity of monoclonal anti-Iat could either suppress or enhance the Tc response to alloantigen, modified self, and tumor antigens. In general, anti-I-A monoclonals greatly suppressed the Tc response, whereas some of the monoclonal anti-I-J augmented the generation of Tc. The results suggest that generation of Tc is dependent on the balance of the activation of Ts and Ta, and the injection of anti-Iat modulates the Tc response by selectively affecting Ts or Ta.

Conclusion

By utilization of monoclonal antibodies and T cell hybridomas, the molecules involved in the regulation and cytotoxic functions of the tumor-specific immune response are being elucidated. The problem is deeply concerned with the antigen-receptor of T cells which are supposed to have dual specificity for the nominal antigen and a self MHC product. The complex structure of TsF and TaF suggests that Igh-linked and I region controlled polypeptides are involved in such a recognition structure. Although Tc may utilize Igh-linked structure for antigen-recognition, the molecular bases for the additional specificity for self is as yet undetermined. The elucidation of molecular composition of these regulatory and effector molecules are of great importance for the future manipulation of immune responsiveness of the tumor-bearing hosts.

References

Fujimoto, S., Greene, M.I. and Sehon, A.H. (1976a) J. Immunol. 116:791.

Fujimoto, S., Greene, M.I. and Sehon, A.H. (1976b) J. Immunol. 116:800.

Greene, M.I., Fujimoto, S. and Sehon, A.H. (1977) J. Immunol. 119:757.

Greene, M.I., Fujimoto, S. and Sehon, A.H. (1978) In: Proteides Biol. Fluids, Proc. Colloq. (H. Peeters, ed) p. 677. Pergamon, New York.

Hiramatsu, K., Ochi, A., Miyatani, S., Segawa, A. and Tada, T. (1982) Nature (London) 296:666.

Owen, F.L., Riblet, R. and Taylar, B.A. (1981) J. Exp. Med. 153:801.

Perry, L.L., Benacerraf, B. and Greene, M.I. (1978) J. Immunol. 121:2144.

Spurll, G.M. and Owen, F.L. (1981) Nature (London) 293: 742.

Tada, T. and Nonaka, M. (1982) In: Isolation, Characterization and Utilization of T Lymphocyte Clones. (C.G. Fathman and F.W. Fitch, eds) p. 97. Academic Press, New York.

Tada, T. and Okumura, K. (1979) Adv. Immunol. 28:1.

CONGRESS SYMPOSIA

TUMOR ANTIGENS AND ANTI-TUMOR ANTIBODY Miescher, P.,
Switzerland, Chairman; Ferrone, S., USA, Co-Chairman;
Flag Pavilion A

Tumor Specific Transplantation Antigens of
Chemically Induced Rodent Tumours. *Evan, G. I.,
Lennox, E. S., Lowe, A. D. and Cohn, J. D.,
Cambridge, England and San Diego, CA USA.

Tumor Antigens as Modified Normal Cell Surface
Antigens. *Parmiani, G., Milan, Italy.

Human Cancer Cell Surface Antigens Defined by
Autologous and Allogeneic Typing. *Shiku, H. and
Yamada, K., Nagoya, Japan. (By Title Only)

The Use of Monoclonal Anti-Idiotype Antibodies
in the Analysis and Treatment of B Cell Lymphoma.
*Maloney, D. G., Miller, R. A. and Levy, R.,
Stanford, CA USA. (By Title Only)

Immune Complexes in Cancer. *Miescher, P. A.
and Carpenter, N. A., Geneva, Switzerland.
(By Title Only)

353

13th International Cancer Congress, Part B
Biology of Cancer (1), pages 355–361
© **1983 Alan R. Liss, Inc., 150 Fifth Avenue, New York, NY 10011**

TUMOUR SPECIFIC TRANSPLANTATION ANTIGENS OF CHEMICALLY
INDUCED RODENT TUMOURS

Gerard I. Evan[*], Edwin S. Lennox[+],
Anthony D. Lowe[+] and Judith D. Cohn[o]
[*]Dept. Microbiology, School of Medicine, U.C.S.F.
[+]MRC Laboratory of Molecular Biology, Hills Rd.,
Cambridge, UK.
[o]Dulbecco Lab, Salk Institute, PO Box 85800,
 San Diego

INTRODUCTION

A basic tenet of tumor immunology is that tumour cells
express surface antigens (Ags) not found on cells of normal
tissues. However, evidence to date for the existence of
such tumour antigens (TAgs) remains equivocal, perhaps the
best candidates for TAgs being the Tumour Specific Transplantation Antigens (TSTAs) of chemically induced rodent
tumours (Lennox, 1980).

TSTAs, as their name implies, are defined in a transplantation rejection assay (Foley, 1953; Baldwin, 1969).
In this assay mice are immunised with syngeneic, lethally
irradiated cells derived from a particular tumour. They
are subsequently challenged with a specified number of live
cells derived from the same tumour. When compared with the
rate of growth of the same "challenge" dose in non-immune
animals, tumour growth in the immunised animals is slowed
or prevented. Such in vivo immunity defines the TSTA specificity of the immunising tumour.

TSTAs are extremely diverse. Seldom, if ever, are
cross reactions observed between any two TSTA-bearing tumours (Basombrio, 1970), even if both are derived from the
same individual by induction at two discrete sites (Sikora
et al., 1979). This diversity does not simply reflect the
inherent diversity of cells present in the normal tissue
acting as target for the carcinogen because independent
tumour lines derived from cloned normal parent cells by in
vitro transformation can each possess a unique TSTA.

TSTA BIOCHEMISTRY

The biochemistry of TSTAs, and of TSTA diversity, thus presents a fascinating problem for the tumour biologist. However, studies of TSTA biochemistry are hampered by the difficulties of preparing anti TSTA sera whose specificities adequately reflect that seen in the in vivo rejection assay. Apart from some rare successes in this sphere (Parker and Rosenberg, 1977; DeLeo et al., 1977) most syngeneic antisera raised against tumours expressing strong TSTAs cross react with a wide variety of tumours. In mice, at least, the major targets for this serological immunity are the ubiquitous murine leukaemia virus (MuLV) components, in particular antigenic determinants on the MuLV envelope glycoprotein gp 70 (Brown et al., 1978).

Without good antibodies to TSTAs, study of TSTA biochemistry is necessarily slow and difficult. In order to generate good anti TSTA antibodies we have therefore made use of hybridoma technology (Lennox et al., 1980, 1981). Mice were immunised with the syngeneic methylcholanthrene-induced tumour C57B10 MC6A (abbreviated to MC6A) which expresses a strong TSTA. Spleens from immune mice were used in fusions to generate hybridomas making anti-MC6A monoclonal antibodies (McAbs). McAbs which bound MC6A were then further selected for their inability to bind the tumour C57B10 MC6B (MC6B). MC6B was induced in the same individual mouse as MC6A, but at a different site, and it expresses a different TSTA to MC6A. Several McAbs binding only MC6A were isolated, and these were further tested for their specificity by assaying their binding to a wide variety of tumour and normal cell lines of varying genetic backgrounds. One McAb, Al/4Bl, was found to have a high specificity for MC6A (Lennox et al., 1982) and we thus considered the antigenic specificity recognised by Al/4Bl as a good candidate for the TSTA of MC6A. Al/4Bl was therefore selected for further study.

BIOCHEMISTRY OF THE Al/4Bl ANTIGEN

Al/4Bl, despite its tantalising specificity, was found to possess a very low affinity for its Ag (Evan and Lennox - in preparation). Nonetheless, using a rapid solid phase immunoaffinity technique (Evan et al. - submitted for publication) we were able to identify the Al/4Bl Ag[*] as a glyco-

protein with an apparent M Wt of 70K on an SDS polyacrylamide gel.

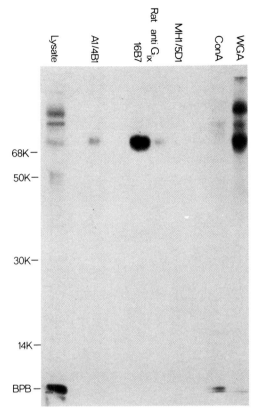

MC6A-3-3 immunoadsorption

[125]I surface labelled MC6A cells were lysed and immunoad-
sorbed as previously described (Evan and Lennox, in preparation). Equal aliquots of the lysate were adsorbed to
agarose-immobilised antibodies or lectins as shown, and
bound material electrophoresed on a 10% SDS polyacrylamide
gel. Al/4Bl and 16-B7 are McAbs specific for the gp70[a]
epitope. Rat anti G_{ix} is a conventional rat antiserum specific for the G_{ix} specificity of **gp70**. MH1/5Dl is a McAb
specific for human blood group A antigen, and acts as a
negative control. Con A is concanavalin A, WGA is Wheat
Germ Agglutinin.

Because of its resemblance to the MuLV envelope glycoprotein (gp70), we decided to examine the possibility that the A1/4B1 Ag was a gp70, in collaboration with Drs. Paul Klein and Chuck Simrell at the University of Florida, Gainesville. To do this, we used a bank of McAbs directed against MuLV envelope gene products (Lostrom et al., 1979). We found one such McAb, 16-B7, which showed an identical and rare pattern of binding to A1/4B1 on a diverse panel of tumour cell lines. Moreover:

a) 16-B7 and A1/4B1 Ags were of identical mobility on SDS polyacrylamide gels.
b) Prior binding of saturating levels of 16-B7 to MC6A cells completely blocked binding of ^{125}I labeled A1/4B1.
c) Depletion of MC6A cell lysates of all 16-B7 binding molecules concomitantly removed all A1/4B1 Ags.
d) One dimensional V8 protease peptide maps of A1/4B1 and 16-B7 Ags were identical.
e) A1/4B1 and 16-B7 both specifically bound density gradient purified AKR ecotropic MuLV.

16-B7 is known to bind an antigenic determinant on the gp70 of AKR ecotropic MuLV, the gp70^a epitope (Lostrom et al., 1979). The above data strongly suggests that A1/4B1 recognises a similar, if not identical, antigenic determinant.

IS THE A1/4B1 SPECIFICITY THE TSTA OF TUMOUR MC6A?

The specificity of A1/4B1 for MC6A out of a wide variety of tumours makes the A1/4B1 Ag a good candidate for the MC6A TSTA. However, the A1/4B1 antigenic determinant is found to lie on a MuLV gp70. If the A1/4B1 antigenic determinant is indeed the TSTA, we are thus presented with two problems:

1) How can the rare A1/4B1 antigenic specificity be carried on MuLV gp70, a species known to be almost ubiquitous in murine tissues and cell lines?
2) How can we reconcile our findings with A1/4B1 and MC6A with the work of DeLeo and others (DeLeo et al., 1977) which has suggested that TSTAs and MuLV components are discrete?

Recent studies of MuLV envelope gene products have shown them to be a highly polymorphic family, both structurally

(Elder et al., 1977a; Rommelaere et al., 1978) and antigenically (Lostrom et al., 1979; Haas and Patch, 1980). Indeed,
many different gp70s can be expressed in a single individual
(Elder et al., 1977b), and often even within a single cell
(Spriggs and Kreuger, 1981; Evan and Lennox, in preparation).
Moreover, the generation of the acute transforming MuLVs,
which are so frequently implicated in cell transformation,
appears to involve recombination between MuLVs. Such recombination seems to occur most readily at sites within envelope
genes, and generates recombinant viruses with unique gp70s.

Multiple, antigenically polymorphic MuLV envelope gene
products obviously meet many of the requirements of TSTAs.
Furthermore, while some antigenic determinants will be shared
amongst a wide variety of gp70s, and thus common to many
different tumour lines, some gp70 antigenic determinants
will be highly restricted. The A1/4B1 determinant is one
such example of the latter case. The system may perhaps be
conceived as being analogous to the public and private antigenic specificities of the major histocompatibility antigens.

In the above mentioned studies of DeLeo et al., tumour
lines were assigned as gp70 negative or positive by whether
or not they bound anti-gp70 sera. It is clear, however, that
this assignment depends entirely on precisely which gp70
antigenic specificities are recognised by the antibody used
in the assay. There are now several cases recorded where
supposedly universal anti gp70 xenoantisera fail to detect
gp70 on certain tumour lines (Krantz et al., 1977; Collins
and Chesebro, 1980), whereas more specific antisera raised
against particular recombinant MuLV gp70s can often do so
(Fischinger et al., 1981). In conclusion therefore, we feel
that the historical evidence against TSTA-gp70 equivalence
is no longer indisputable.

In the case of MC6A, we are now almost convinced that
the TSTA is the polymorphic gp70 antigenic specificity
recognised by A1/4B1. We suggest that TSTA diversity may in
general be a product of MuLV envelope gene polymorphism.

OUTLOOK

At present we are conducting several lines of study to
further test our above hypothesis. Firstly, we are attempt-
ing to see whether A1/4B1 expression correlates with

transplantation activity. In an extensive search of mouse tumour lines we have identified a few which also express the A1/4B1 antigenic specificity. Though at present preliminary, our results do suggest that A1/4B1 positive tumour lines specifically protect against MC6A in an in vivo transplant-ation assay (Lennox et al., 1982). Secondly, we are attempt-ing to purify the A1/4B1-binding gp70 of MC6A in quantities large enough to allow its use as an immunogen. We will then assay the TSTA activity (and specificity) of the purified molecule. Finally, we are attempting to test our hypothesis on other tumour lines which also express unique TSTAs.

ACKNOWLEDGEMENTS

We wish to thank Lorraine Croft for her technical help, members of the MRC Laboratory of Molecular Biology for their discussion and criticism, and the Medical Research Council (U.K.) for support.

*Footnote. For the sake of simplicity, I have adopted the following convention: the term "antigen" (Ag) is used to imply the whole molecule bound by an antibody; the terms "antigenic determinant" and "antigenic specificity" are used to describe the epitope recognised by an individual antibody molecule.

REFERENCES

Baldwin R and Embleton M (1969). Int J. Cancer 4:430.
Basombrio M (1970). Cancer Res 30:2458.
Brown J, Klitzman J, Hellstrom J, Nowinski R, and Hellstrom
  K (1978). Proc Nat Acad Sci USA 75:955.
Collins J and Chesebro B (1980). J Immunol 125:1325.
DeLeo A, Shiku H, Takahashi T, John M and Old L (1977).
  J Exp Med 146:720.
Elder J, Gautsch J, Jenson F, Lerner R, Hartley J and Rowe
  W (1977a). Proc Nat Acad Sci USA 74:4676.
Elder J, Jensen F, Bryant M, and Lerner R (1977b). Nature
  267:23.
Fischinger P, Thiel H, Ihle J, Lee J, and Elder R (1981).
  Proc Nat Acad Sci USA 78:1920.
Foley E (1953) Cancer Res 13:835.
Haas M and Patch V (1980). J Exp Med 151:1321.
Krantz M, Strand M, and August J (1977). J Virol 22:804.

Lennox E and Sikora K (1977). In Borek C, Feroglio C and King D (eds): "Cancer Biology V Differentiation and carcinogenesis" p 68.

Lennox E (1980). In Fougereau M, Dausset J (eds): "The Antigens of Chemically Induced Tumours, Immunology 1980 - Progress in Immunology IV. New York, Academic, p 659.

Lennox E, Cohn J and Lowe A (1980). Transplantation Proc 13:1754.

Lostrom M, Stone M, Tam M, Burnette W, Pinter A and Nowinski R (1979). Viology 98:336.

Parker G and Rosenberg S (1977). J Nat Cancer Inst 58:1303.

Rommelaere J, Faller D and Hopkins N (1978). Proc Nat Acad Sci USA 75:495.

Sikora K, Koch G, Brenner S, and Lennox E (1979). Brit J Cancer 40:8.

Spriggs D and Kreuger R (1981). Virology 108:474.

13th International Cancer Congress, Part B
Biology of Cancer (1), pages 363–371
© 1983 Alan R. Liss, Inc., 150 Fifth Avenue, New York, NY 10011

TUMOR ANTIGENS AS MODIFIED NORMAL CELL SURFACE ANTIGENS

Giorgio Parmiani, MD

Division of Experimental Oncology B
Istituto Nazionale Tumori
20133 Milan, Italy

Tumor antigens can be defined as those cell surface molecules which can induce an immune response in the syngeneic or autologous host. I propose that the three classes of tumor antigens detected in man by autologous serological typing (Old, 1981) should be used to define also antigens of experimental tumors. Table 1 describes these classes of tumor antigens.

Table 1. Classification of cell surface antigens of experimental tumors.

Class	Characteristics	Distribution
1	Individual antigens	Restricted to a single tumor
2	Shared antigens	Present on different tumors, not on normal tissues
3	Normal (differentiation) antigens	Present on normal and neoplastic cells

The nature of most tumor antigens is unknown. The possibility that at least some tumor antigens may originate through a genetic or epigenetic modification of normal cell surface structures has been a subject of intensive investigations during the last five years (see Parmiani, 1980). Table 2 summarizes the possible modifications of normal cell surface antigens on tumor cells which may lead to the appearance of new antigens by direct of indirect mechanisms.

Table 2. Possible modifications of normal cell surface antigens on tumor cells.

Type of modification	Antigens involved
Quantitative:	
a) reduction	H-2K, H-2D, Ia
b) deletion	H-2K, H-2D, H-2L
Qualitative (new, alien-like, alloantigens)	H-2K, H-2D, MiHA*, Ia, ML, TL
Interaction antigens	H-2K, gp70

* MiHA: minor histocompatibility antigens.

Class 1 tumor antigens

Class 1 tumor antigens include the most studied tumor specific transplantation antigens (TSTA) of chemically induced neoplasms of rodents, but individual type of antigens are expressed in a variety of other tumors induced by viruses or physical means (i.e. UV). The molecular basis of the diversity of TSTA is still unknown. Based on many similaritis between TSTA and hystocompatibility antigens (HA), we proposed that TSTA may derive from a modification of the H-2 on non-H-2 normal antigens (Invernizzi and Parmiani, 1975). We have, therefore, examined a certain number of chemically and virally induced murine tumors to evaluate the presence of alterations in the profile of H-2K,D,L (class 1) and non-H-2 antigens and the relationship of such alterations to TSTA. In some cases, evidence for altered expression in terms of unexpected presence of alien antigens of both H-2 and/or non-H-2 HA on tumor cells was found in experiments of cell-mediated, serological and transplantation immunity (Parmiani et al., 1980a;

Schirrmacher et al., 1980; Greenberg et al., 1981). Immunogenetic and biochemical studies of our BALB/c tumors, however, have subsequently shown that TSTA and both normal or foreign HA were separate structures on the surface of neoplastic cells (Parmiani et al., 1978; Rogers et al., 1980), although in a system of ENU-induced lung tumors of C3H mice a K^k variant molecule was discovered which may function like TSTA (Martin et al., 1977; Callahan et al., 1981).

Biochemical analyses of class I products of the MHC of some other chemically induced, TSTA-bearing fibrosarcomas showed no obvious differences between H-2K or H-2D glycoproteins of the tumor as compared to those of normal cells (Ballinari et al., 1982), but the procedure used would have missed subtle differences at the level of the glycosilated groups.

An apparent lack of class I H-2 antigens has been reported in several H-2^k lymphomas (Schmidt et al., 1979) which, however, were not evaluated for the presence of TSTA. In a recent study we found that a certain percentage of TSTA-bearing, chemically induced BALB/c fibrosarcomas apparently lacked the products of the H-2L^d gene but not of the K^d and D^d regions (Ballinari et al., submitted) (Table 3). The relationship, if any, between this deletion of L^d gene products and the TSTA is currently under investigation.

Table 3. Lack of expression of L^d antigens on the C-1
BALB/c fibrosarcoma as evaluated by transplantation methods.

Recipients	Immunizing cells	No.of mice with tumor/ No.of mice injected with tumor		
		C-1	C-3	GI-17
BALB/c-H-2^{dm2}	---	5/5	9/9	
	BALB/c	8/8	0/11	
BALB/c	BALB/c	8/8	8/8	
BALB/c-H-2^{dm2}	C-1	1/8	6/6	6/6
	C-3	8/8	0/8	2/8

The individual TSTA might also derive from a modification of MiHA or appearance of other determinants as already
suggested (Parmiani, 1980). Results supporting this conten-
tion have been presented by some authors (Parmiani et al.,
1980a; Russell et al., 1979) but we could show, at least
for one tumor, that also alien-like MiHA and TSTA were born
by different cell surface structures (Parmiani et al.,
1980b).

Also class II antigens encoded by the I-region of MHC
have been reported to function as TSTA in a guinea-pig
leukemia system (Forni et al., 1975) and in the reticulum
cell sarcomas of SJL mice (Wilbur and Bonavida, 1981) but
no clear conclusions could be reached in these systems on
the relationship between Ia-like molecules and TSTA. Also
it was not clearly established whether TSTA were of the
class 1 or 2.

Class 2 tumor antigens

Among the tumor-restricted, cross-reacting antigens we
can limit our attention to the viral and fetal antigens.
Virus-coded antigens have been shown to serve as weak TSTA

in chemically induced tumors (Hellström et al., 1978) and in many virus induced tumor systems. Due to the polymorphism of some viral antigens like gp70, these molecules have been proposed as source of TSTA activity (Lennox, 1981). The possibility that both RNA or DNA-virus antigens may interact with other normal cell surface structures to give rise to a new antigenic entity on the tumor cell has been suggested by several experimental findings (Blank and Lilly, 1977; Kvist et al., 1978; Callahan et al., 1979), although no evidence was provided on the TSTA activity of such new antigens.

Expression on tumor cells of antigens shared with embryonic or fetal cells is know from many years. Less clear is, however, whether fetal antigens per se have TSTA activity (Chism et al., 1978). In any event, although it is not yet established which is the molecular nature of fetal antigens (Evans et al., 1981), these cell surface structures may be modified on tumor cells in such a way to lead to the appearance of molecules endowed with the capacity to elicit transplantation immunity. Example of alien minor histocompatibility-like antigens have been described on experimental tumor cells (Parmiani et al., 1980a; Russell et al., 1979; Parmiani et al., 1982) which are shared by different tumors, especially BALB/c or DBA/2 lymphomas. Although the nature of these antigens is still unknown, they are likely to be either true MiHA or antigens resulting from the interaction between viral-related molecules and other cell surface structures.

Class 3 tumor antigens

This is probably the broadest class of antigens present on tumor and normal cells. These antigens may be found in higher quantity on the neoplastic counterparts as compared from the normal tissue from which the tumor derives. The presence of this type of antigens has been revealed from studies dealing with the serology of human neoplasms (Old, 1981) a subject which will be dealt upon by others in this session. I would like to limit myself to a few but important differentiation-like antigens of experimental tumors like TL and ML which may function also like tumor antigens. The thymus-leukemia (TL) antigens is the first example of a differentiation antigens which is repressed on normal thymocyte of some strains but which can reappear after a leukemogenic transformation (Old, 1981). Since TL antigen modulates, however, it cannot induce a transplantation immunity but only a humoral immune response.

As for the ML (mammary leukemia) antigens, this appears like a lymphoid differentiation alloantigens expressed by C3H mammary tumor cells and DBA/2 leukemia but not by normal mammary epithelial cells. This serologically defined antigen, however, may function also as TSTA as shown by Fujiwara et al. (1978). Monoclonal antibodies have been raised to this antigen and used to define its strain and tissue distribution in normal and neoplastic tissues (Rapp and Fuji, 1982).

This is, therefore, a clear example of a differentiation antigens which may appear on tumor cells and function as TSTA.

In conclusion, several normal cell surface antigens can appear on neoplastic cells or be quantitatively increased to become immunogenic to the host and thus functionning as tumor antigens.

Acknowledgment

The author's work was supported by Grant No. 80.02371.96 of the Finalized Project "Control of Tumor Growth" of the CNR (Rome).

REFERENCES

Ballinari D, Pierotti MA, Grazioli L, Cattaneo M, Rogers MJ, Parmiani G (1982). Biochemical analysis of a public H-2 specificity revealed by an anomalous reaction of an alloantiserum with a chemically induced C57BL/10 fibrosarcoma. J Immunogenetics 9: in press.

Blank KJ, Lilly F (1977). Evidence for an H-2 viral protein complex on the cell surface as the basis for the H-2 restriction of cytotoxicity. Nature 269: 808.

Callahan GN, Allison JP, Pellegrino MA, Reisfeld RA (1979). Physical association of histocompatibility antigens and tumor-associated antigens on the surface of murine lymphoma cells. J Immunol 122: 70.

Callahan GN, Walker LE, Martin WJ (1981). Biochemical comparison of H-2K antigen isolated from C3HfB/HeN and C3H/HeN mice. Immunogenetics 12: 561.

Chism SE, Burton RC, Warner NL (1978). Immunogenicity of oncofetal antigens: a review. Clin Immunol Immunopathol 11: 346.

Evans DL, Chung M, Johnson KD (1981). Antigenic differences between tumor-associated fetal antigens and rat histocompatibility antigens. Cell Immunol 60: 274.

Forni G, Rhim JS, Pickeral S, Shevach EM, Green I (1975). Antigenicity of carcinogen and viral induced sarcomas in inbred and random bred guinea pigs. J Immunol 115: 204.

Fujiwara H, Aoki H, Tsuchida T, Hamaoka T (1978). Immunologic characterization of tumor-associated transplantation antigens on MM102 mammary tumor eliciting preferentially helper T cell activity. J Immunol 121: 1591.

Greenberg PD, Cheever MA, Fefer A (1981). Definition of alien H-2 determinants on a Friend leukemia by analysis of alloreactivity of CTL from primary MLC. J Immunogenetics 8: 493.

Hellström KE, Hellström I, Brown JP (1978). Unique and common specific transplantation antigens of chemically induced mouse sarcomas. Int J Cancer 21:317.

Invernizzi G, Parmiani G (1975). Tumor-associated trans
    plantation antigens of chemically induced sarcomata
    cross-reacting with allogeneic histocompatibility
    antigens. Nature 254: 713.

Kvist S, Ostberg L, Person H, Philipson L, Peterson P
    (1978).Molecular association between transplantation
    antigens and cell surface antigen in adenovirus
    transformed cell line. Proc.Nat.Acad.Sci.USA 75: 5674.

Lennox ES, Lowe AD, Cohn J, Evan G (1981). Specific
    antigens on methylcholanthrene-induced tumors of
    mice. Transpl Proc 12: 1759.

Martin WJ, Gipson TG, Rice JM (1977). $H-2^a$ associated
    alloantigen expressed by several transplacentally
    induced lung tumors of C3Hf mice. Nature 265: 738.

Old LJ (1981). Cancer immunology: the search for speci
    ficity. Cancer Res 41: 361.

Parmiani G (1980). Histocompatibility antigens and tumour
    antigens. Cancer Immunol Immunother 8: 215.

Parmiani G, Ballinari D, Sensi ML (1980a). Tumor-associated
    alien alloantigens of BALB/c tumors encoded by the
    MHC and by non-H-2 genes: a histogenetic study.
    J Immunol 134: 662.

Parmiani G, Colombo MP, Ballinari D (1980b). Expression
    of alien minor histocompatibility antigens distinct
    from tumor-specific transplantation antigen on a murine
    fibrosarcoma. Int J Cancer 26: 461.

Parmiani G, Meschini A, Invernizzi G, Carbone G (1978).
    Tumor-associated transplantation antigen distinct from
    $H-2^k$-like antigens on a BALB/c ($H-2^d$) fibrosarcoma.
    J Natl Cancer Inst 61: 1229.

Parmiani G, Sensi ML, Carbone G, Colombo MP, Pierotti MA,
    Hilgers J, Hilkens J (1982). Cross-reactions between
    tumor cells and allogeneic normal tissues. Inhibition of
    a syngeneic lymphoma outgrowth in H-2 and non-H-2
    alloimmune BALB/c mice. Int J Cancer 29: 323.

Rapp L, Fuji H (1982). Differential antigenic expression of
    the DBA/2 lymphoma L1210 and its subline cells
    and cross-reactivity with C3H mammary tumors as defined
    by syngeneic monoclonal antibody.

Proc Amer Ass Cancer Res 23: 270.

Rogers MJ, Law LW, Pierotti MA, Parmiani G (1980). Separation of the tumor associated transplantation antigen (TATA) from the alien H-2^k antigen expressed on a methylcholanthrene induced tumors. Int J Cancer 25: 105.

Russel JH, Ginns LC, Terres G, Eisen HN (1979). Tumor antigens as inappropriately expressed normal alloantigens. J Immunol 122: 912.

Schirrmacher V, Hubsch V, Garrido F (1980). Syngeneic tumor cells can induce alloreactive T killer cells: a biological role for transplantation antigens. Proc Natl Acad Sci USA 77: 5409.

Schmidt W, Atfield G, Festenstein H (1979). Loss of H-2K^k gene product(s) on AKR spontaneous leukemia. Immunogenetics 8: 311.

Wilburn SM, Bonavida B (1981). Expression of hybrid Ia molecules on the cell-surface of reticulum cell sarcoma that are undetectable on host SJL/J lymphocytes. J Exp Med 153: 501.

CONGRESS SYMPOSIA

IMMUNOLOGICAL ASPECTS OF CELL MEMBRANE STRUCTURE
AND FUNCTION Perlmann, P., Sweden, Chairman;
Dreyer, W., USA, Co-Chairman; Flag Pavilion A

Molecular Phenomena at the Cell Surface.
*Singer, S. J., La Jolla, CA USA. (By Title Only)

Distinct Recognition Sites on Histocompatibility
Antigens for Antibodies and Cytotoxic T
Lymphocytes. *Hammerling, G. J., Kuon, W. and
Rusch, E., Heidelberg, W. Germany.

Immunologic Effects of Interferons on the Cell
Membrane. *Nathanson, L., Stony Brook, NY USA.

Effector-Target Cell Interactions: Approaches
Towards Definition of Recognition Structures.
*Henney, C. S. and Urdal, D., Seattle, WA USA.
(By Title Only)

Generation of Tumorcidal Macrophages and Direct
Selective Destruction of Tumor Cells by Membrane
Active Adjuvants. *Munder, P. G., Modolell, M.,
Andreesen, R., Berdel, W., Pahlke, W., Oepke, R.,
and Westphal, O., Freiburg, W. Germany.

Please note: Papers that are listed as "By Title
Only" were presented at the 13th International
Cancer Congress, but are not included in these
volumes.

13th International Cancer Congress, Part B
Biology of Cancer (1), pages 375–385
© **1983 Alan R. Liss, Inc., 150 Fifth Avenue, New York, NY 10011**

DISTINCT RECOGNITION SITES ON HISTOCOMPATIBILITY ANTIGENS
FOR ANTIBODIES AND CYTOTOXIC T LYMPHOCYTES

G.J. Hämmerling, W. Kuon and Evi Rüsch

Institut für Immunologie und Genetik
Deutsches Krebsforschungszentrum, Heidelberg
Im Neuenheimer Feld 280, D-6900 Heidelberg, FRG

ABSTRACT

Studies with monoclonal antibodies show that allodeterminants are concentrated on H-2 molecules in several
distinct epitope regions. Different parts of H-2 molecules
can also be recognized by alloreactive or H-2 restricted
cytotoxic T lymphocytes, but these parts do not appear to be
identical to those recognized by antibodies. These data
show that an H-2 molecule can be subdivided into several
specialized regions and that the B and T cell compartments
of the immune system recognize different regions on H-2
molecules.

INTRODUCTION

One of the most important breakthroughs in the study of
major histocompatibility complex (MHC) antigens was the detection that cytotoxic T lymphocytes (CTL) recognize cell-
bound foreign antigens, such as tumor or viral antigens,
only in conjunction with their own MHC products (Zinkernagel and Doherty 1974). Thus, T lymphocytes with specificity for foreign antigen in association with their own
MHC are not able to attack the same antigen if this is presented together with a different MHC. This observation has
raised many questions, e.g. if and how the foreign antigen
combines with MHC structures, if T lymphocytes have two receptors, one for foreign and another one for their own MHC
or if they have only one receptor which can recognize neo-
determinants created by association of foreign antigen and
self-MHC.

Since it is a frequent phenomenon in nature that specialized functions are confined to particular regions on protein molecules (i.g. enzymes, antibodies, etc.) the expectation is that MHC molecules mediate their function also via certain regions. This question was analyzed using CTL and monoclonal antibodies (mAb) against H-2 antigens. In these studies the target determinants for mAb were found to be clustered in several distinct epitope regions on the H-2 molecule, but these regions do not seem to correlate with those recognized by CTL.

RESULTS

Allodeterminants Are Clustered in Spatially Distinct Regions on H-2 Molecules

Antibody blocking studies were performed to determine the spatial relationship of allodeterminants on H-2 molecules. For this a set of mAb (Lemke et al 1979) was labeled with ^{125}Iodine, and the ability of cold mAb to block the binding of labeled mAb was determined. The results show that the mAb fall into two or three distinct groups, depending on the set of mAb and the respective H-2 allele analyzed. Thus, only mAb of one group block each other but they do not interfere with the binding of mAb of the other groups. From these studies it was concluded that allodeterminants are clustered on H-2 molecules in several spatially separated epitope regions. So far the H-2K^k, H-2D^b (Lemke and Hämmerling 1982), H-2K^b (Hämmerling et al 1982), H-2^r, H-2^s (unpublished) molecules have been investigated with similar results. Biochemical studies have shown that the determinants in the different epitope regions reside indeed on the same H-2 molecule (unpublished).

In order to analyze which aminoacids of the H-2 protein sequence would influence the antigenic structure of the epitope region several well defined H-2K^b mutants (bm strains of mice) with known aminoacid sequence were utilized. Some pertinent results are schematically summarized in Table 1 (Hämmerling et al 1982).

On the wild type H-2K^b antigen with mAb against H-2K^b three epitope regions could be identified, designated arbitrarily A, B and C. From the same set of mAbs only members of groups B and C were still reactive with the bm3 mutant which has two aminoacid substitutions at Pos. 77 and 89. These data demonstrate that these substitions modify only one

Table 1.   Reactivity of anti-K^b mAb with H-2K^b mutant strains

Strain	Substitution at position	Group A 9-136 10-56 B8 Y-25	Group B 141-11 142-23 142-45 Y-3	Group C 7-65 7-309 9-178 5F1
C57Bl/6	–	+	+	+
bm3	77+89	–	+	+
bm1	155+156	+	+	–
bm6	116+121	+	+	+

Reactivity of mAb was determined by binding of ^{125}I labeled mAb to speen cells. + = same binding as on C57Bl/6 cells, - = no binding; mAb of a group crossblock each other in inhibition experiments and define an epitope region. Y-25 and Y-3 are a gift of E. Lerner, Yale University, B8-I-24 is from G. Köhler, Basel, 5F1 from L. Sherman, Scripps Clinic. The other mAb are described by Hämmerling et al 1982.

epitope region but not the other two. In contrast substitutions 155 and 156 (mutant bm1) destroy only the target determinants for mAb of group C, but not those of groups A and B. On the other hand mutations at positions 116 and 121 (mutant bm6) do not affect the binding of mAb of any group.

Altogether such data indicate that a given aminoacid substitution changes only the structure of one antigenic region, but not of the other ones. However, this applies only to determinants defined by mAb because, as will be shown below, the same mutations drastically affect the recognition of H-2 antigens by cytotoxic T lymphocytes.

Target Inhibition of Alloreactive and H-2 Restricted CTL with mAb Against the H-2K^k Antigen

In order to approach the question if the distinct epitope regions described by mAb will also serve as recognition structures for CTL, target inhibition of CTL was performed with H-2K^k specific mAb. With these mAb two distinct epitope regions have been identified on the H-2K^k molecule (Lemke and Hämmerling 1982). Alloreactive H-2K^k specific CTL (DBA 2-anti-A/J) were generated in bulk culture. The lytic activity was determined on day 4 in the presence or absence of different mAb during the 4 hr ^{51}chromium release period. The results obtained by Weyand et al 1981a are depicted in Fig. 1, which shows that the lytic activity of the CTL population is decreased by increasing concentrations of mAb because the mAb bind to the target H-2 antigen and thus prevent accessability of CTL binding to the region covered by the antibody.

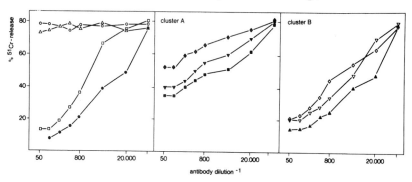

Fig. 1. Target inhibition by anti-K^k mAb of lysis of L929 H-2K^k) targets by K^k specific CTL (DBA/2 A/J). Effector: target ratio = 50:1. Left frame: , medium control; , control ascites 13/18; , hyperimmune BALB/c anti-A/J alloantiserum; , mixture of six monoclonal anti-K^k antibodies. Middle frame, anti-K^k antibody describing cluster A: ,=H100-5R28; , H100-27R55; ,H116-22R7. Right frame, monoclonal anti-K^k antibody describing cluster B: , H100-3OR23; , H142-23/3; , H142-45/2.

It is obvious that the mAb fall into two groups depending on their blocking capacities. These two groups happen to correlate with the two distinct epitope regions on the H-2K^k molecule. Thus, mAb to cluster B are much more effective in blocking than mAb to cluster A. Since most of the mAb used here have similar affinity and are of the IgG class (with the exception of 142-45) the more efficient inhibition by cluster B antibodies does not seem to be due to different affinities, etc.. In addition, under different experimental conditions CTL can be generated which are predominantly blocked by cluster A or cluster B antibodies, as will be shown below.

Altogether the data suggest that CTL can recognize different regions of the H-2 molecule. Calculation of lytic units shows that about three times more CTL exist in a bulk culture which are specific for those parts of the H-2 molecule that are covered or modified by binding of antibodies to cluster B compared to antibodies to cluster A.

A very similar picture was obtained when H-2 restricted CTL were studied. As a model system H-2K^k restricted TNP specific CTL (CBA anti-CBA-TNP) were chosen. Again the data suggest that more CTL use epitope region B as restriction sites. At first sight these data seem to suggest that antibodies and both alloreactive and H-2 restricted CTL recognize the same polymorphic epitope regions on H-2 molecules, but, as will be seen later, contrasting results were obtained with other H-2 molecules.

Demonstration of Different CTL Subpopulations which Recognize Different H-2 Epitopes

For a clonal analysis of the fine specificity of CTL for H-2 epitopes alloreactive H-2K^k specific CTL clones were generated in a limiting dilution system. Increasing numbers of DBA/2 responders were stimulated with 1 x 10^6 A/J stimulator cells in the presence of TCGF (crude rat Con A supernatant) for 7 days. Lytic activity was then measured against L929 cells. In more than 30 limiting dilution experiments we found almost regularly multiphasic Poisson distributions. A typical triphasic plot is presented in Fig. 2 which depicts three sets of experimental values each fitting to a straight line. The lines cross the ordinate at approx. 1.0 suggesting that in each case only one cell type is limiting. With increasing numbers of responder cells a linear increase of wells with cytolytic activity is observed. From these data a precursor frequency for this CTL population of about 1/400 can be estimated. However, a further increase of responders results in a decrease of positive wells suggesting action of a suppressive mechanism on the frequent CTL$_1$ population. Then, with higher responder cell numbers a second linear increase is found indicating the existence of a second CTL population with a precursor frequency of about 1/1500 to 1/1200. At higher cell doses this population becomes also suppressed which allows a third CTL population to become visible (f = 1/3000 to 1/4000).

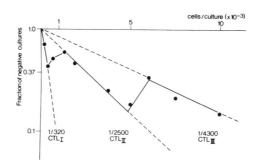

Fig. 2 (Adapted from Weyand et al (1981b) Three alloreactive
H-2K^k specific CTL populations revealed by limiting
dilution analysis. Graded numbers of DBA/2 responders were
stimulated with 10^6 A/J stimulators for 7 days in the presence of TCGF (crude supernatant from rat splenocytes stimulated with Con A). Cytolytic activity was measured against
L929 cells.

Altogether, the zig zag curves indicate the presence
of three CTL populations with different precursor frequencies.
Frequently, we observe only biphasic curves with either
population CTL_I and CTL_{II} or CTL_{II} and CTL_{III}. In the first
case the existence of population CTL_{III} is not revealed by
the Poisson plot but it is suggested by decrease and subsequent increase of ^{51}Cr-release values at higher numbers of
responder cells. The reasons for the variations in our limiting dilution system are not clear but the batch of TCGF, the
origin of mice, etc. may be critical.

Target Inhibition of Different CTL Clonotypes by Anti-H-2

Next, we used target inhibition by anti-H-2 mAb for determination of H-2 epitope specificity of CTL clones in CTL
subpopulations. Each limiting dilution well was split into
two aliquots and cytolytic activity was measured in the presence and in the absence of excess mAb (ascites fluid
diluted 1:25 or 1:50).

From the resulting data the percentage of CTL can be
calculated which are directed against that area of the H-2
molecule which is covered or modified by binding of the respective mAb. The results are summarized in Table 2.

Table 2:   Target inhibition with anti-H-2K^k mAb of H-2K^k
             specific CTL clones

Inhibitor (anti-H-2 mAb)	Cluster	% microwells inhibited of CTL subpopulations		
		CTL$_I$	CTL$_{II}$	CTL$_{III}$
H100-5/28 (m3)	A	74	53	29
H100-27/55 (m4)	A	52	41	24
H116-22/7 (m1)	A	48	10	8
H100-30/23 (m5)	B	0	55	65
H141-23/3 (m9)	B		52	68
H142-45/2 (m10)	B	0	59	72
Mixed mAb	A+B	85	90	95
Balb/c a-A/J serum	A+B	76	85	80
Ratio of A:B		1:0	1:1.6	1:3.6

CTL clones were generated in a limiting dilution system
DBA/2 anti-A/J (Weyand et al 1981b). Wells were split into
two equal aliquots and cytolytic activity was measured in the
absence or in the presence of anti-H-2 (ascites fluid 1:25).
CTL subpopulations correspond to those shown in Fig. 2. The
percentage of inhibited CTL clones has been caculated by comparison of the frequency of clones against all H-2K^k determinants with frequency of clones against antibody covered sites.
It can be seen that each mAb inhibits only a certain percentage of microwells. These findings demonstrate the existence
of distinct CTL clonotypes with specificity for different H-2
determinants. The most surprising observation is the differential inhibition obtained with mAb against the two clusters
(epitope regions) of H-2 determinants. Thus, only mAb against
cluster A were able to block CTL clones from the high frequent
CTL$_I$ population. In contrast, CTL$_{II}$ clones were blocked to
about the same degree by mAb to cluster A and B. CTL$_{III}$ clones,
however, were about three times more efficiently blocked by
cluster B antibodies. These results suggest that the high frequent CTL$_I$ population is predominantly specific for cluster A
of the H-2K^k molecule. After suppression of this population
at higher cell doses other populations become visible with
preferential specificity for cluster B. Population CTL$_{III}$ is
probably very similar to CTL generated in bulk cultures which
are also predominantly reactive against cluster B. It can

be concluded from these findings that cluster A specific CTL precursors are suppressed under mass culture conditions.

When TNP-specific H-2 restricted CTL were analyzed in this limiting dilution system again a triphasic curve was observed similar to the one depicted in Fig. 2. Target inhibition of TNP-specific CTL wells with mAb show also that the low frequent CTL_{III} population could be much more efficiently inhibited by mAb to cluster B than the high frequent CTL_I population.

The mechanism of target inhibition by mAb is not clear. It could be either steric hindrance or due to conformational changes induced by a mAb which prevents binding of a CTL. Inspite of this uncertainty several main conclusions can be drawn from the limiting dilution data. First, a differential inhibition of CTL subpopulations by mAb is indicative that alloreactive CTL exist which have specificity for different parts of a given H-2 molecule. The same conclusion applies for H-2 restricted CTL. Thus, H-2 molecules appear to express distinct regions which serve as recognition sites for both alloreactive and H-2 restricted CTL. These data are suggestive that CTL and antibodies recognize basically the same epitope regions, but the following set of experiments will demonstrate that this is not the case.

CTL And Antibodies Do Not Recognize the Same Epitope Region on H-2 Molecules

In one of the previous paragraphs we have described that point mutations in the $H-2K^b$ polypeptide chain modify only allodeterminants in one epitope region but not in the other ones. Hence, the expectation was that CTL raised in a K^b mutant against the wild type would also mainly recognize the corresponding epitope region. To test this hypothesis CTL were generated in bm3 mice against wild type B6, and the specificity of CTL was investigated by target inhibition with mAb against $H-2K^b$. Since bm3 mice have two aminoacid substitutions at positions 77 and 89, the resulting CTL are expected to be directed against that epitope region on the wild type H-2 which is influenced by aminoacids 77 and 89. When antibodies were used, such a corresponding epitope region could be defined by mAb of Group A which do not bind to bm3 mutants (see Table 1). Therefore it was anticipated that mAb of Group A would be most effective in target inhibition but not mAb of Groups B and C.

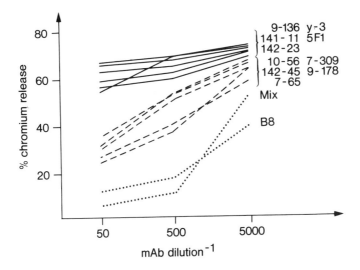

Fig. 3. Target inhibition by anti-K^b mAb of lysis of H-2^b targets (ConA blasts) by K^b specific CTL (B10.D2 B10.A(5R). Effector: target ratio = 50:1.

Conversely CTL raised in bm1 against B6 should be best inhibited by mAb of Group C, but not by Group A or B, because only the epitope region defined by Group C mAb is modified by the aminoacid substitution of bm1 (Table 1). A typical target inhibition experiment is presented in Fig. 3, and the results of several different experiments are schematically summarized in Table 3. Three different CTL populations were investigated. 1. B10D2 (H-2^d against H-2K^b wild type), 2. bm3 (77/89) against K^b wild type, and 3. bm1 (155/156) against K^b wild type.

It can be seen that the various mAb fall into three distinct groups according to their effect in the target inhi- bition experiments, and that the same hierarchy of inhibitory capacity is observed regardless of which CTL population is investigated. For example, although CTL bm3 against B6 were expected to be best inhibited by antibodies belonging to cluster A (see Table 1) it is obvious that not all members of Group A but also mAb of the other epitope regions are able to block. The very same mAb block also CTL B10.D2 against B6 or CTL bm1 against B6. Since the mechanism of target inhibition

Table 3. Summary of target inhibition by anti-K^b mAb
of CTL raised in K^b mutants against K^b wild type

CTL	Specificity	Inhibitory capacity of mAb		
		strong	medium	none
BALB/c				
anti-B10.A(5R)	K^b	Mix	10-56 (A)	9-136 (A)
bm3				
anti-C57Bl/6	77,89[1]	B8 (A)[2]	142-45 (B)	141-11 (B)
bm1				
anti-C57Bl/6	155,156[1]		7-65 (C)	142-23 (B)
			7-309 (C)	Y-3 (B)
			9-178 (C)	5F1 (C)

Target inhibition performed as described in Figs. 1 and 3.
The inhibitory capacity of mAb was deduced from the inhibition
curves.
1. CTL are directed against those determinants which are
different between mutant and wild type due to aminoacid substitutions at positions 77 and 89 or 155 plus 156.
2. Letters in parenthesis indicate membership to epitope
regions as defined by crossblocking studies (see Table 1).

is not known, which could be due to steric hindrance or to
conformational changes, it is more important to note that there
are mAb from each epitope region which do not block suggesting
that these epitope regions are no major targets for CTL. We
assume that affinity or antibody class are not responsible for
this differential blocking effect. For example, mAb 141-11 is
an IgM antibody and it seems to be of rather high affinity,
but it does not block, whereas 10-56 which has intermediate
inhibitory capacity is an IgG antibody of rather low affinity
(unpublished). In conclusion no clear correlation between epitope regions defined by antibodies and the fine specificity
of CTL can be seen.

Altogether the data presented here for the H-2K^k and
the H-2K^b molecule appear to lead to contrasting conclusions.
For the H-2K^k molecule one is tempted to assume that B and
T cells recognize the same epitope regions. This may be a mis-
interpretation of the data because the H-2K^b system shows
clearly that antibodies and CTL do not recognize the same

epitope region on the K^b molecule. Since here for each epitope region mAb can be found which block CTL it cannot be stated which H-2 sites are the target for CTL. Somewhat more informative are those mAb which do not block. Because each epitope region contains mAb without significant inhibitory capacity this suggests that none or only a small area of the epitope regions defined by antibodies is also recognized by CTL. More studies will be required for definition of those H-2 regions which serve as recognition and restriction sites for CTL and which may interact with foreign antigens, such as virus or tumor associated antigen.

Hämmerling GJ, Rüsch E, Tada N, Kimura S, Hämmerling U (1982). Localization of allodeterminants on H-2K^b antigens determined with monoclonal antibodies and H-2 mutant mice (Major histocompatibility complex/antigenic structure). Proc Nat Acad Sci. In press.

Lemke H, Hämmerling GJ, Hämmerling U (1979). Fine specificity analysis with monoclonal antibodies of antigens controlled by the major histocompatibility complex and by the Qa/TL region in mice. Immunol Rev 47:175.

Lemke H, Hämmerling GJ (1982). Clustering of antigenic determinants on H-2 molecules. J Immunol 128:2465.

Weyand C, Hämmerling GJ, Goronzy J (1981a). Recognition of H-2 domains by cytotoxic T lymphocytes. Nature 292:627.

Weyand C, Goronzy J, Hämmerling GJ (1981b). Recognition of polymorphic H-2 domains by T lymphocytes. I. Functional role of different H-2 domains for the generation of alloreactive cytotoxic T lymphocytes and determination of precursor frequencies. J Exp Med 154:1717.

Zinkernagel RM, Doherty PC (1974). Activity of sensitized thymus derived lymphocytes in lymphotic choriomeningitis reflects immunological surveillance against altered self components. Nature 251:547.

13th International Cancer Congress, Part B
Biology of Cancer (1), pages 387–392
© 1983 Alan R. Liss, Inc., 150 Fifth Avenue, New York, NY 10011

IMMUNOLOGIC EFFECTS OF INTERFERONS ON THE CELL MEMBRANE

Larry Nathanson, M.D.

Nassau Hospital, Mineola, NY
School of Medicine, SUNY at Stony Brook

INTRODUCTION

Interferons are a group of related proteins characterized by antiviral activity and species specificity. Three
major interferon subtypes in humans and murine species
include viral induced leukocyte type alpha interferon
(IFN-α); a polyribonucleotide induced fibroblast type beta
(IFN-β); and immune or mitogen induced T-lymphocyte type
gamma (IFN-γ). International reference preparations are
now available for standarization of all these interferon
types. In addition, the corresponding recombinant DNA
produced interferons which include pure and hybrid leukocyte A and D interferon (IFLrA, IFLrD and IFLrA/D).[10]
In addition to the antiviral activity [2,6] demonstrated by
interferons, other effects include: direct cytostatic
effects [5,6] primarily seen in G-1 phase (but also in S
and G-2 phase) of cell cycle; activation of macrophages, NK
cells and nonsensitized lymphocytes; effects on absorption
alloantigens, enhanced expression of H-2 Ag; and reduced
tumorgenicity. A specific membrane receptor for interferons
has been demonstrated by means of radio labeled interferon
studies. [1,7,12]

Broadly speaking, biological activity of interferons
are of three major types: first, induction of an antiviral
state; second, inhibition of cell growth, and third,
modulation of the immune system. This latter effect, and
the possible role which cell surface alterations produced
by interferon may play in it, is the topic of this brief
review.

CELL SURFACE EFFECTS

Table I summarizes eight known effects of interferon on the cell surface.[5] Most of these studies have been demonstrated using cells obtained from murine species, and most relate to effects probably produced by a crude mixture of interferons which may include both alpha and beta subtypes.

TABLE I
INTERFERONS:CELL SURFACE EFFECTS

1. Increase Membrane Protein-Lipid Ratio
2. Increase Intramembranous Particles
3. Increase Net Negative Surface Charge
4. Inhibits Membrane Binding Labeled TSH
   and Cholera Toxin. Increases Binding
   Con A (L1210)
5. Increases Cytotoxicity of Sensitized
   Splenic Lymphocytes (via Surface Effect)
   L1210
6. Increase Expression Histocompatibility
   Ag L1210 cells
7. Changes in Ganglioside Orientation of
   Enzyme Treated Plasma Membrane
8. Stimulation of Cyclic AMP (but not
   Adenylate Cyclase)

Analysis of plasma membranes prepared from normal cells has shown significant alterations in membrane density probably indicating that protein lipid ratios are increased in the membranes of interferon treated cells. In addition, interferon has been shown to increase the concentration of intramembranous particles in such cells, as demonstrated by freeze fracture electron microscopy. These two effects may be related, as a major component of intramembranous particles is glycoprotein, hence, suggesting these particles as a major target site for interferon. Cells placed in electrophorectic apparatus show increased anodal mobility following interferon treatment. Thus, the negative charge on cell surfaces appears to increase following such treatment. The binding of thyroid stimulating hormone (TSH) and cholera toxin to cell surfaces has been studied. Interferons significantly inhibit binding of TSH, and to a lesser extent, cholera toxin to specific cell receptors. Conversely, inteferon treatment may increase the binding of concanavalin A to the surface of L1210 cells.

Interferon has been shown to enhance specifically
induced cytotoxicity of splenic lymphocytes for L1210 cells.
This only occurs in such spleen cells following their
specific sensitization to L1210 antigens and, therefore,
strongly suggests a cell surface effect of interferon.
This may correlate with the additional observation that
interferons enhance the expression of cell surface histocompatibility antigens in L1210 cells and tumor associated
antigens on melanoma cells.[10] When cell membranes were
enzymatically treated and then subjected to analysis of
ganglioside components in the plasma membrane, it has been
found that interferon had a significant effect on the
orientation of such gangliosides in the membrane.

An additional effect of interferon in the stimulation
of cyclic AMP has also been shown. Because this effect is
not related to any change in adenylate cyclase, it may be
inferred that it is due to some nonspecific change in the
cell membrane resulting from interferon treatment.
However, receptor dependant influence of interferons on
the cyclase-cAMP system has not been excluded.

IMMUNOLOGIC EFFECTS
Interferons alter the function of all the major
effector cells of the immune system whether studied in
vitro or in vivo as shown in Table II.[5] With regard to
B-cell function, interferon has a significant direct
effect on antibody synthesis.[8] There is an inhibition
in such synthesis when interferon treatment of B-cell
precedes Ag exposure, but an increase in antibody formation
when interferon follows Ag exposure (both in vitro and
in vivo). T-cell function is altered in vivo as demonstrated by diminished graft versus host reactions and
delayed graft rejection, as well as reduced delayed type
hypersensitivity. However, H2 Ag expression on cell
surface in vivo is augmented. In vitro, a decrease is
observed in mixed lymphocyte reaction and an increase
H2 Ag expression and mitogen responses. Increased
lymphokine production by mitogen treated T-cells is seen
when such cells are exposed to interferon.[3] Nonspecific
(NK cell) cytolytic activity [4,9,11] and specific antibody dependant K cell activity has been shown to be
augmented, both in in vivo and in vitro, in interferon
treated cells. Significant stimulation of macrophages has

been noted with increased phagocytosis and antitumor cell
activity in vitro as well as in vivo. Again, it should be
emphasized that much of this work has been carried out with
impure and mixed interferon preparations so that the precise effects of individual interferons are as yet unclear.
Furthermore, in certain cases it is possible that humeral
lymphokines present in trace amounts in interferon preparations could have accounted for some of the activities
attributed to interferons themselves.

TABLE II
IMMUNOLOGIC EFFECTS OF INTERFERONS
FUNCTION AND EFFECT OF INTERFERONS

EFFECTOR CELL	IN VITRO	IN VIVO
B	Antibody Formation IF Before Ag-decreased IF After Ag-increased	Antibody Formation decreased increased
T	Mixed Lymphocyte reaction decreased H-2 Ag expression- increased Mitogenic response- increased Lymphokine Produc- tion-increased	Graft vs. host re- action-decreased H-2 Ag expression- increased Delayed-type hyper- sensitivity (sensitization) and response)- decreased Allograft rejec- tion-delayed
K	Killer or natural killer activity- increased	Killer or natural killer activity- increased
Macrophage	Phagocytosis-increased Antitumor cell activity- increased	Phagocytosis- increased Antitumor cell activity- increased

After RM Friedman (5)

CORRELATIONS

A precise picture of the molecular mechanisms by which
the multiple immunolgic effects of interferon are mediated
is still unclear. However, it does appear that interferons
bind to a specific membrane receptor, that they have
multiple physical and biochemical effects on the cell
membrane, and that these effects include enhanced expression
of surface histocompatibility antigens. They appear to
augment the cytotoxicity of sensitized lymphocyte effector
cells by virtue of a membrane effect. In addition, changes
in a membrane cyclic AMP may be related to these molecular
events.

Further work will be required to define the cell surface
alterations which follow interferon treatment, and allow us
to manipulate such changes to achieve specific experimental
or clinical goals.

1. Aguet M, Gresser I, Hovanessian AG, Bandu MT, Blanchard B, Blangy D (1981). Specific high-affinity binding of 1251-labeled mouse interferon to interferon resistant embryonal carcinoma cells in vitro. Virology 114(2):585.
2. Baglioni C, Nilsen T (1981). The action of interferon at the molecular level. Amer Sci 69:392.
3. Blomgren H, Einhorn S (1981). Lymphokine production by PHA-stimulated human lymphocytes is enhanced by interferon. Int Arch Allergy Appl Immunol 66(2):173.
4. Djeu JY, Timonen T, Herberman RB (1981). Augmentation of natural killer cell activity and induction of interferon by tumor cells and other biological response modifiers. In Chirigos MA et al (eds): "Mediation of Cellular Immunity in Cancer by Immune Modifiers", Vol 19, New York:Raven Press p 161.
5. Friedman RM (1981). "Interferons-A Primer", New York: Academic Press.
6. Friedman RM, Czarniecki CW et al (1981). Mechanisms of interferon action on cell growth and on murine leukemia, vesicular stomatitis, and encephalomyocarditis viruses. In Munk K, Kirchner H (eds): "Interferon-Properties, Mode of Action, Production, Clinical Application", Vol 11, New York:S. Karger·Basel.
7. Grollman EF, Lee G et al (1978). Relationships of the structure and function of the interferon receptor to hormone receptors and establishment of the antiviral state. Can Res 38:4172
8. Harfast B, Huddlestone JR, Casali P, Merigan TC, Oldstone MB (1981). Interferon acts directly on human B Lymphocytes to modulate immunoglobulin synthesis. J Immunol 127(5):2146.
9. Lee SH, Kelley S, Chiu H, Stebbing N (1982). Stimulation of natural killer cell activity and inhibition of proliferation of various leukemic cells by purified human leukocyte interferon subtypes. Can Res 42:1312.
10. Liao SK, Kwong PC, Khosravi M, Dent P (1982). Enhanced expression of melanoma associated antigens and β_2-microglobulin on cultured human melanoma cells by interferon JNCI 68:No.1.
11. Lotzova E, Savary C, Gutterman J, Hersh E (1982). Modulation of natural killer cell-mediated cytotoxicity by partially purified and cloned interferon-α. Can Res 42:2480
12. Mogensen KE, Bandu MT, Vignaux F, Aguet M, Gresser I (1981). Binding of 1251-labelled human alpha interferon to human lymphoid cells. Int J Cancer 28(5):575.

13th International Cancer Congress, Part B
Biology of Cancer (1), pages 393–402
© 1983 Alan R. Liss, Inc., 150 Fifth Avenue, New York, NY 10011

GENERATION OF TUMORCIDAL MACROPHAGES AND DIRECT SELECTIVE DESTRUCTION OF TUMOR CELLS BY MEMBRANE ACTIVE ADJUVANTS

Paul G. Munder, M. Modolell, R. Andreesen, W. Berdel, W. Pahlke, R. Oepke and O. Westphal
Max-Planck-Institut für Immunbiologie
D-7800 Freiburg
Federal Republic of Germany

Host defense mechanisms can be modified in vivo by a variety of compounds. Numerous organic and inorganic substances have been described which enhance the immunological response of the organism. Although many of them are chemically not related, good immunological adjuvants have the ability in common to cause local reactions with cell destruction granuloma formation and local as well as systemic cell proliferation. In the attempt to define a possible common denominator which could explain this biological activity of widely different compounds the observation was made that surface activity might play a central role (Dresser, 1961; Gall, 1966; Munder, 1968; Munder 1980). Many of the immunolgical adjuvants are either surface active themselves (retinoids, saponin, Freunds complete adjuvants) contain membrane active structures like the cell walls of different bacteria (Mycobacteria, C. parvum) and induce the formation of surface active lysophosphatidylcholine (2-LPC) in macrophages like the inorganic adjuvant silica (Munder, 1977). The increased formation of endogenous 2-LPC is caused by the activation of a cellular phospholipase A after the phagocytosis of the mentioned adjuvants, which leads to the breakdown of phosphatidylcholine and accumulation of 2-LPC and free fatty acids. These biochemical studies led to the working hypothesis that the increased formation of surface-active lysophospholipids might be the lowest common denominator for the explanation of adjuvant activity. Natural 2-LPC did indeed act as an adjuvant when given together with or shortly before the antigen (Munder 1980). As this substance is, however, a very important intermediate in the cellular phospholipid metabolism it is rapidly metabolized. To inhibit its turnover and to prolong thereby its biological activity a series of 2-LPC analogs were synthesized. Fig. 1 demonstrates schematically examples of the modifications used so far in vivo and in vitro.

I.

ES_n-OH

$$CH_2 - O - \overset{\overset{O}{\underset{\|}{}}}{C} - C_nH_{2n \cdot 1}$$
$$|$$
$$HC - OH$$
$$|$$
$$CH_2 - O - \boxed{PC}$$

II.

ET_n-OH

$$CH_2 - O - C_nH_{2n \cdot 1}$$
$$|$$
$$HC - OH$$
$$|$$
$$CH_2 - O - \boxed{PC}$$

III.

ET_n-H

$$CH_2 - O - C_nH_{2n \cdot 1}$$
$$|$$
$$CH_2$$
$$|$$
$$CH_2 - O - \boxed{PC}$$

IV.

ET_n-OCH_3

$$CH_2 - O - C_nH_{2n \cdot 1}$$
$$|$$
$$HC - O - CH_3$$
$$|$$
$$CH_2 - O - \boxed{PC}$$

The most important alterations in the molecule are:

1) the replacement of the acyl-bond in sn-1 of 2-LPC by an alkyl-bond, preventing thereby the degradation by a lysophospholipase (EC 3.1.1.5) and

2) the substitution of the OH-group in sn-2 inhibiting the acylation of the lysophospholipid 2-LPC to the biological inactive phosphatidylcholine. Further analogs have been prepared in which the length of the aliphatic side chain has been varied and the polar head group in sn-3 has been modified. Additional biologically interesting compounds are analogs in which the C-O-C bond in sn-1 has been replaced by a C-S-C bond abolishing any platelet aggregating activity (PAF) and some pure enantiomeric D-compounds (Hanahan 1981). Combination of these modifications in one molecule leads in principle to numerous analogs. Only a minor part has been synthesized and tested biologically so far. The following substances have been used extensively in our studies on the antitumor-activity of lysophospholipids: Rac. 1-octadecyl-2-methoxy-sn-glycero-3-phosphocholine ($ET-18-OCH_3$); rac. 1-octadecyl-sn-glycero-3-phosphocholine ($ET-18-OH$); 1-octadecyl-propanediol-3-phosphocholine ($ET-18-H$); rac. 1-hexadecyl-sn-glycero-3-phosphocholine ($ET-16-OH$); 1-hexadecyl-propanediol-3-phosphocholine ($ET-16-H$). A systematic study on the biological activity of further analogs is at present under way. In the abbreviations used, ET -denotes the ether- or alkyl-bond, 12-18 the number of carbon atoms of the aliphatic side chain and H or CH_3 the substituting group in sn-2 of the molecule.

So far as the physico-chemical characteristics are concerned all the listed analogs are almost identical in this respect. Their surface activity, solubility, and affinity to proteins is rather similar to the natural parent compound 2-LPC. But the metabolic fate is quite different causing presumably the biological effects discussed below (Modolell, 1979).

The first indication for a modified biological effect of 2-LPC analogs was the observation of an increased and prolonged humoral immune response against soluble and particulate antigens (Munder, 1980).If activation of phospholipase A and increased formation of 2-LPC in macrophages mediates the classical adjuvant activity the enhanced adjuvant effect of analogs was thought to be mediated by these cells after contact with analogs. Recent results on the phagocytic and antibacterial activity of ET-18-OH$_3$ confirm this notion (Vassileff 1982).

When the influence of ALP on cellular immune mechanism were studied a remarkable anti-tumor effect was noted (Munder 1981). Figure 1 shows the typical growth pattern of a methyl-cholanthrene induced sarcoma (Meth A-sarcoma) under daily application of ET-18-OH.

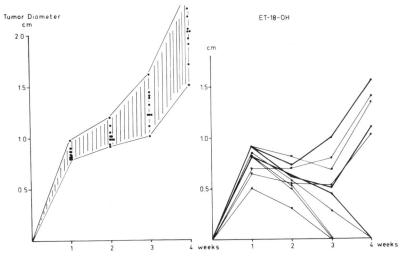

Figure 2. Growth of MethA sarcoma tumor under the influence of ET-18-OH. 1 x 10^5 tumor cells were injected i.c. 10 mice (C57/B6 x Balb/c)F$_1$ were used per group. Tumor growth was determined by measuring 2 diameters of the tumor weekly and calculating the volume by the formula: . On day + 5 treatment was started by feeding 50 µg ET-18-OH daily for 20 days.

Originally the compounds were given intravenously only but oral application prooved to be equally effective. As indicated in Fig. 2, half of the animal show complete regression of the transplanted tumors whereas in other animals the tumor stops growing temporarly but resumes normal growth after three to four weeks. In a small percentage of treated animals no effect at all can be observed. In no instance, however, an enhanced tumor growth has ever been seen. The lowest effective dose is about 10 µg/mouse/day. Doses above 100 µg ALP usually do not improve the results.

Only lysophospholipids with an alkyl-bond have antitumor activity. Natural 2-LPC has no effect. In Fig. 3 the results of experiments are shown in which two ALP's were compared with 2-LPC and cyclophosphamide.

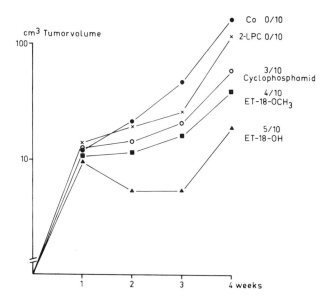

Figure 3. Growth of MethA sarcoma under treatment with different lysophospholipids. 1×10^5 tumor cells were injected i.c. into (C57/b6x Balb/c) Fl mice. Treatment was started on day +5 (50 µg/mouse/day). 50 µg cyclophosphamide was also given orally. 0/10 : Survivor/Total.

It is evident that 2-LPC has no effect. This indicates the necessity of the alkyl-bond for the antitumor activity. Surprising is the constantly observed antitumor effect of ET-18-OH which should theoretically be inactivated by acylation in sn-2. It might, however, been active as it is a racemic compound in which the D-enantiomer could be the effective part.

ALP was also tested in other tumor systems like 3-Lewis lung carcinoma, leukemia 1210, different myelomas and Ehrlich ascites carcinoma (Munder, 1981). In all these tumors ALP analogs had antitumor activity. In some of these experiments, the analogs were injected intraperitoneally (i.p.) before the tumor cells were transplanted at the same site (Tarnowski 1978; Munder 1981). Under those conditions, mice were protected against a more than a thousandfold higher number of tumor cells which killed mice in the control groups. The protection lasted for about 30 days. Assuming an important role of macrophages in this defense reaction peritoneal cells were incubated in vitro with various tumor cells together with the ALP ET-18-OCH$_3$. As shown in Figure 4 Meth A tumor cells are killed in vitro depending 1) on the amount of ALP added and 2) the number of macrophages present in the culture. Tumor cell survival was measured by thymidine incorporation and morphological observation. Decreased or absent ^{3}H-thymidine incorporation was always correlated with increased tumor cell destruction.

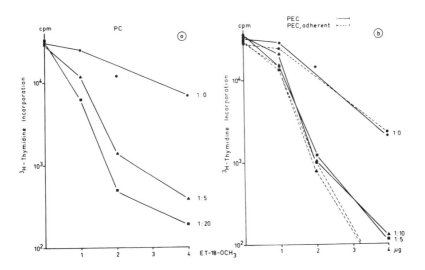

Figure 4. Tumor cell destruction in vitro by ET-18-OCH3 incubated peritoneal PC (a) and peritoneal exudate cells (b). Each point represent the mean of 6 cultures. SD$_x$< 8%. Effector and target cells were cultivated for 3 days. 2 x 10^3 tumor cells/well. Neither normal nor peritoneal exsudate cells destroy Meth A tumor cells in vitro. But both cell populations can be activated by ALP to kill tumor cells.

Increased tumor cell destruction by ALP activated peritoneal cells depends apparently on the adherent cells (Fig. 3b). The killing of tumor cells by peritoneal cells in culture containing ALP is not confined to a specific strain of mice or tumor.

Fig. 5 demonstrates the killing of Abelson lymphoma 8.1 cells by peritoneal cells in the presence of ET-18-OCH$_3$. ^{3}H-thymidine incorporation, absolute number of surviving tumor cells, and alkaline phosphatase activity in the cultures (Culvenor, 1981) were determined as parameters for cellular destruction. All three parameter decline in parallel depending on the amount of ALP added and the number of PC present.

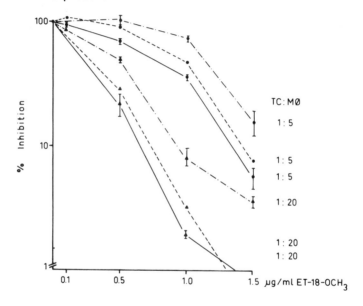

Figure 5. Destruction of Abelson 8.1 lymphoma cells in vitro by ALP activated peritoneal cells. 2 x 10^3 tumor cells/well. Incubation for 3 days. –·–·Alk. phosphat.,– – –^{3}H-thymidine incoporation, •—• absolute number of surviving tumor cells. Each value in % inhibition of the measured parameter in tumor cells alone. 6 cultures/value.

The studies with peritoneal cells raised the question whether the membrane active analogs act directly on macrophages or whether they liberate activating lymphokines from admixed lymphocytes. For this reason, pure bone marrow derived macrophages were used which had been obtained by culturing bone marrow in vitro (Metcalf 1977).In numerous experiments ET-18-OCH$_3$ activated bone marrow derived macrophages are as effective as peritoneal cells making a mediating effect of lymphocytes rather unlikely.

For the activation ALP does not have to be present during the interaction of macrophage and tumor cell. In the experiment shown in figure 6 bone marrow derived macrophages were first incubated with 10 µg and 15 µg ET-18-OCH$_3$ for 24 hours, washed, resuspended in fresh medium and then cultured with tumor cells. Two different strains of mice and two different tumors were used.

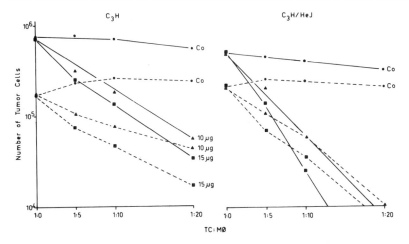

Figure 6. Destruction of BP 8 and myeloma X 5563 tumor cells by bone marrow macrophages preactivated with ET-18-OCH$_3$. BP 8: - - - -■ X 5563: •————•

Cytotoxicity of the activated macrophages was measured by counting the remaining tumor cells after 72 hours in culture. It should be noted that macrophages from C3H/HeJ mice which cannot be activated by lymphokines become highly cytotoxic after preincubation with ALP.

The anti-tumor activity of alkyllysophospholipids is not only mediated by the cytotoxic action of ALP activated macrophages. The substances have also a direct killing effect on neoplastic cells. This has been reported fro ET-18-OCH$_3$ incubated with human malignant cells (Runge, 1980, Andreesen 1978, Tidwell 1981, Berdel 1981). The direct cytotoxic effect is most likely caused by a specific inhibition of the phospholipid metabolism in neoplastic cells (Modolell 1979). The strength of this cytotoxic reaction depends strongly on the molecular structure of the lysophospholipid used as demonstrated in figure 7.

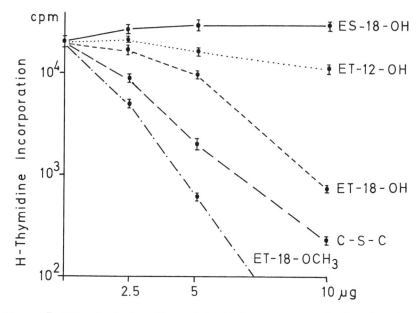

Figure 7. Direct destruction of MethₐA sarcoma cells in vitro by various alkyllysophospholipids. 1 x 10⁴ tumor cells were incubated in MEM + 10% fetal calf serum for 48 h. C-S-C.: 1-hexadecylmercapto-2-methoxymethyl-3-phosphorylcholine (Boehringer, Mannheim, FRG) ET-12-OH: 1-dodecyl-glycero-3-phosphorylcholine.

Figure 7 demonstrates several facts about the direct cytotoxicity of ALP: 1. Only alkyl- but not acyllosophospholipid like ES-18-OH are active. 2. The presence of a free -OH group in sn-2 decreases but does not abolish the killing. 3. Compounds with a C-S-C structure in sn-1 are also highly active. 4. ALP with a shorter aliphatic chain like ET-12-OH are less cytotoxic. Similar results were obtained when three different lysophospholipids were compared in its activity towards a number of established cell lines of murine and human origin. Some of the results are summarized in table 1.

It is evident that natural 2-LPC is not cytotoxic for any of the tested tumor cells. ET-18-OH, which can partially be metabolized is highly cytotoxic for some but nor for all. ET-18-OCH₃ kills all the cells except the untransformed fibroblasts 3T3 and ST-U. L 929 is also not affected (Munder 1981). This difference between malignant and normal cells excludes cytolysis due to the surface activity of ALP as cause for the tumor cell kill. In that case, no difference between the substances and the effect on the various cells should have had been noted.

Table 1. Direct Cytotoxicity of ALP

Tumor cells[a]		2-LPS	ET-18-OH	ET-18-OCH$_3$
EL 4		110.4	54.9	0.2
L1210		114.6	10.6	0.1
P 815		107.0	20.2	1.2
Abelson	8.1	103.8	9.1	0.2
WEHI	7.1	97.5	92.4	31.6
--	22.1	88.9	24.1	0.2
--	231.1	108.2	89.1	1.4
--	279.1	103.8	3.4	0.5
EBV transformed human cells				
Raji		90.6	0.6	0.1
Kaplan		95.7	62.2	1.6
B 95/8		109.3	0.1	0
Virus transformed fibroblasts				
3T3		104.0	109.7	79.8
SV 3T3		107.2	101.5	5.1
ST-U		107.0	90.8	90.3
FV-STU		109.2	91.1	19.5

a) cells were cultured in DMEM + 10% FCS for 48 h in the presence of 15 µg ALP/ml quadruplicate cultures; S.D.: < 9%; b) percentage ^{3}H-incorporation of tumor cells alone; c) The WEHI cells were kindly supplied by A. Harris, W. and E. Hall Institute, Melbourne; d) embryonic fibroblasts; e) transformed by Friend leukemia virus

Summarizing these data it is postulated that the membrane active alkyl-lysophospholipids kill tumor cells in vivo and in vitro by generating tumor cytotoxic macrophages and by a selective disturbance of the phospholipid metabolism of tumor cells. (Modolell, 1979). This combination of two different antitumor principles in one molecule makes ALP to a new antineoplastic agent. Data during phase I studies in chemotherapy resistant patients indicate a possible therapeutic value for ALP in the treatment of cancer patients (Berdel, 1982).

References

Andreesen R, Modolell M, Weltzien HU, Eibl H, Common H, Löhr G, Munder P (1978). Selective destruction of human leucemic cells by alkyl-lysophospholipids. Canc Res 38:3894.

Andreesen R, Modolell M., Munder P (1979). Selective sensitivity of chronic myelogenous leucemia cell populations to akyl-lysophospholipids. Blood 54:519.

Berdel W, Fink U, Egger B, Reichert A, Munder P, Rastetter J (1981). Alkyl-lysophospholipids inhibit the growth of hypernephroid carcinomas in vitro. J Cancer Res Clin Oncol 101:325.

Berdel W, Fink U, Maubach P, Permanetter B, Rastetter J (1982). Response of acute myelomonocytic leucemia to alkyl-lysophospholipids. Blut 44:177.

Culvenor JG, Harris AW, Mandel TE, Whitelaw E, Ferber E (1981). Alkaline phosphatase in hematopoietic tumor cell lines of the mouse: high acitivty in cells of the B lymphoid lineage. J Immunol. 126:1974.

Dresser DW (1966). Adjuvanticity of Vitamin A. Nature 217:527.

Gall D (1966). The adjuvant activity of aliphatic nitrogenous bases. Immunology 11:369.

Hanahan DJ, Munder PG, Satouchi K, McManus L, and Pinkard RN (1981). Potent platelet stimulating activity of enantiomers of acetyl glyceryl ether phosphorylcholine. Biochem Biophys Commun 99:133.

Metcalf D (1977). Hemopoietic colonies. In Recent results in cancer research. Springer, Berlin, Heidelberg, New York.

Modolell M, Andreesen R, Pahlke W, Brugger U, Munder P (1979). Distrubance of phospholipid metabolism during the selective destruction of tumor cells induced by alkyl-lysophospholipids. Cancer Res 39:4681.

Munder PG, Ferber E, Modolell M, Fischer H (1968). The influence of various adjuvants on the metabolism of phospholipids in macrophages. Int Arch Allergy 36:117.

Munder PG, Lebert S (1977). The activation of phospholipase A in macrophages after the phagocytosis of silica and other cytotoxic dusts. In Walton WH (ed): "Inhaled particles IV", Oxford New York, Pergamon Press p. 531.

Munder PG, Modolell M, Andreesen R, Weltzien HU, Westphal O (1980). Lysophosphatidylcholine (lysolecithin and its synthetic analogues. Immunmodulating and other biological effects. In Chedid L, Miescher P, Meuller-Eberhard HJ (ed): "Immunstimulation", Berlin Heidelberg New York: Springer Verlag, p. 177.

Munder P, Modolell M, Bausert W, Oettgen HF, Westphal O (1981). Alkyl-lysophospholipids in cancer therapy. In Hersh EM, Chirigos MA, Mastrangelo MJ (ed) "Augmenting agents in cancer therapy", New York: Raven Press, p. 441.

Runge M, Andreesen R, Pfleiderer A, Munder P (1980). Destruction of human solid tumors by alkyl-lysophospholipids. JNCI 64:1301.

Tarnowski GS, Mountain IM, Stock CC, Munder P, Weltzien HU, Westphal O (1978). Effect of lysolecithin and analogs on mouse ascites tumors. Cancer Res 38:339.

Tidwell T, Gurman G, Vogler WR (1981). The effects of alkyl-lysophospholipids on leucemic cell lines. Differential action on two human leucemic cell lines, HL 60 and K562. Blood 57:794.

Vassileff TL, Munder P, Jann K (1982). Effect of a lysolecithin analog on nonspecific resistance in mice. Infect Immun, in press.

CONGRESS SYMPOSIA

FUNCTIONAL ASPECTS OF CELL MEMBRANES Burger, M.,
Switzerland, Chairman; Bernacki, R., USA,
Co-Chairman; Rainier Room

The Role of Somatomedin/Insulin-Like Growth
Factors and Their Receptors in Skeletal Growth
and Fetal Development: A Mini-Review.
*Perdue, J. F., Montreal, Quebec, Canada.

Analysis of the Transport Mechanism for
Methotrexate in L1210 Mouse Leukemia Cells.
*Henderson, G. B., La Jolla, CA USA.

Regulation of Membrane Function by Lipids;
Implications for Tumor Development.
*Shinitzky, M., Skornick, Y., Gorelik, E. and
Sindelar, W., Rehovot, Israel and Bethesda, MD USA.

Is Membrane Modification an Important Mechanism
of Anti-Cancer Drug Action? *Amos, H.,
Gonzalez, F., Sens, D. A. and Mandel, K. G.,
Boston, MA USA. (By Title Only)

Antigenic Changes Related to Drug Action.
*Fioretti, M. C., Romani, L. and Bonmassar, E.,
Perugia ,Italy and Rome, Italy.

Please note: Papers that are listed as "By Title
Only" were presented at the 13th International
Cancer Congress, but are not included in these
volumes.

403

13th International Cancer Congress, Part B
Biology of Cancer (1), pages 405–413
© 1983 Alan R. Liss, Inc., 150 Fifth Avenue, New York, NY 10011

THE ROLE OF SOMATOMEDIN/INSULIN-LIKE GROWTH FACTORS AND THEIR
RECEPTORS IN SKELETAL GROWTH AND FETAL DEVELOPMENT: A MINI-
REVIEW

James F. Perdue, Ph.D.

Lady Davis Institute for Medical Research
Sir Mortimer B. Davis Jewish General Hospital
Montreal, Quebec, Canada H3T 1E2

Chemistry and Function: Studies of growth hormone (GH)-
dependent skeletal growth have correlated its magnitude with
the serum concentrations of a factor initially called «sulfation factor» and later termed somatomedin (Sm) (Phillips
and Vassilopoulou-Sellin, 1980). Subsequent purification of
Sm's from human serum resolved them into two classes with
similar molecular weights, i.e. 7.5 kilodaltons (Kdaltons)
and biological properties (Zapf, Schoenle and Froesch, 1978)
but with different amino acid sequences and isoelectric
points (pI). These factors are now called somatomedin/
insulin-like growth factors (Sm/IGF) and recent studies indicate that the plasma of rats has homologous peptides.
IGF-I is a representative molecule of the alkaline class of
growth factors while IGF-II is representative of those factors with neutral to acidic pI's. In humans, the concentration of IGF-I in the blood is highly correlated with GH
levels. Using a radioimmunoassay (RIA), Zapf et al (1981)
determined IGF-I concentrations to be 193 ± 58 ng/ml for
normal adults, 712 ± 255 ng/ml in acromegalic patients and
24 ± 14 ng/ml for GH-deficient, i.e. hypopituitary patients.
Although serum levels of IGF-II are not influenced by hyper-
secretion of GH, e.g. normal patients have 647 ± 126 ng/ml
and acromegalics 641 ± 187 ng/ml, they are decreased to
252 ± 98 ng/ml in GH-deficient patients. Recently, Schoenle
et al (1982) demonstrated a direct effect of these factors
on the growth of an animal. They continuously infused designated concentrationsof IGF-I or -II into hypox rats and
proportionally stimulated the rate of (a) body weight gain,
(b) DNA synthesis in costal cartilage, and (c) widening of
the tibial epiphyseal plate.

Although current evidence argues against a role for IGF-I in fetal development, IGF-II and their receptors may be critical for this specialized period of growth. In humans, the levels of IGF-II have been correlated with the infant's birth weight and length (D'Ercole and Underwood, 1981). In rats, Moses et al (1980) and Daughaday et al (1981) both observed a temporal relationship between stages of prenatal and postnatal development and IGF-II levels. Twenty to 100- and 6-fold higher concentrations of this peptide have been observed by these investigators, respectively, in the plasma of 19 to 22 day old embryos compared with maternal serum. These levels were maintained for 6 to 7 days following birth but declined over a period of 25 days to the concentrations present in adults. These changes in circulating levels of IGF-II were paralleled by changes in IGF-II receptor affinity and number. Gavin et al (1982) observed that ^{125}I-IGF-II binding to fetal liver plasma membranes increased gradually from day 17 to day 21 and was markedly greater than was found in maternal liver. Day 17 to 19 embryos had a single class of high affinity IGF-II receptors but following birth and neonatal development, curvilinear Scatchard plots indicative of both high and low affinity sites were observed. By day 9 postpartum, the IGF-II binding capacity and K_d for the neonatal rat liver was similar to that of the maternal animal.

The growth of some malignancies may also be influenced by altered IGF-I and -II levels. Daughaday et al (1981) and Zapf et al (1981) found a marked lowering of IGF-I concentration in the serum of some patients with non-islet cell tumors but displaying hypoglycemia. Daughaday et al (1981) also found that the IGF-II levels in the sera from 10 of 14 patients were significantly greater than normal controls. Since the site of production of the additional IGF-II is not known, its presence may reflect ectopic synthesis and secretion by the tumor as was recently described for human Transforming Growth Factor (Marquardt and Todaro, 1982). There is presently no data on the effect of cell transformation on Sm/IGF receptor number or affinity other than the loss of receptors, presumably through a «down regulation» mechanism.

Structure of the Receptors: Based on the competition for binding of ^{125}I-IGF-I or -II to membranes by specified concentrations of unlabelled IGFs, insulin, etc., specific receptors that bind IGF-I (hereafter called Type I) and IGF-II, e.g. Type II receptors, were postulated to exist (Zapf et al, 1978). Large differences between the quantities of IGF-I or IGF-II bound by membranes from adipocytes, liver, muscle, placenta or cultured cells and from different species are considered to reflect the preponderance of one of the receptor types. This is illustrated in Table 1 using a single concentration of ligand but these results are comparable with those where the concentrations of growth factor were varied and the binding data analyzed by the method of Scatchard.

Table 1. Insulin-like Growth Factor and Insulin Binding to Membranes from Cultured Cells or Tissues

Tissue or Cell Type	% of Available Ligand Bound Specifically		
	^{125}I-IGF-I	^{125}I-IGF-II	^{125}I-Insulin
Chick embryo cells	4.5	20.0	2.7
Human placenta	8.7	8.6	38.8
Human foreskin fibroblasts	3.0	5.0	ND*
Mouse placenta	1.0	29.7	ND
Mouse embryo cells	2.0	15.0	ND
Rat placenta	1.7	17.7	1.3
Rat embryo cells	4.4	26.0	ND
Rat chondrosarcoma	8.4	35.0	1.0

One hundred μg of membrane protein was incubated at 22°C for 60 min in 350 μl of medium containing 50 mM-Na$_2$HPO$_4$-1 mM PMSF, 350 μg of bovine serum albumin and 0.1 ng of ^{125}I-IGF-I or -II or 0.5 ng of ^{125}I-insulin ± 10 μg of unlabelled ligands. Following incubation, three - 100 μl aliquots of the suspension were centrifuged at 100,000 x g for 8 min on the Beckman Airfuge and the quantity of specifically bound radioactivity determined. The results are representative of two to ten experiments for each membrane examined. *ND = not determined.

Type II receptors are the major ones present in rat and mouse placenta and embryonic cells. Although we have not examined them, adipocytes and liver membranes from these two species also bound IGF-II exclusively (Zapf et al, 1978). Human placenta and cultured human foreskin fibroblasts bind similar quantities of the two growth factors. Since the equilibrium dissociation constant, the K$_D$, is similar for IGF-I, IGF-II and insulin, e.g. it is 1 nM, insulin receptors are presumably present in the human placenta in far greater numbers than the Sm/IGF receptors. Insulin receptors can barely be detected in the tissues from the rat. In the case of adipocytes, a target cell for insulin's action, 1.1-1.4% of the available ^{125}I-insulin was bound specifically (Zapf et al, 1978).

The hypothesized presence of Type I and Type II receptors and tissue and species specific distribution was substantiated concomitant with their identification by cross-linking each to their respective ^{125}I-labelled ligands with the photoactivatable reagents (Bhaumick et al, 1981) or with disuccinimydl suberate (DSS). In brief, membranes are incubated with unmodified ^{125}I-Sm/IGF or its arylazide derivative ± unlabelled growth factors (as a measure of nonspecific interaction). Following incubation, receptor-associated ligand is separated from unbound ligand by centrifugation and the particulate material either photoactivated or incubated for 15 min at 0-4°C with 100 μM DSS. The cross-linked ^{125}I-ligand-receptor complexes are identified by autoradio-autography following electrophoresis in polyacrylamide gels containing sodium dodecyl sulfate (SDS-PAGE).

The structure of the Type I receptor is very similar to the insulin receptor. Under non-reducing conditions both appear on gels as large complexes of 320 to 350 Kdaltons. When the cross-linked ^{125}I-insulin complex is reduced prior to SDS-PAGE, radioactivity is associated predominantly with a 140 Kdalton α-subunit and almost indistinguishably with a 90 Kdalton β-subunit (Yip, Moule and Yeung, 1982; Massagué and Czech, 1982b). Under the same conditions of electrophoresis, ^{125}I-IGF-I is linked predominantly to a polypeptide of 130 Kdaltons (Bhaumick, Bala and Hollenberg, 1981; Chernausek, Jacobs and Van Wyk, 1981; Kasuga, Obberghen and Rechler, 1981; Massagué and Czech, 1982a) and almost imperceptually to another of 98 Kdaltons. Since (a) in vivo ^{35}S incorporation into newly synthesized insulin receptors, (b) chemical analysis of receptors isolated from human placenta, and (c) labelling of the insulin receptor with arylazide groups placed in different positions of the ^{125}I-insulin molecule all indicate the β subunit is present in quantities that are stoichiometrically equal to that of the α subunit, it is likely that the cross-linking reagents used to identify the subunits are not reacting with those that are distant from the ligand binding site. Massagué and Czech (1982a) proposed that both receptors are formed from two α subunits and two β subunits linked by disulfide bonds in a stoichiometry of (β-S-S-α)-S-S-(β-S-S-α). The hydrodynamic properties, i.e. the shape and MW determined from the Stokes

radius and sedimentation constant of the recently isolated
Type I receptor (Bhaumick, Armstrong, Hollenberg and Bala,
1982) is consistent with this interpretation.

The Type II, i.e. IGF-II, receptor appears to be a single
chained polypeptide of 220 Kdaltons that is held together by
intra-chain disulfide bonds as evidenced by the increase in
MW to 250 Kdaltons upon reduction prior to electrophoresis
(Massagué and Czech, 1982a; Kasuga, Van Obberghen, Nissley
and Rechler, 1981). This is illustrated in Figure 1 for rat
placenta. Although not shown in this figure, we have also

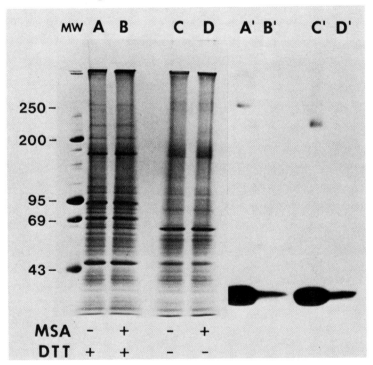

Figure 1. Identification of the rat placental Sm/IGF receptors. One hundred µg of R_3 membrane protein was incubated
with 15,000 CPM's of ^{125}I-IGF-II $\pm$ 50 µg of unlabelled MSA
(a rat IGF-II-like peptide), cross-linked with 100 µM DSS and
the proteins resolved by SDS-PAGE $\pm$ 100 mM dithiothreitol (DTT).
MW - proteins of standard molecular weight. The autoradiographs of the Coomassie blue stained membrane proteins in
lanes A, B, etc. are identified A', B', etc. A,A': R_3 + ^{125}I-
IGF-II. B,B': as in A + 50 µg MSA. C,C': unreduced R_3 +
^{125}I-IGF-II. D,D': as in C + 50 µg MSA.

identified a specifically labelled 50 Kdalton or 75 Kdalton
(when reduced) IGF-II cross-linked protein in membranes from
the Swarm rat chondrosarcoma and rat placenta when the autoradiographs have been exposed for a long period of time.
Using identical conditions of incubation, ^{125}I-IGF-I could
not be cross-linked to mouse or rat placental membrane or
membranes prepared from the Swarm rat chondrosarcoma. This
differential in the ability of ^{125}I-IGF-I or -II to bind and
cross-link to Type I or II receptors in different tissues has
also been observed by Massagué and Czech (1982) and is
summarized for the different species in Table 2. Note that
these results show a high correspondence with the binding
data presented in Table 1. It is of interest that the chicken

Table 2. Tissue Distribution and Relative Amounts of Types I
and II IGF Receptors and Insulin Receptor

	IGF receptors		Insulin
	Type I	Type II	receptors
Human			
Placenta	high	low	high
Skin fibroblasts	low	high	low
IM-9 (lymphocytes)	high	low	high
RPMI 6666 (lymphoblasts)	–	–	low
RPMI 7666 (lymphoblasts)	–	–	low
TE85 (osteogenic sarcoma)	low	low	low
A875 (melanoma)	low	low	low
Nonhuman			
Rat adipocyte	–	high	high
Rat liver	–	high	high
Rat lymphocytes	low	high	low
Rat H-35 hepatoma	low	high	low
Rat placenta	–	high	low
Rat Swarm chondrosarcoma	–	high	low
Mouse liver	–	high	high
Mouse 3T3-L1 fibroblasts	low	high	low
Mouse 3T3-L1 adipocytes	high	high	high
Mouse placenta	low	high	low
Chicken embryo fibroblasts	high	–	–
Rabbit superior cervical ganglia	low	low	low

embryo fibroblast binds the IGF-II slightly better than it does IGF-I (Table 1) and yet the only cross-linked receptor that has been identified in this tissue is one of 300 Kdaltons or 130 Kdaltons when reduced (Kasuga, Van Obberghen, Nissley and Rechler, 1982). Just as it is believed the Sm/IGF have evolved from a family of peptides of which proinsulin is a member, it is possible the avian species contains the primitive receptor from which Type I and II later evolved.

In summary, IGF-I and -II are essential mitogens for in vitro replication and presumably for in situ development and skeletal growth. IGF-II and its receptors appear more important than IGF-I for fetal development and may account for the hypoglycemia observed in some patients with non-pancreatic malignancies. The binding of ^{125}I-labelled IGF-I or -II to membranes isolated from different tissues, e.g. liver and adipocyte, and different species was not equal and indicated that two receptor forms existed. This was confirmed by cross-linking each to their specific ligands and analyzing the cross-linked species by SDS-PAGE. Type I receptors bind IGF-I and are formed from 140 and 95 Kdalton subunits into a 350 Kdalton complex. The Type II receptor is most commonly seen as a 220 Kdalton protein although some recent evidence suggests that other subunits may be part of the complex.

At present, there is no information on the mechanisms which translate Sm/IGF receptor occupancy into the pleotypic events culminating in cell replication and growth. Studies of insulin's effects on glycolysis, glucose transport and gluconeogenesis have implicated (a) proteases with the generation of small 1,000-3,000 dalton secondary messengers and (b) phosphorylation-dephosphorylation of regulatory enzymes. Because of the structural similarities between proinsulin and the Sm/IGFs and between the insulin receptor and the Type I receptor, one might anticipate that similar mechanisms are operating to stimulate the replication of cells.

Acknowledgements: I wish to acknowledge the technical assistance of Ms. Ghislaine Letendre and Carole Thibault, and the typing of Ms. Sandra Fraiberg. This work was supported in part from Research Grant MT-5749 from the Medical Research Council of Canada.

Bhaumick B, Bala RM, Hollenberg MD (1981). Somatomedin receptor of human placenta: Solubilization, photolabeling, partial purification, and comparison with insulin receptor. Proc Nat Acad Sci 78:4279.

Bhaumick B, Armstrong GD, Hollenberg MD, Bala RM (1982). Characterization of the human placental receptor for basic somatomedin. Can J Biochem (in press).

Chernausek SD, Jacobs S, Van Wyk JW (1981). Structural similarities between human receptors for somatomedin C and insulin: analysis by affinity labeling. Biochemistry 20: 7345.

Daughaday WH, Trivedi B, Kapadia M (1981). Measurements of insulin-like growth factor II by a specific radioreceptor assay in serum of normal individuals, patients with abnormal growth hormone secretion, and patients with tumor-associated hypoglycemia. J Clin Endocrinol Metab 43:289.

D'Ercole AJ, Underwood LE (1981). Growth factors in fetal growth and development. In: «Fetal Endocrinology», Academic Press, p. 155.

Gavin JR, Kent J, Trivedi B (1982). Ontogenesis of hepatic insulin-like growth factor II (IGF-II) receptors in rats. 64th Annual Meeting of the Endocrine Society, San Francisco, Abstract 404.

Kasuga M, Van Obberghen E, Nissley SP, Rechler MM (1981). Demonstration of two subtypes of insulin-like growth factor receptors by affinity cross-linking. J Biol Chem 256: 5305.

Kasuga M, Van Obberghen E, Nissley SP, Rechler MM (1982) Structure of the insulin-like growth factor receptor in chicken embryo fibroblasts. Proc Nat Acad Sci 79:1864.

Massagué J, Czech MP (1982a). The subunit structure of two distinct receptors for insulin-like growth factors I and II and their relationship to the insulin receptor. J Biol Chem 257:5038.

Massagué J, Czech MP (1982b). Role of disulfides in the subunit structure of the insulin receptor. J Biol Chem 257: 6729.

Marquardt H, Todaro J (1982). Human transforming growth factor: Production by a melanoma cell line, purification and initial characterization. J Biol Chem 257:5220.

Moses AC, Nissley SP, Short PA, Rechler MM, White RM, Knight AB, Higa OZ (1980). Increased levels of multiplication-stimulating activity, an insulin-like growth factor, in fetal rat serum. Proc Nat Acad Sci 77:3649.

Phillips LS, Vassilopoulou-Sellin R (1980). Somatomedins. N Engl J Med 302:371.

Schoenle E, Zapf J, Froesch ER (1982). Insulin-like growth factors I and II stimulate growth in hypophysectomized rats. 64th Annual Meeting of the Endocrine Society, San Francisco, Abstract 325.

Yip CC, Moule ML, Yeung CWT (1982). Subunit structure of insulin receptors of rat adipocytes as demonstrated by photo-affinity labeling. Biochemistry 21:2940.

Zapf J, Schoenle E, Froesch ER (1978). Insulin-like growth factor I and II: Some biological actions and receptor binding characteristics of two purified constituents of nonsuppressible insulin-like activity of human serum. Eur J Biochem 87:285.

Zapf J, Walter H, Froesch ER (1981). Radioimmunological determination of insulin-like growth factors I and II in normal subjects and in patients with growth disorders and extra-pancreatic tumor hypoglycemia. J Clin Invest 68:1321.

13th International Cancer Congress, Part B
Biology of Cancer (1), pages 415–423
© **1983 Alan R. Liss, Inc., 150 Fifth Avenue, New York, NY 10011**

ANALYSIS OF THE TRANSPORT MECHANISM FOR METHOTREXATE IN L1210 MOUSE LEUKEMIA CELLS

Gary B. Henderson, Ph.D.

Division of Biochemistry
Department of Basic and Clinical Research
Research Institute of Scripps Clinic
La Jolla, California 92037

Summary. Studies on the transport mechanism for methotrexate in L1210 mouse leukemia cells are summarized. The results support the utilization of an obligatory anion exchange mechanism in which the uptake of methotrexate is coupled to the efflux of an intracellular anion. Gradients of anions could then serve as the energy source for the observed concentrative uptake of methotrexate. Intracellular anions which may participate in this exchange cycle are suggested to include phosphate and AMP.

Introduction. The importance of membrane transport in the chemotherapeutic efficacy of methotrexate (MTX) was first demonstrated by Kessel et al. (1965) who showed that a close correlation existed between the sensitivity of various tumor cells to MTX and their ability to accumulate the drug. Subsequent studies in various laboratories (reviewed in Goldman 1971; Huennekens et al. 1978; Sirotnak 1980) established the general properties of MTX transport. Employing saline buffers as the suspending media, the drug was found to enter L1210 and other mouse leukemia cells by means of a membrane-associated transport system which under physiological conditions mediated the uptake of 5-methyltetrahydrofolate and other folate compounds. K_t values for half maximal rates of influx were determined to be ca. 2, 4, 5 and 200 μM for 5-methyltetrahydrofolate, 5-formyltetrahydrofolate (folinate), MTX, and folate, respectively. This transport system also appears to be the only route for the uptake of various folate compounds including the vitamin, folate. Previous conclusions suggesting a separate uptake route for folate are incorrect (Huennekens et al. 1981) since preparation of [H]folate employed in these studies contained low levels of a breakdown product (6-hydroxymethylpterin) which rapidly enters the cells via a separate transport system (Suresh, Huennekens 1982).

MTX can be accumulated by L1210 cells although concentration gradients typically do not exceed 2.0. Ironically, metabolic inhibitors enhance the ability of the cells to accumulate MTX (Goldman 1971; Rader et al. 1974; Henderson, Zevely 1980), and, conversely, glucose decreases net uptake (Goldman 1971; Henderson, Zevely 1980). These observations led to speculation that MTX influx and efflux might proceed via separate routes with different energy requirements (Goldman 1971). MTX transport is also sensitive to inhibition by various anions. This anion effect was observed initially for phosphate by Kessel and Hall (1967) and later extended to other anions by Goldman (1971).

Possible Transport Mechanisms for MTX. A requirement for membrane-associated carrier proteins to translocate MTX across cell membranes would be expected since MTX (at pH 7.4) is a highly water-soluble divalent anion. In addition, the minus 2 charge on MTX dictates that the movement of the drug into cells is in opposition to the membrane potential ($\Delta \psi$). The latter is -77 mV (interior negative) in L1210 cells when calculated from the distribution of [^{14}C]tetraphenylphosphonium ions across the L1210 cell membrane (unpublished results). Thus, if it were assumed that MTX enters L1210 cells via a passive carrier-mediated process, the Nernst equation predicts that concentration gradients of free intracellular drug at the steady-state should not exceed 0.05. Since actual concentration gradients of MTX exceed 1.0 in both L1210 and other cells of hematopoietic origin, it can be concluded that an energy source and a corresponding coupling mechanism must be involved in MTX uptake.

A variety of transport mechanisms could potentially be utilized for the active movement of MTX into L1210 cells, although at least two possibilities appear unlikely from previous observations on this system. A direct coupling mechanism using the hydrolysis of ATP(or other high-energy phosphate compounds) as the driving force is contradicted by the inhibition of MTX uptake by glucose and the corresponding stimulation of uptake by metabolic inhibitors. Similarly, co-transport with Na$^+$ can be eliminated since the transport process is Na$^+$-independent (Kessel et al. 1965; Goldman 1971). A third possibility is that MTX transport occurs via an anion exchange process. A mechanism of this type could explain the sensitivity of MTX influx to inhibition by anions, and also the effects of metabolic inhibitors on net uptake if the latter have an enhancing effect on the intra-cellular concentration of exchange anions. In addition, if the uptake of extracellular MTX is accompanied by the efflux of an intracellular divalent anion, then the process would be electroneutral and thus uncoupled from $\Delta\psi$. Gradients of anions could then serve as the energy source for driving the concentrative uptake of MTX.

Experimental Evaluation of the Anion Exchange Model. Initial Studies (Henderson, Zevely 1979; Henderson, Zevely 1980) on the effects of anions on MTX influx led to the reali-zation that the various saline buffers used to examine MTX transport in previous studies contained anions (phosphate,

Table 1

Effect of Buffer Composition on MTX Transport Parameters in L1210 Cells

Buffer	K Influx	V_{max}	$t_{\frac{1}{2}}$ Efflux	Concentration Ratio at Steady State
	µM	pmoles/min/mg	min	
PBS	10.	16	18	2
HBS	4.3	18	24	8
Na-HEPES	1.6	18	38	23
Mg-HEPES-sucrose	0.7	19	100	107

Transport measurements were performed in the indicated buffers as described previously (Henderson, Zevely 1980). Buffer compositions were as follows: PBS (phosphate-buffered saline) 138 mM NaCl, 2.7 mM KCl, 8.1 mM Na$_2$HPO$_4$, 1.5 mM KH$_2$PO$_4$, 1.0 mM CaCl$_2$, and 0.5 mM MgCl$_2$, pH 7.4); HBS (HEPES-buffered saline), 140 mM NaCl, 10 mM KCl, 20 mM HEPES, and 1 mM MgCl$_2$, pH 7.4 with KOH; Na-HEPES, 160 mM HEPES and 2 mM MgCl$_2$, pH 7.4 with NaOH; and Mg-HEPES-sucrose, 20 mM HEPES and 225 mM sucrose, pH 7.4 with MgO.

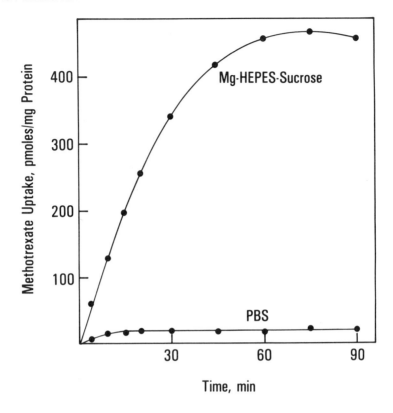

Fig. 1. Comparison of MTX uptake by L1210 cells suspended in PBS and in Mg-HEPES-sucrose. Transport measurements were performed as described previously (Henderson, Zevely 1980). Extracellular [^{3}H]MTX was: initially, 2.0 µM; at steady-state, 1.08 and 1.90 µM in Mg-HEPES-sucrose and PBS, respectively. For buffer composition, see Table 1.

chloride, and bicarbonate) which inhibited MTX influx. The inhibitory effects of these anions are illustrated by the dramatic decline in the K_t for MTX influx (Table 1) when phosphate and chloride are selectively removed from the suspending buffer and replaced with either HEPES (a zwitterion) or sucrose (a non-electrolyte). K_t values in these buffers ranged from 10 µM in PBS to 0.7 µM in a buffer (Mg-HEPES-sucrose) which lacked added anions. The V_{max} for MTX influx was the same in each buffer (16-19 pmoles/min/mg protein) indicating that phosphate and chloride (and, to some extent, HEPES) are competitive inhibitors of MTX influx and, in addition, the presence of HEPES and sucrose or the absence of saline constituents have no adverse effects on the cell or the transport system. Further studies using this series of buffers showed that the ability of the cells to accumulate MTX improves remarkably (up to 50-fold) as anions are removed from the medium (Table 1). The magnitude of this effect is illustrated in Fig. 1 which compares the uptake profiles for MTX obtained in PBS with that in Mg-HEPES-sucrose. MTX efflux is likewise affected by buffer composition (Table 1). The efflux rate was the most rapid in PBS ($t_{1/2}$ = 18 min) and declined progressively as anions (phosphate and chloride) were removed from the medium. The slowest rate of efflux was observed in Mg-HEPES-sucrose ($t_{1/2}$ = 100 min). It was thus apparent that the kinetics of MTX transport are affected to a considerable degree by various anions and that the assessment of the effects of individual anions on the transport process would require the use of buffer systems devoid of interfering anionic constituents.

Subsequent studies with L1210 cells suspended in buffers lacking anions led to the following observations on the MTX transport system:
(A) MTX influx is competitively inhibited by a broad spectrum of anions (Henderson, Zevely 1979; Henderson, Zevely, Huennekens 1979; Henderson, Zevely 1980; Henderson et al. 1980; Henderson, Zevely 1981a; Henderson, Zevely 1982a; Henderson, Zevely 1982b). Several of the more effective anions and their respective K_i values were: 5-methyltetrahydrofolate (0.3 µM), bromosulfophthalein (2 µM), thiamine pyrophosphate (3 µM), dicarboxybenzene (20 µM), and AMP (50 µM). Inhibition constants of intermediate value were observed with phosphate (400 µM), sulfate (540 µM), and other divalent inorganic anions, while small monovalent anions, such as chloride (K_i = 30 mM), were the least effective. Measurements comparing mono-, di-, tri- and tetracarboxybenzene gave K_i values of 1100, 20, 50 and 460 µM, respectively, confirming that divalent anions are bound most effectively by the transport protein. The binding site thus has sufficient flexibility to accomodate both folate compounds and various other anions of diverse structure.

(B) Removal of extracellular anions and their replacement with HEPES or sucrose decreases MTX efflux by approximately 5-fold. Conversely, efflux in buffered sucrose solutions can be increased (trans-stimulated) up to 5-fold by the re-addition of certain anions to the medium (Henderson, Zevely 1981a). Enhancement is produced by folate compounds and p-aminobenzoylglutamate, small monovalent (e.g., chloride, acetate, or lactate) and divalent (e.g., phosphate and sulfate) anions, a few nucleotides (e.g., AMP and dAMP), and thiamine pyrophosphate. Moreover, this enhancement was shown to involve the MTX carrier since anions with the ability to promote efflux lost this capacity upon exposure of the cells to an irreversible inhibitor (NHS-MTX)[1] of the MTX transport system. A close correlation could also be established between K_t values for inhibition of MTX influx and anion concentrations for 50% stimulation of MTX efflux (Henderson, Zevely 1981a). The various anions which inhibited influx but failed to promote MTX efflux included trivalent anions (citrate, tricarboxypropane, and tricarboxybenzene), most nucleotides (e.g., ATP, ITP, GMP and CMP), and compounds with bulky aromatic substituents (e.g., bromosulfophthalein, NAD, and probenecid).

(C) Evidence has been obtained suggesting that the MTX carrier protein can also transport phosphate and sulfate. A phosphate transport component was identified (Henderson, Zevely 1982a) which is sensitive to competitive inhibition by MTX and to irreversible inhibition by an active ester of MTX. In addition, fifty percent inhibition of this phosphate transport component occurred at a concentration of MTX (2 μM) that was similar to the K_t for MTX influx (1.4 μM) under the conditions employed. L1210 cells also contain a sulfate transport component which could be inhibited by low concentrations (1-10 μM) of MTX (Henderson, Zevely 1982b). The principal transport routes for phosphate (a Na^+-dependent system) and for sulfate (the general anion carrier system) in L1210 cells are not inhibited by MTX (Henderson, Zevely 1982a; Henderson, Zevely 1982b).

(D) The same carrier protein appears to mediate both the influx and efflux and MTX. This conclusion was deduced from the observations that these processes are equally

---

[1]The synthesis of NHS-MTX (N-hydroxysuccinimide ester of MTX) and its inhibitory effects on MTX transport will be described elsewhere.

sensitive to inhibition by p-chloromercuriphenylsulfonate (Henderson, Zevely 1981b) and by NHS-MTX (unpublished results), and they also respond in parallel to inhibition or promotion, respectively, to various external anions (Henderson, Zevely 1981a).

Proposed Mechanism for MTX Transport in L1210 Cells. The characteristics of MTX transport in L1210 cells can be accommodated into a single unified transport mechanism. The proposed model is that the MTX carrier protein mediates an obligatory exchange of MTX and anions across the L1210 cell membrane, in much the same fashion as the general anion transport system of erythrocytes mediates the exchange of chloride and bicarbonate (Cabantchik et al. 1978; Passow et al. 1980). To facilitate MTX uptake, the binding site on the carrier protein is suggested to interact with MTX at the external membrane surface, mediate its translocation across the lipid bilayer, and release the drug into the cytoplasm. Reversal of the process would then occur only upon binding of an intracellular anion, the translocation of the anion to the outer membrane surface, and the release of the anion into the medium. The obligatory nature of the proposed mechanism allows further for the use of anion gradients as an energy source for active transport of MTX. The large concentration gradients of MTX (ca. 100-fold) that are observed in cells suspended in a buffer (Mg-HEPES-sucrose) lacking anions could then be explained by the utilization of the large intracellular anion gradients generated under these conditions to drive MTX uptake. Intracellular anions which exchange for MTX have not been identified, although various findings suggest the involvement of phosphate and/or AMP. The latter each exhibit a relatively high affinity for the transport protein, are good transport substrates (i.e., promote MTX efflux), and are available in high amounts within the cell. Moreover, the participation of phosphate or AMP in the coupling process could also explain the effects of energy modulators on MTX uptake. Gradients of phosphate and AMP both increase upon exposure of the cells to metabolic inhibitors and thus could provide the additional driving force for the enhanced uptake of MTX that is observed under conditions of ATP depletion. In a reciprocal fashion glucose might decrease MTX uptake by lowering intracellular levels of phosphate and AMP at the expense of ATP synthesis.

References

Cabantchik Z, Knauf P, Rothstein A (1978). The anion transport system of red blood cells. Biochim Biophys Acta 515:239-302.

Goldman ID (1971). The characteristics of the membrane transport of amethopterin and the naturally occurring folates. Ann NY Acad Sci 186:400-422.

Henderson GB, Grzelakowska-Sztabert B, Zevely EM, Huennekens FM (1980). Binding properties of the 5-methyltetrahydrofolate/methotrexate transport system of L1210 cells. Arch Biochem Biophys 202:144-149.

Henderson GB, Zevely EM (1979). Energetics of methotrexate transport in L1210 mouse leukemia cells. In Kisliuk R, Brown G (ed): "Chemistry and Biology of Pteridines," New York: Elsevier/North Holland Inc. pp 549-554.

Henderson GB, Zevely EM (1980). Transport of methotrexate in L1210 cells: effect of ions on the rate and extent of uptake. Arch Biochem Biophys 200:149-155.

Henderson GB, Zevely EM (1981a). Anion exchange mechanism for transport of methotrexate in L1210 cells. Biochem Biophys Res Commun 99:163-169.

Henderson GB, Zevely EM (1981b). Transport of methotrexate in L1210 cells: mechanism for inhibition by p-chloromercuriphenylsulfonate and N-ethylmaleimide. Biochim Biophys Acta 640:549-556.

Henderson GB, Zevely EM (1982a). Intracellular phosphate and its possible role as an exchange anion for active transport of methotrexate in L1210 cells. Biochem Biophys Res Commun 104:474-482.

Henderson GB, Zevely EM (1982b). Functional correlations between the methotrexate and general anion transport systems of L1210 cells. Biochem Internatl 4:493-502.

Henderson GB, Zevely EM, Huennekens FM (1979). Photoinactivation of the methotrexate transport system of L1210 cells by 8-azidoadenosine 5'-monophosphate. J Biol Chem 254:9973-9975.

Huennekens FM, Vitols KS, Henderson GB (1978). Transport of folate compounds in bacterial and mammalian cells. Adv Enzymol 47:313-346.

Huennekens FM, Vitols KS, Suresh MR, Henderson GB (1981). Transport of folate compounds in L1210 cells: components and mechanism. In Sartorelli A (ed): "Molecular actions and targets for cancer chemotherapeutic agents," New York: Academic Press. pp 333-347.

Kessel D, Hall TC (1967). Amethopterin transport in Ehrlich ascites carcinoma and L1210 cells. Cancer Res 27:1539-1543.

Kessel D, Hall TC, Roberts D (1965). Uptake as a determinant of methotrexate response in mouse leukemias. Sci 150:752-753.

Passow H, Fasold H, Gartner EM, Legrum B, Ruffing W, Zaki L (1980). Anion transport across the red cell membrane. Ann NY Acad Sci 341:361-383.

Rader JI, Niethammer D, Huennekens FM (1974). Effects of sulfhydryl inhibitors upon transport of folate compounds in L1210 cells. Biochem Pharmacol 23:2057-2059.

Sirotnak FM (1980). Correlates of folate analog transport, pharmacokinetics, and selective antitumor action. Pharmacol Ther 8:71-103.

Suresh MR, Huennekens FM (1982). Transport of 6-hydroxy-methylpterin by L1210 mouse leukemia cells. Biochem Internatl 4:533-541.

Acknowledgments

I would like to acknowledge the encouragement and helpful discussions of Dr. F.M. Huennekens during the course of these studies. Supported by grants CA 23970 and CA 06520 from the National Cancer Institute and CH-229 and CH-31S from the American Cancer Society.

13th International Cancer Congress, Part B
Biology of Cancer (1), pages 425–433
© 1983 Alan R. Liss, Inc., 150 Fifth Avenue, New York, NY 10011

REGULATION OF MEMBRANE FUNCTION BY LIPIDS; IMPLICATIONS FOR TUMOR DEVELOPMENT

M. Shinitzky[1], Y. Skornick[2], E. Gorelik[3]
W. Sindelar[3]
Department of Membrane Research, The Weizmann
Institute Of Science, Rehovot, Israel[1]; Depart-
ment of Surgery, Rokach Hospital, Tel-Aviv, Israel[2]
Surgery Branch, The National Cancer Institute
Bethesda, MD. 20205, U.S.A.[3]

Synopsis

Increase in the lipid fluidity of membranes increases the turnover number of each diffusible unit, but in general decreases its accessibility to ligand binding. As a result, many membranal functions reach a maximal activity at a specific lipid fluidity. These effects of membrane fluidity bear direct implications on tumor development with significant clinical potential. Two main avenues, by which lipid manipulation could be applied in cancer treatment are now being studied in experimental animals and cancer patients. In the first, the immunogenicity of tumor cells in syngeneic and autologous systems increase upon increase of the membrane microviscosity which is in line with the findings that membrane antigens become more exposed upon such treatment. Irradiated tumor cells with increased membrane microviscosity (e.g. by incorporation of cholesteryl hemisuccinate, CHS) thus act as strong and specific vaccine against the viable untreated tumor cells of the same kind. The second lipid manipulation relates to restoration of suppressed immune competence. A special mixture of lipids (Active Lipid, AL) designed to efficiently fluidize cell membranes was found to restore various immunological functions of leukocytes from cancer patients. The combination of augmentation of tumor immunogenicity and restoration of immune functions by such lipid manipulations is expected to constitute an innocuous active immunotherapy regimen for cancer treatment.

Lipid Fluidity and Membrane Function

Membranal processes can be grossly divided into those
driven by metabolic energy (active processes) and those
carried out through diffusion (passive processes). The
latter are spontaneous and comply with the thermodynamics of
protein diffusion and position where the membrane lipid fluidity is a critical determinant. Manipulation of passive
membranal processes by in vitro or in vivo alteration of
lipid composition and fluidity bears a great potential for
restoration of impaired functions amenable for clinical
treatments. Immunotherapy of cancer based on lipid treatments is discussed in the following sections.

The overt effect of the lipid fluidity on a passive
membranal process is mainly mediated through the degree of
accessibility of the functional site and its rates of rotational and lateral diffusions. Increase in the lipid microviscosity decreases the lipid free volume and in turn decreases the solubilization of the proteins in the hydrocarbon
core (Shinitzky, 1979). In parallel, the energy of interactions between the protein residues and the lipid chains
decreases (Gerson, 1982) and the net effect is a shift in
the equilibrium position towards the aqueous domain in
either sides of the membrane ("vertical displacement",
Borochov and Shinitzky, 1976; Shinitzky, 1979). Changes in
lipid microviscosity can alternatively be compensated for by
protein-protein association through "lateral displacement",
which in extreme cases can create segregated domains of
lipids and proteins.

As in other equilibria, thermal fluctuations around the
median vertical position of the function site (e.g. an antigen) are expected. This can be simulated by a quasi-equili-
brium between an operating and a cryptic forms of the site
which are at constant shuttling. For most cases the dependence of the fraction of operating receptors, α, on the membrane lipid microviscosity, $\bar{\eta}$, is given by :

$$\alpha = \frac{1}{1+(\frac{\bar{\eta}}{\bar{\eta}_{\frac{1}{2}}})^{-m}} \qquad (1)$$

where $\bar{\eta}_{\frac{1}{2}}$ is the specific microviscosity at which half of the sites are in the operating form. The power m is an expansion factor which characterizes the sensitivity of the receptor accessibility to changes in the lipid microviscosity (Yuli et al., 1981). This feature relates to the receptor *plasticity* and is expressed in the slope of the function $\alpha = f(\bar{\eta}/\bar{\eta}_{\frac{1}{2}})$. Modulation of accessible fraction, α, of Antigens (Shinitzky and Souroujon, 1979; Miller and Shinitzky, 1981) receptors (Heron et al., 1980; Heron et al., 1981) and transport channels (Yuli et al., 1981) by changes in membrane lipid fluidity approximately obeys the dependence given in Eq. 1.

The overt activity of a passive membranal process can be presented in terms of Michaelis Menten, Kinetics. Accordingly, V_{max} is a product of the number of operating sites C_+ and the average rate of activity, k, of an isolated unit:

$$V_{max} = k \cdot C_+ = k \cdot \alpha \cdot C_o \qquad (2)$$

C_o is the total operateable sites stored in the membrane (the site capacity). Since for almost all instances K is inversely proportional to $\bar{\eta}$ combination of Eqs. 1 and 2 yields

$$\frac{1}{V_{max}} = A \cdot \bar{\eta}[1 + (\frac{\bar{\eta}}{\bar{\eta}_{\frac{1}{2}}})^{-m}] \qquad (3)$$

This dependence could be verified for glucose and amino acid transports in intact cells (Yuli et al., 1981; Yuli et al., 1982). A summary of such an experiment is shown in Figure 1.

Cell growth and function are regulated to a large extent by the membrane lipid fluidity presumably through its effect on the degree of submergence at equilibrium as well as lateral and rotational mobilities of the diffusible functional proteins. In relation to tumor growth, modulation of membrane lipid fluidity can increase the expression of tumor associated antigens (TAA) and to potentiate the anti-tumor activity of the host's leukocytes.

Active Immunotherapy in Experimental Tumors

The vertical displacement notion implies that latent TAA on cell surfaces can become accessible to the immune competence systems upon rigidification of the membrane lipid layer. This was demonstrated indirectly by tumor rejection in mice

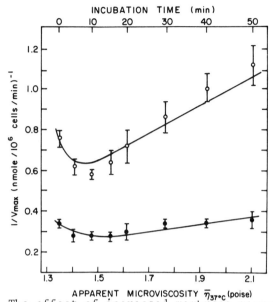

Fig. 1. The effect of increased membrane microviscosity on
the basal (o) and insulin stimulated (•) maximal rates of
3$_H$-aminoisobutyric acid uptake by 3T3 fibroblasts at 37°C.
Microviscosity was increased by incorporation of CHS at
different incubation times. The lines were computed for
data fitting according to Eq. 2 (from Yuli et al., 1982).

which were pretreated with irradiated syngeneic tumor cells
(T and B lymphomas, fibrosarcoma and mammary adenocarcinoma)
of lipid rigidified membranes, most effectively induced by
incorporation of cholesteryl hemisuccinate (CHS)(Shinitzky
et al., 1979). When 2-3 immunizations at 7 days interval
were given prior to challenge over 80% of the mice rejected
the tumor (i.e. survival beyond 100 days). This type of
immunization was found to be specific when cross reactivity
was examined by immunization with one kind of syngeneic
tumor cells (e.g. B or T lymphoma) followed by challenge
with another kind of syngeneic tumor cells (e.g. fibrosarcoma) and vice versa. Some cross reactivity was observed,
however, between chemically and viral induced T-lymphoma
lines, suggesting that common TAA reside in the various
T-lymphomas. The route of immunization, whether humoral or
cellular, was examined independently by analyzing for
specific tumor antibodies and specific effector cells in
mice which were preimmunized with CHS enriched tumor cells.

In all lines tested the level of specific anti-tumour antibodies in mice pretreated with CHS-enriched tumor cells was
only slightly, and for most cases insignificantly, higher
than the level detected in mice treated with only irradiated
tumor cells or in untreated mice. This observation suggested
that the anti-tumor activity elicited by our tumor vaccine is
predominantly, if not exclusively, cellular. This could be
verified by strong delayed type hypersensitivity (DTH)
reaction in the immunized mice (unpublished results).

It should be noted that the increase in membrane microviscosity can reach a critical point where proteins can be
shed off into the supernatant (Muller and Shinitzky, 1981).
The shed material upon "hyperrigidification" can be in the
form of membrane fragments, vesicles, molecular aggregates
or even isolated proteins coated with lipids (Muller and
Shinitzky, 1981). Therefore, treatment with CHS for increasing immunogenicity should be monitored for each specific
cell to verify the optimal microviscosity beyond which the
immunogenicity can sharply decline. The shed antigens may
preserve their immunogenic potential (Skornick and Sindelar,
1981) and may thus provide a vaccine which can be used also
allogeneically.

Inasmuch as active immunetherapy of cancer can be effective for treatment of small tumor masses only, our method
could be of clinical potential in elimination of metastases
after removal of the bulk tumor mass. This approach was
recently tested in mice infected with murine tumors which
are known to disseminate at a certain stage of development
(Skornick et al., 1982). These were the MC-103 sarcoma,
P-815 mastocytoma and 3LL Lewis lung carcinoma. The local
tumor was introduced into the foot pad and was excised by
amputation when visceral metastases were established. Immunotherapy consisted of 10^7 CHS-treated cells of the same
kind which were injected intraperitoneally either on the
day of amputation or 24 hours later. A second identical
treatment was given 6 days later. Three groups of mice
served as control: untreated, untreated but with excision
of the primary growth and treated with only irradiated cells
after excision.

Survival after immunotherapy was significantly longer in
all three tumor lines tested as compared with animals in the
three control experiments. With the 3LL tumor immunization
was also assessed by suppression of pulmonary metastases 11

days after excision of the primary growth. This was scored
by number of metastatic modules, by the weight of the lung
and by [125]IUdR incorporation into the metastatic cells. All
of these parameters were reduced 3-6 folds in the mice
treated with the vaccine as compared with the mice in any of
the 3 control experiments, which were insignificantly
different. The data of this experiment are summarized in
Figure 2.

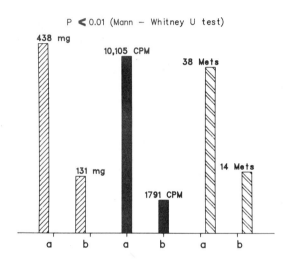

Fig. 2. Pulmonary metastases in mice infected with local
3LL evaluated by total lung weight, [125]IUdR incorporation
and number of metastatic modules, in immunized (b) and
control (a) mice groups (Skornick et al., 1982).

Human Studies and Clinical Strategy

To test the therapeutic potential of autologous human
tumor cells enriched with CHS, skin tests with such cells
were carried out in patients with solid tumors (Skornick et
al., 1981; Skornick and Sindelar, 1981). A strong skin
reaction of typical delayed hypersensitivity patterns was
elicited only with CHS enriched cells. With untreated cells
the skin reaction was negative or very weakly positive.
Patients who did not respond to the CHS treated cells (about

10% of the cases) were at an advanced stage of the disease
and anergic as tested by conventional recall antigens, indicating that the lack of response originated from severely
suppressed immune competence. A fair correlation was observed between the level of skin reaction with CHS-treated
cells and the clinical stage of the tumor. Control skin
tests performed with normal cells isolated from the growth
or with peripheral blood lymphocytes which were enriched
with CHS and irradiated, were negative. This indicated that
the observed delayed hypersensitivity reaction with autologous tumor cells with rigidified membranes relates to
potentiation of the immunogenicity inherent in the tumor
cells and which can then sensitize memory cells to evoke
proliferation of effector cells (monocytes and T-lymphocytes) directed against the tumor. In analogous in vitro
experiments the patients pheripheral blood lymphocytes were
sensitized with the autologous irradiated tumor cells. The
capacity to sensitize the lymphocytes was found to increase
considerably upon incorporation of CHS into the tumor cell
membranes (Shinitzky et al., 1981).

When clinical application of active immunotherapy is
designed one has to consider both the impaired immune competence of the patient and the weak antigenicity of his
tumor cells. Currently, most of the clinical immunotherapy
protocols are based on immune sensitization by non-specific
adjuvants such as BCG (Baldwin and Pimm, 1978). In a few
trials autologous untreated tumor cells were used as
vaccine to evoke specific sensitization against the tumor
(Bontlett and Zhar, 1972; Stein et al., 1978; Adler et al.,
1980). These reports indicate that when these two approaches
are combined significant delay in tumor development can be
achieved.

Replacing the untreated tumor cells with CHS enriched
cells should increase markedly the efficacy of the treatment. The proposed dose per treatment should range from
$10^7 - 10^8$ cells which in most cases is readily available.
Currently, a phase I immunotherapy study with this vaccine
is being carried out both at the National Cancer Institute,
Bethesda MD, and in the Rokach Hospital, Tel-Aviv, in
patients with solid tumors who have exhausted standard
therapeutic options.

The impaired immune competence of cancer patients is
presumably one of the etiological factors in the uncontrolled

tumor development. It is possible, but yet unproven, that
the suppressed immune response is partially due to an im-
proper lipid composition of the leukocyte plasma membranes
(e.g. elevated cholesterol level). In this case, it may be
possible to design a special lipid mixture given in the diet
or as hyperalimentation for restoration of membrane fluidity
and of immune function. In phase II of this study, which is
planned to start in a few months, the tumor vaccine will be
given in conjunction with Active Lipid (prepared by AL Labs,
P.O. Box 1215, Ojai, California), a potent membrane fluidizer
composed of phospholipids and glycerides from hen egg-yolk,
which was found to be very effective in restoration of immune
functions in aged mice both in vitro and in vivo. Its effectiveness in rectification of immune competence in cancer
patients is currently under investigation. All materials in
this combined immunotherapy approach are of physiological
innocuous nature and no adverse effect of the treatment may
be therefore expected.

ACKNOWLEDGEMENT

     Part of the animal studies were supported by Grant No.
RO1-CA-27471 awarded by the National Cancer Institute. Part
of the human studies were supported by a grant from the
Israel Cancer Association.

REFERENCES

Adler A, Stein JA, Goldfarb AJ, Levy E, Inbar M, Altboim I,
    Rozin RR, Teva Z and Czernobilsky B (1980) Cancer Immunol
    Immunother 10:45.
Baldwin RW and Pimm MV (1978) Adv Cancer Res 28:91.
Bontlett LG and Zbar B (1972) J Natl Cancer Inst 48:1709.
Borochov H, Shinitzky M (1976) Proc. Natl Acad Sci USA 73:
    4526.
Gerson DF (1982) Biophys J 37:145.
Heron DS, Israeli M, Hershkovitz M, Samuel D and Shinitzky
    M (1981) Eur J Pharmacol 72:361.
Heron DS, Shinitzky M, Hershkovitz M, Samuel D (1980) Proc
    Natl Acad Sci 77:7463.
Muller CP, Shinitzky M (1981) Exp Cell Res 136:53.
Shinitzky M (1979) Dev Cell Biol 4:173.

Shinitzky M, Danciger E, Skornick Y, Zakut V and Spirer Z (1982 (1982) in the proceedings of the Annual Meeting of the European Academy of Allergolopy and Clinical Immunology, 1981, Lavoisier Edition, Paris.

Shinitzky M, Skornick Y and Haran-Ghera N (1979) Proc Natl Acad Sci USA 76: 5313.

Shinitzky M, Souroujon M (1979) Proc Natl Acad Sci USA 76: 4438

Skornick Y, Danciger E, Rozin RR and Shinitzky M (1981) Cancer Immunol Immunother 11, 93.

Skornick Y, Gorelik E and Sindelar WF (1982) submitted for publication

Skornick Y, Sindelar WF (1981) Surgical Forum 32:432

Stein DA, Adler A, Goldfarb AJ and Czernobilsky B (1978) Cancer Immunol Immunother 5:31.

Yuli I, Incerpi S, Luly P, Shinitzky M (1982) Experientia, in press.

Yuli I, Wilbrandt W, Shinitzky M (1981) Biochemistry 20:4250.

13th International Cancer Congress, Part B
Biology of Cancer (1), pages 435–445
© 1983 Alan R. Liss, Inc., 150 Fifth Avenue, New York, NY 10011

ANTIGENIC CHANGES RELATED TO DRUG ACTION

M.C.Fioretti, L.Romani, E.Bonmassar[°]

Inst.of Pharmacology, Univ.of Perugia, Via del
Giochetto, 06100 Perugia; [°]Department of Experimental Medicine, Second University of Rome,
00100 Rome, Italy.

An impressive number of laboratory data are presently
available showing that cancer cells of various animal species
including man, express antigenic determinants not detectable
in normal tissues. However the complex immunological barriers
of the host,potentially capable of recognizing tumor-associated antigen(s) (TAA), do not appear in most instances to
result in effective control of the malignancy. Although no
exhaustive answer has been provided to furnish a satisfactory explanation to this problem, much emphasis was given to
the low levels of tumor cell immunogenicity(Hewitt 1978;
Galili et al. 1978).

The starting project of our laboratory was to generate
in vivo novel antigenic structures on cancer cells while
they are growing in the tumor-bearing host,using a pharmaco-
logical device (i.e. drug-induced xenogenization of the tumor in vivo). This would produce artificially the antigenic
target required for effective control of the disease by immunological means.

The studies illustrated and summarized in this presentation, provide evidence that our goal has been achieved in
animal models. Cancer cells collected from tumor-bearing mice subjected to treatment with antineoplastic agents,can
show indeed profound changes of their immunogenicity-anti-
genicity. In selected conditions this resulted in either increase of pre-existing TAA (Mihich 1969; Mihich 1973; Fuji
et al. 1979), or induction of antigen(s) not detectable, in
ordinary conditions, in the tumor line of origin (Houchens
et al.1976; Fioretti et al. 1980; Romani et al. 1979).

Preliminary studies performed in the sixties suggested
that new transplantation antigen(s) could have been produced

in Ehrlich carcinoma by in vivo treatment of tumor-bearing mice with antineoplastic agents, such as 5-Fluorouracil(Bonmassar et al.1965),or dl-phenylalanine mustard(Bonmassar et al. 1968).

More recently definite evidence that strong transplantation antigens can be generated by drug treatment in vivo, was obtained using 5-(3-3'-dimethyl-1-triazeno)imidazole-4-carboxamide(DTIC, Bonmassar et al. 1970).

In this study (BALB/c x DBA/2)F_1 (CD2F_1) mice bearing histocompatible L1210 leukemia, were treated with DTIC (50-100 mg/Kg/day i.p. for 10 days). Leukemic cells were collected from DTIC-treated donors and inoculated i.p. into 3 groups of mice, A, untreated; B, treated with DTIC; C, immunodepressed by pretreatment with Cyclophosphamide (Cy,200 mg/Kg i.p., 1 day before tumor challenge). Group B was always used as donor-recipient of the DTIC-treated line(s)(L1210/DTIC) for subsequent transplant generations(TG-n). At TG-0(i.e. using "parental" untreated L1210 line), DTIC-treated animals survived longer than untreated controls, as expected on the basis of the antileukemic effect of the drug. At TG-2 survival times of group A and B were comparable, thus indicating the emergence of DTIC-resistant leukemic cells. However from TG-4 onward, the majority of untreated recipients(group A) survived beyond the 60-day of observation period. All DTIC-treated or Cy-pretreated mice, instead, died within 20 days after challenge. These results were compatible with the hypothesis that L1210/DTIC cells acquired strong transplantation antigen(s) following a limited number of TG in DTIC-treated recipients, and were rejected by intact mice..On the contrary animals of group B and C, severely immunodepressed by DTIC(Bonmassar et al. 1972; Giampietri et al. 1979) or Cy (Giampietri et al. 1979; Houchens et al. 1975) respectively, succumbed with generalized leukemia, not being competent of rejecting the highly immunogenic L1210/DTIC cells. This hypothesis was supported by further studies showing that DTIC-treated leukemia sublines grow and regress in the peritoneal cavity of mice with a kinetic pattern similar to that of H-2-incompatible lymphomas inoculated into allogeneic recipients (Riccardi et al. 1978). On the other hand progressive and lethal growth of L1210/DTIC cells was observed in congenitally athymic "nude" mice(Campanile et al. 1975), severely deficient for T-dependent graft responsiveness.

Results comparable to those obtained with L1210 leukemia, have been detected with a number of murine lymphomas of various origin (Houchens et al. 1976; Fioretti et al. 1980; Nicolin et al.1976; Silvestrini et al.1977;Bonmassar et al.

1975; Bonmassar et al. 1979). Increased   immunogenicity for the host histocompatible with the parental line, was also obtained in leukemic cells treated with drugs
other than DTIC, and triazeno derivatives (see below).In
these cases,however,the cell-associated immunogenic strenght
was considerably less pronounced than that mediated by triazeno compounds (Nicolin et al. 1972).

Several hypotheses, illustrated in Table 1, have been
advanced for explaning the failure of lethal growth of DTIC-
treated leukemia cells in intact hosts.

TABLE 1
Hypotheses concerning the failure of lethal growth of DTIC-
treated cells in intact histocompatible mice.

HYPOTHESIS	RELEVANT DATA	CONCLUSION
1 Decreased oncoge- nic potential	DTIC-lines grow and regress in intact mice(Riccardi et al.1978).Growth rate of DTIC tumors is similar to that of parental lymphomas in vitro or in immunodepressed hosts (Silvestrini et al. 1977; Contessa et al. 1981).	Rejected
2 Increased density of preexisting TAA on cell membrane	Mice rendered tolerant to the parental line still reject DTIC sublines(Hou- chens et al.1976). High im- munogenicity is obtained in lymphomas not expressing de- tectable TAA(Fioretti et al. 1980). Specifically cytoto- xic T lymphocytes (CTL) do not lyse the parental line (Romani et al. 1979; Santo- ni et al. 1978).	Rejected
3 Increased immuno- sensitivity	Susceptibility to cell-medi- ated immunity against allo- antigens of DTIC lines is similar to that of parental tumors (Taramelli et al.1981).	Rejected
4 Emergence of pre- existing highly immunogenic clones in immunodepressed	Parental lines passaged in immunodepressed hosts do not acquire strong antigenicity (Campanile et al. 1975).The	Rejected

host	DTIC phenomenon is demonstrable in absence of drug-induced selection(Bonmassar et al. 1972).	
5 DTIC bound to cell membrane as haptenic group	DTIC lines retain high immunogenicity following numerous passages in immunodepressed hosts not treated with DTIC (Bonmassar et al. 1972).	Rejected
6 Induction of drug-mediated tumor antigen(s)(DMTA) not detectable in the parental line	All the above mentioned data speak in favour of this hypothesis	Accepted

It should be pointed out that hypotheses 1-5 have been rejected, since they could not furnish the rational bases for explaining the entire picture of the experimental data available. However hypothesis 6, which has been favoured by the majority of studies performed with triazeno derivatives, is not mutually exclusive with the others. No doubt exists that hypotheses 1-5 could well illustrate part of the mechanisms underlying the increased immunogenicity of tumor cells following DTIC-treatment in vivo, or in vitro(Contessa et al. 1981).

A typical example of DTIC-mediated induction of strong immunogenic properties in mouse lymphoma cells, not expressing TAA detectable by ordinary transplantation resistance studies, is illustrated in Table 2. Histocompatible B10(H-2b)

TABLE 2

Mortality of syngeneic B10 mice inoculated i.v. with 10^6 cells of LSBM-1 lymphoma and treated with DTIC (100 mg/Kg/day i.p. for 5 days after challenge) for a number of transplant generations.

TRANSPLANT GENERATIONS	Mortality of [a]			
	Intact hosts		Immunodepressed hosts[b]	
	MST[c]	D/T[d]	MST	D/T
0	8	8/8	8	8/8
7	11	8/8	10	8/8
14	20	2/8	12	8/8
21	>60	0/8	11	8/8

a) B10 mice presensitized with $50x10^6$ irradiated LSBM-1 lymphoma cells did not impair the lethal growth of the chal-

lenge with as few as 10 cells inoculated i.p. on day +15
after sensitization.
b) Pretreated with Cy (180 mg/Kg i.p.) 24 hrs before challenge.
c) MST, Median Survival Times in days.
d) D/T, Dead mice over total animals tested, after 60-day
observation period.

mice were inoculated with chemically-induced LSBM-1 lymphoma
cells, non-immunogenic for the host (see footnote a) of the
Table), and treated with DTIC for a number of transplant generations. At TG-21 all intact mice rejected the tumor,which
produced instead a rapid and fatal generalized disease in immunodepressed hosts.

Studies on the structure-activity relationship concerning DTIC and various triazene derivatives revealed 2 important features relative to DMTA induction, i.e. (a)the presence of the imidazole ring, a constituent of the DTIC molecule, is not essential for the activity; (b) dimethyltriaze-
nes, including DTIC, are not active "per se" but require metabolic demethylation by microsomal enzymes(Contessa et al.
1979). The chemical structure, abbreviation requirement of
metabolic activation and strenght of the immunogenicity generated in L1210 Ha leukemic cells, for a number of triazene
compounds, is illustrated in Table 3.

The level of drug-induced immunogenicity was comparative-
ly evaluated taking into account essentially the number of
transplant generations in vivo or of exposures to the drug
in vitro required for attaining "full immunogenicity" of L1210
Ha leukemia (Bonmassar et al. 1972). The "full immunogenicity"
endpoint has been defined as the degree of the immunogenic
strenght, causing the complete rejection of the challenge of
10^5 leukemic cells by intact CD2F$_1$ recipients.

The summary data of Table 3 provide clear evidence that
the imidazole moiety present in DTIC,is not essential for
attainig increased immunogenicity, since DM-CH$_3$ and DM-Cl are
even more active than DTIC. Moreover all dimethyl compounds
(i.e. DM-derivatives) require metabolic activation either in
vivo or in vitro.

Generation of DMTA by treatment in vivo or in vitro with
DTIC has been demonstrated by a number of in vitro studies in
which specifically sensitized cytotoxic T lymphocytes(CTL)
were tested against ^{51}Cr-labeled target DTIC-lymphoma cells
in a 4 hr ^{51}Cr-release assay. Effector CTL were obtained in
primary responses in vivo (Nicolin et al. 1974), or in vitro
(Romani et al. 1979), or in secondary responses in vitro

TABLE 3

Chemical structure and properties of aryltriazenes capable of mediating increase of tumor cell immunogenicity _in vivo_ or _in vitro_.

$$R - \langle O \rangle - N = N - N \begin{smallmatrix} CH_3 \\ R_1 \end{smallmatrix}$$

R	R_1	Abbreviations	Requirement of metabolic activation	Strength of immunogenicity elicited in L1210 Ha leukemia[a]
$-CH_3$	H	$MM-CH_3$	−	+
$-Cl$	H	$MM-Cl$	−	+
$-NO_2$	H	$MM-NO_2$	−	+
$-CONH_2$	H	$MM-CONH_2$	−	$\underline{+}$
$-CH_3$	$-CH_3$	$DM-CH_3$	+	+++
$-Cl$	$-CH_3$	$DM-Cl$	+	+++
$-NO_2$	$-CH_3$	$DM-NO_2$	+	++
$-CONH_2$	$-CH_3$	$DM-CONH_2$	+	++
$-COOK$	$-CH_3$	$DM-COOK$	+	++

a) Tested _in vivo_ in drug-treated CD2F1 mice bearing L1210 Ha leukemia, or _in vitro_ on the same leukemic cells in presence of liver microsomes when metabolic activation was required. The strenght of reference compound DTIC can be classified as ++.

using _in vivo_ presensitized responder lymphocytes(Santoni et al. 1978). The results of these studies are consistent with the hypothesis that DMTA are not detectable in the tumor line of origin, although their presence in subliminar amounts cannot be ruled out. Moreover it was found that DTIC lines contain different clones of immunogenic cells expressing distinct subsets of DMTA (Fioretti et al. 1978), along with limited levels of TAA cross-reacting with those of the line of origin(Santoni et al. 1978; Campanile et al. 1975).

The presence of DMTA in all tumor cells of DTIC lines appears to be a prerequisite for the line to be rejected by intact hosts, since even a single non-immunogenic cell of the experimental tumors used is often sufficient to produce lethal growth in the host. Further support to this concept was afforded by experiments of "dilution" cloning, showing that all tested clones were highly immunogenic(Fioretti et al. 1978). Additional experiments along this line of research

were performed with Ara-C-resistant clone(s) isolated from a
fully-immunogenic L5178Y/DTIC line. The Ara-C-resistant sub-
line(L5178Y/DTIC/Ara) was obtained in immunodepressed CD2Fl
mice treated chronically with high doses of Ara-C for a number of transplant generations. In vitro secondary CTL were
obtained by coculturing "responder" splenocytes, presensitized in vivo with the tumor, with irradiated sensitizer lymphoma cells for 5 days in 5% CO_2 atmosfere at 37°C. Effector
CTL were then tested against ^{51}Cr-labeled target cells, as
illustrated in Table 4. The results show that (a) primary

TABLE 4

Primary and secondary cytotoxic response in vitro against
L5178Y/DTIC and its Ara-C-resistant subline(L5178Y/DTIC/Ara)

Effector lymphocytes[a]		Target cells[b]	% Lysis mean$\pm$SE
Presensitized in vivo against[c]:	Sensitized in vitro against:		
L5178Y/DTIC	–	L5178Y/DTIC	10.5$\pm$1.4
L5178Y/DTIC	L5178Y/DTIC	L5178Y/DTIC	43.0$\pm$1.2
L5178Y/DTIC	L5178Y/DTIC	L5178Y	ND[d]
L5178Y/DTIC/Ara	–	L5178Y/DTIC/Ara	18.0$\pm$2.8
L5178Y/DTIC/Ara	L5178Y/DTIC/Ara	L5178Y/DTIC/Ara	86.3$\pm$1.9

a) Spleen cells of CD2Fl donors.
b) Effector to target ratio, 40:1.
c) 10^7 viable cells given ip 50 days before spleen cell
   collection.
d) ND, not detectable.

in vivo CTL immune against L5178Y/DTIC or L5178Y/DTIC/Ara
sublines were slightly cytotoxic against the same cells used
for sensitization; (b) secondary CTL against both lines were
strongly cytolytic for target cells of the sensitizing tumor; (c) secondary CTL immune against L5178Y/DTIC was inactive against the L5178Y line of origin. These data confirm
that Ara-C-resistant clone(s) of L5178Y/DTIC line, selected
by Ara-C treatment in vivo, express high levels of DMTA.
Therefore "chemical cloning" provided an additional piece of
information consistent with that obtained with "dilution"
cloning.
    The appearance of DMTA on tumor cell membrane following
drug-treatment in vivo or in vitro could conceivable produce
sensible rearrangement of the entire antigenic makeup of the
cancer cells. Therefore interest has been focused on the
expression of normal histocompatibility antigens on the membrane of DTIC-treated cells. In this respect, experiments

were performed in which cytotoxic lymphocytes were generated in vitro against alloantigens of the H-2 complex of subregions of it. This effector cells were tested against ^{51}Cr-
labeled parental line in the presence of "cold" DTIC-treated
cells as inhibitor. The results showed that little or no
difference in the expression of H-2 antigens recognized by
cytotoxic lymphocytes could be detected between parental and
DTIC-treated subline(Taramelli et al. 1981).

One of the most crucial questions arising in the course
of investigations on the antigenic changes mediated by DTIC
concerns the biochemical mechanisms underlying DMTA appearance. Being the DTIC-hapten hypothesis ruled out as indicated
in Table 1, additional hypotheses have been proposed, such
as (a) drug-mediated viral activation capable of inducing
virus-coded antigen(s) on cell membrane; (b) drug-mediated
somatic mutation of cancer cells affecting gene(s) involved
in the expression of membrane antigen(s).

The "viral activation" hypothesis is weakened by the
observation that DTIC lines contain a number of different
clones with distinct DMTA(Fioretti et al. 1978). On the contrary, the "somatic mutation" hypothesis appears to be rein-
forced by this finding and by a recent investigation showing
that treatment in vivo with Quinacrine, an antimutagenic compound, prevents the emergence of DMTA in L1210 Ha cells following DTIC treatment of tumor-bearing mice(Giampietri et
al. 1980). Moreover Quinacrine does not appear to antagonize
the antitumor and immunodepressive effects of the drug (Giampietri et al. 1980). The hypothesis of somatic mutation is
also supported by the studies conducted by Van Pel et al.
1979, who found results similar to those obtained with DTIC,
using treatment of tumor cells in vitro with chemical mutagens. In addition DTIC was found to by markedly mutagenic
for bacteria and mammalian cells.

Very recent results showed also that L5178Y leukemia
subjected to combined treatment with DTIC+Quinacrine became
chemoresistant to DTIC, but did not show immunogenic changes.

Subsequent treatment of the line with DTIC alone resulted in rapid increase of tumor cell immunogenicity(Fioretti et al. in preparation). These findings imply that (a)
DTIC-resistant clones are not immunogenic; (b) "DTIC phenomenon" is not the result of selection mechanisms mediated by
the drug.

In conclusion 12-year studies on drug-mediated xenogenization of tumor cells in vivo and in vitro provided
sufficient information to propose this model, fully developed in a preclinical design (Giampietri et al. 1971), as

a promising new approach to cancer immunotherapy.

AKNOWLEDGMENTS - We thank Dr.J.Mayo, Mr.C.Reeder and Dr. V. L. Narayanan, National Cancer Institute, Bethesda Md., for supplying many of the animals and drugs that we used.

Supported by Progetto Finalizzato "Controllo della Crescita Neoplastica" Contract No. 82.00304.96 (Consiglio Nazionale delle Ricerche, Rome, Italy).

REFERENCES

Bonmassar E, Bonmassar,A, Vadlamudi S, Goldin A (1970). Immunological alteration of leukemic cells in vivo after treatment with an antitumor drug. Proc Natl Acad Sci 66:1089.

Bonmassar E, Bonmassar A, Vadlamudi S, Goldin A (1972). Antigenic changes of L1210 leukemia in mice treated with 5-(3,3-Dimethyl-1-Triazeno)-imidazole-4-Carboxamide. Cancer Res 32:1446.

Bonmassar A, Frati L, Fioretti MC, Romani L, Giampietri A, Goldin A (1979). Changes of the immunogenic properties of K36 lymphoma treated in vivo with 5-(3,3-Dimethyl-1-Triazeno)-Imidazole-4-Carboxamide (DTIC). Europ J Cancer 15: 933.

Bonmassar E, Melan F, Testorelli C (1968). Sulla sensibilità alla sarcolisina di tumori asciti di Ehrlich in topi "vaccinati" con cellule tumorali tratte da animali variamente trattati con la sarcolisina stessa e con altri farmaci antiblastici(Tioguanina, Actinomicina D). Arch Ital Pat Clin Tumori 9:229.

Bonmassar E, Prada A, Giannattasio G, Testorelli C (1965). Combined antitumor effects of 5-Fluorouracil therapy and specific immunization. Arch Ital Pat Clin Tumori 8:231.

Bonmassar E, Testorelli C, Franco P, Goldin A, Cudkowicz G (1975). Changes of the immunogenic properties of a radiation-induced mouse lymphoma following treatment with antitumor drugs. Cancer Res 35:1957.

Campanile F, Houchens DP, Gaston M, Goldin A, Bonmassar E (1975). Increased immunogenicity of two lymphoma lines after drug treatment of athymic (nude) mice. J Natl Cancer Inst 55:207.

Contessa AR, Bonmassar A, Giampietri A, Circolo A, Goldin A, Fioretti MC (1981). In vitro generation of a highly immunogenic subline of L1210 leukemia following exposure to 5-(3,3-Dimethyl-1-Triazeno)-imidazole-4-Carboxamide. Cancer Res 41: 2476.

Contessa AR, Giampietri A, Bonmassar A, Goldin A (1979). Increased immunogenicity of L1210 leukemia following short-term exposure to 5-(3,3-Dimethyl-1-Triazeno)-Imidazole-4-carboxamide(DTIC) in vivo or in vitro. Cancer Immunol Immunother 7:71.

Fioretti MC, Romani L, Bonmassar A, Taramelli D (1980). Appearance of strong transplantation antigens in non-immunogenic lymphoma following drug-treatment in vivo. J. Immunopharm 2:189.

Fioretti MC, Romani L, Taramelli D, Goldin A (1978). Antigenic properties of lymphoma sublines derived from a drug treated immunogenic L5178Y leukemia. Transplantation 26:449.

Fuji H, Mihich E, Pressman D (1979). Differential tumor immunogenicity of DBA/2 mouse lymphoma L1210 and its sublines. II. Increased Expression of tumor associated antigens on subline cells recognized by serologic and transplantation methods. J Natl Cancer Inst 62:1503.

Galili N, Devens B, Noor D, Becker S, Klein E (1978). Immune responses to weakly immunogenic virally-induced tumors. I. Overcoming low responsiveness by priming mice with syngeneic in vitro tumor line or allogeneic cross-reactive tumor. Eur J Immunol 8:17.

Giampietri A, Bonmassar E, Goldin A (1979). Drug induced modulation of immune responses in mice: effects of 5-(3,3'-dimethyl-1-triazeno)-imidazole-4-carboxamide(DTIC) and cyclophosphamide (Cy). J Immunopharm 1:61.

Giampietri A, Bonmassar A, Puccetti P, Circolo A, Goldin A Bonmassar E (1981). Drug-mediated increase of tumor immunogenicity in vivo for a new approach to experimental cancer immunotherapy. Cancer Res 41:681.

Giampietri A, Fioretti MC, Goldin A, Bonmassar E (1980).Drug-mediated antigenic changes in murine leukemia cells: antagonistic effects of Quinacrine, an antimutagenic compound. J Natl Cancer Inst 64:297.

Hewitt HB (1978). The choice of animal tumors for experimental studies of cancer therapy. Adv Cancer Res 27:149.

Houchens DP, Bonmassar E, Gaston MR, Kende M, Goldin A (1976). Drug-mediated immunogenic changes of virus-induced leukemia in vivo. Cancer Res 36:1347.

Houchens DP, Iorio A, Barzi A, Goldin A, Bonmassar E (1975). Inhibition of antilymphoma allograft response in normal and lethally irradiated mice by Cyclophosphamide (NSC 26271) and Isophosphamide (NSC 109724). Cancer Chemotherapy Reports 59:967.

Mihich E (1969). Modifications of tumor regression by immunological means. Cancer Res 29:2345.

Mihich E (1973). Tumor Immunogenicity in Therapeutics. In Mihich (ed): "Drug Resistance and Selectivity: Biochemical and cellular basis", Academic Press, New York, p 391.

Nicolin A, Bini A, Franco P, Goldin A,(1974). Cell-mediated response to a mouse leukemic subline antigenically altered following drug treatment in vivo. Cancer Chemoter Rep 58: 325.

Nicolin A, Spreafico F, Bonmassar E, Goldin A (1976). Antigenic changes of L5178Y lymphoma after treatment with 5-(3,3-Dimethyl-1-Triazeno)-Imidazole-4-Carboxamide in vivo. J Natl Cancer Inst 56:89.

Nicolin A, Vadlamudi S, Goldin A (1972). Antigenicity of L1210 leukemic sublines induced by drugs. Cancer Res 32: 653.

Riccardi C, Fioretti MC, Giampietri A, Puccetti P, Goldin A (1978). Growth and rejection patterns of murine lymphoma cells antigenically altered following drug treatment in vivo. Transplantation 25:63.

Romani L, Fioretti MC, Bonmassar E (1979). In vitro generation of primary cytotoxic lymphocytes against L5178Y leukemia antigenically altered by 5-(3,3-Dimethyl-1-Triazeno)-Imidazole-4-Carboxamide in vivo. Transplantation 28:218.

Santoni A, Kinney Y, Goldin A (1978). Secondary cytotoxic response in vitro against Moloney lymphoma cells antigenically altered by drug-treatment in vivo. J Natl Cancer Inst 60:109.

Silvestrini R, Testorelli C, Goldin A, Nicolin A (1977). Cell kinetics and immunogenicity of lymphoma cells treated with 5-(3,3-Dimethyl-1-Triazeno)-Imidazole-4-Carboxamide(DIC) in vivo. Int J Cancer 19:664.

Taramelli D, Romani L, Bonmassar A, Goldin A, Fioretti MC (1981). Expression of normal h stocompatibility antigens in murine lymphomas treated with 5-(3,3-Dimethyl-1-Triazeno)-Imidazole-4-Carboxamide (DTIC) in vivo. Europ J. Cancer 17:411.

Van Pel A, Georlette M, Boon T (1979). Tumor cell variants obtained by mutagenesis of a Lewis lung carcinoma cell line: immune rejection by syngeneic mice. Proc Natl Acad Sc 76:5282.

Index

PROGRESS IN CLINICAL AND BIOLOGICAL RESEARCH